How To Know

THE

FRESHWATER

ALGAE

How To Know

THE
FRESHWATER
ALGAE

G. W. Prescott

University of Montana

WM. C. BROWN COMPANY PUBLISHERS
Dubuque, Iowa

Library of Congress Catalog Card Number: 79-128177

ISBN 0–697–04859–4 (Cloth)
ISBN 0–697–04858–6 (Paper)

Tenth Printing, 1972

THE PICTURED-KEY NATURE SERIES

How To Know The—

AQUATIC PLANTS, Prescott, 1969
BEETLES, Jaques, 1951
BUTTERFLIES, Ehrlich, 1961
CACTI, Dawson, 1963
EASTERN LAND SNAILS, Burch, 1962
ECONOMIC PLANTS, Jaques, 1948, 1958
FALL FLOWERS, Cuthbert, 1948
FRESHWATER ALGAE, Prescott, 1954, 1970
FRESHWATER FISHES, Eddy, 1957, 1969
GRASSES, Pohl, 1953, 1968
GRASSHOPPERS, Helfer, 1963
IMMATURE INSECTS, Chu, 1949
INSECTS, Jaques, 1947
LAND BIRDS, Jaques, 1947
LICHENS, Hale, 1969
LIVING THINGS, Jaques, 1946
MAMMALS, Booth, 1949, 1970
MARINE ISOPOD CRUSTACEANS, Schultz, 1969
MOSSES AND LIVERWORTS, Conard, 1944, 1956
PLANT FAMILIES, Jaques, 1948
POLLEN AND SPORES, Kapp, 1969
PROTOZOA, Jahn, 1949
ROCKS AND MINERALS, 1970
SEAWEEDS, Dawson, 1956
SPIDERS, Kaston, 1952
SPRING FLOWERS, Cuthbert, 1943, 1949
TAPEWORMS, Schmidt, 1970
TREMATODES, Schell, 1970
TREES, Jaques, 1946
WATER BIRDS, Jaques-Ollivier, 1960
WEEDS, Jaques, 1959
WESTERN TREES, Baerg, 1955

Printed in United States of America

INTRODUCTION

ARDLY any body of water or moist spot on the face of the earth is devoid of algae; they are distributed almost as widely as bacteria. The variety of form and color exhibited by algae are seemingly endless and Nature has shown no bounds in designing these ornate plants, many of which have bizarre shapes and diverse specialized habits.

Algae attract attention for many reasons, partly because of their bright colors or because of profuse and conspicuous growths in ponds, streams and along ocean shores. The more evident growths in fresh water are usually referred to by those unacquainted with algae as "water moss," "frog spittle," or pond-scums, pond-silks, *etc.* This illustrated, 'how-to-know' key is designed to give the student who is equipped with a microscope an opportunity to explore the world of fresh-water algae, and to give the correct scientific names (at least genus names) to the more common forms. The student may find to his surprise that a clot of "moss" will include half a dozen or more distinct and recognizable plants, each with its own characteristic form, method of reproduction, and life history. In some collections taken from acid bogs as many as 200 or more different species may be found.

It is hoped that this book will aid in identifying 530 fresh-water algal genera. To be sure, the naming of a plant or animal is not necessarily an end unto itself—but identification and naming must serve as a basis for any study of structure, physiology, life history, ecology and economic importance. Just as when one knows the name of a person and so then can learn more about him (or her), so the identification of algae can be the beginning of further investigations, for scientific pursuits ·or for the pure pleasure of getting better acquainted with the world of aquatic life.

Having found the generic names of fresh-water algae, the student may wish to identify plants according to their specific names. (See p. 3 for definitions). For this he will want to turn to some of the works listed in the bibliography. An attempt has been made in illustrating the genera to depict their most common species. In many instances, among the one-celled and colonial genera especially, there is considerable variation in form among the species included in a genus. The student will need to keep this point in mind when matching a plant under consideration with the illustrations in the key. A plant in question may be a species somewhat or quite unlike the one shown.

The generic names used in the key for the most part are those of long-standing and the ones to be found in floras and handbooks the world over. In several instances new names are employed thus reducing to synonymy the older and perhaps more familiar ones. Synonymous names are given in parentheses herein. The advanced student is urged to refer to the publications of specialists if he wishes to make comparisons of taxonomic terminologies.

G. W. Prescott

CONTENTS

WHAT ARE ALGAE

LTHOUGH most fresh-water algae are microscopic, many kinds are gregarious and occur in such numbers as to form the well-known "water-blooms" or pond scums. A few genera are individually large enough to be seen easily without the aid of a microscope, *e.g.*, the stone-worts (Characeae) or some of the fresh-water red algae such as *Batrachospermum,* or colonial forms such as the blue-green alga *Nostoc.*

If it were possible for fresh-water algae to grow as large as some other plants (mosses and ferns for example) and to live upon land, they would be considered highly attractive indeed and would be much cultivated as ornamentals. The symmetry of form and the patterns of external decorations possessed by many of them are not excelled in beauty by larger plants. The varied shapes of both marine and fresh-water algae, coupled with their many colors and hues have made them the subject of ob-  servation and wonderment for a long time, especially since the invention of the microscope. Indeed, the microscopic size of most of the fresh-water algae renders them all the more intriguing, and since the early days of the first microscopical club they have been used for pleasurable observation and speculation.

It is not the aesthetic quality of fresh-water algae alone, of course, which explains the amount of interest shown them. For small though they are, fresh-water algae (like some of their microscopic kin in the oceans) have many economic importances and considerable biological significance. Their relationship to aquatic biology problems of various kinds, their troublesome contamination of water supplies, and their use in general physiological research constitute just a few of the many aspects which lead to a study of them. Purely scientific problems, such as the role of algae in organic evolution, the biology of their reproduction and life histories, and their ecology are common subjects of investigation. Although much is still to be learned from them, the solution, or at least clarifications, of many problems in general biology and physiology have been obtained from studies of algae. At this time, for example, much attention is being given algae in culture for the study of highly important and practical problems in photosynthesis and the products of algal metabolism. Some genera of unicellular algae are being used for the assay and detection of biologicals (vitamins and growth-promoting or growth-inhibiting substances). Some cancer research involves studies in the physiology and reproduction of algal cells. The use of algae in sewage oxidation and for oxygenation in space flights are other well-known fields of study.

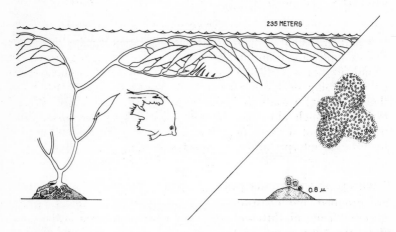

Whatever the interests in fresh-water algae may be, the student who has access to a microscope can find many hours of fascination in a few drops of pond water.

The term "algae" derived from the Latin name for sea-wrack, has come to be applied to all relatively simple (thalloid) marine and freshwater vegetation. Actually, of course, many different kinds of organisms are included among the plants which lie outside (or below) the realm of mosses (Bryophyta), the ferns (Pteriodophyta), and the seed-bearing plants (Spermatophyta). Included under "algae" are the smallest and most simple of chlorophyll-bearing organisms, the entire plant being but a single cell. Some of these may be less than 1 micron in diameter. At the other extreme, some of the brown algae, kelps (Phaeophyta) are the longest plants in the world. *Macrocystis* of the Pacific Ocean, for example is commonly over 100 feet in length, and greater lengths up to 700 feet have been claimed.

The student soon learns that "algae" includes several divisions or phyla of the plant kingdom, and that there are incorporated even some groups of organisms which, strictly speaking, belong neither to the plant nor to the animal kingdom (Euglenophyta, Pyrrhophyta, and many of the yellow-green algae such as *Synura* and *Dinobryon*). These are forms which usually are treated as chlorophyll-bearing protozoans in a reference work dealing with one-celled animals. Several of the swimming, protozoanlike forms have definitely plantlike or even non-motile relatives, however, which more than justify their being given a place among the plant-like algae.

The reader who is not familiar with the classification of plants and animals, nor with the terminology used for the different categories, may wish to refer to the following definitions.

Species

A particular kind of plant or animal population is called a species. For example, a certain kind of rose, or a particular alga such as a "pond silk," or a particular bird is known as a species and is given an identifying or specific name. Because there are so many (although slight) variations between individuals which are, in general, very much alike, the limitations or precise circumscriptions of a species of a plant or animal are often difficult, and subject to different interpretations by specialists.

Genus

All plants which obviously are roses, but not all the same kind, are grouped and constitute what is known as a genus (plural, genera). Thus, all different species of roses are placed in the genus *Rosa,* the Latin name for the genus. All species of "pond-silk" are placed in the genus *Spirogyra.* The genus name, *Spirogyra,* and a species name (a particular kind) together constitute the *scientific* name. For example, *Spirogyra elongata* is the scientific name of a species which has long cells; *Rosa cinnamonea* is the cinnamon rose. This method of naming each kind of plant or animal with a double name is known as the binomial system of nomenclature. The double name identifies not only a particular kind of individual but also indicates to what group (genus) it belongs. From a taxonomic point of view a "species" is regarded as a *population* of similar organisms, genetically distinct and which, ordinarily, will not cross with members of another 'population.'

Family

The genus *Rosa* has much in common with the strawberry genus *Fragaria,* and is much like the prune genus, *Prunus.* Similarly *Spirogyra* has much in common with another group of species which constitutes the genus *Mougeotia*. Therefore, *Rosa, Fragaria, Prunus,* and other genera that have characteristics much in common are grouped to form what is called a family. In this instance, the Rosaceae or Rose Family. *Spirogyra, Mougeotia, Zygnema* and some other algal genera which have characteristics in common and which seem, therefore, to be related are grouped to form the family Zygnemataceae. All genera in a family and all species in a genus are assumed to have a common ancestor.

Order

In turn, families which are distinct from one another but which, nevertheless, have some few characteristics in common are grouped to form what is known as an *Order*. Thus we have the Rosales, the Zygnematales, *etc.*

Division or Phylum

Several related orders form a major category known as a Division or Phylum of the plant kingdom (or of the animal kingdom). Thus several orders of the green algae constitute the division (phylum) Chlorophyta. In many instances it may be convenient to subdivide the phylum into groups of orders called *Classes*. Hence in the Chlorophyta there are recognized 2 classes (or Sub-phyla), Chlorophyceae and Charophyceae. In the key which follows only the genus names are given, with illustrations of 1 or 2 common species. In so far as possible, the most distinctive features of the genus are shown in the illustrations.

In some instances a genus may be monotypic, *i.e.,* contains only 1 species, or a family may have only 1 known genus. For example, the family Microsporaceae includes only the genus *Microspora* (Fig. 261). Likewise, it is possible for a phylum or organisms to have but 1 order; all such compositions being subject to interpretations of specialists. Categories of classification are often referred to as *taxa* (singular, taxon).

USE OF THE KEY

HE task of the writer in describing fresh-water algae is not made easier by their relatively small (mostly microscopic) size. Hence it is necessary to employ special descriptive terms to differentiate these minute organisms, and to assign them properly to the families and phyla to which they belong. Many of the terms are defined in the Pictured Glossary.

In such a treatment as is presented here, only the more common and best-known genera can be given a place. Included are not only most of the genera reported from the United States, but also a number known from Europe which can be expected in North America. The reader should keep in mind that all genera are not considered when using the key. He should avail himself of other less abridged or specialized works if satisfactory identification of a plant in which he is interested does not appear possible by the use of the following key. But the almost world-wide distribution of a majority of fresh-water genera gives such a key a usefulness beyond geographical limits. Such a key cannot be made as easy to use as are many keys to larger organisms. An attempt has been made to overcome some of the usual difficulties inherent in a key by leading to the same genus name at several different points; especially is this true for those genera which are so variable that selection of any one set of differentiating criteria for them is impossible unless one should write out a full description of the genus.

A beginning student or one with limited familiarity with the algae must exercise patience until he has developed some degree of judgment and has become well-acquainted with the meaning of terms, and until he has discovered to what degree a plant may vary from the more usual character which is employed in making an identification. Many times the user will find it profitable, if not necessary, to 'back-track' in the key and to follow down both dichotomies of choice before arriving at a satisfactory determination. As mentioned before, in making use of the illustrations it must be remembered that only 1 or 2 species of a genus are illustrated, and that the plant in question may not appear exactly like the forms which are figured. This is true for many of the genera in the Chlorococcales (*Scenedesmus, Oocystis, Tetraedron, etc.*) and of the Desmids (*Cosmarium, Euastrum, Micrasterias, e.g.*) also

5

in the Chlorophyta, genera which have very many species and which show considerable variation.

One of the primary difficulties with which the inexperienced student is confronted when first using a general key to the algae is that of detecting and identifying colors, green, blue-green, yellow-green, *etc.* to which the key makes reference. Pigmentation in the different algal groups is a fundamental characteristic, in the main, and one which is very helpful in making, especially the primary, identification. But yellow-green algae at times may appear decidedly grass-green, and the brown-pigmented algae may have a distinct tinge of green, especially when artificial light is used for the microscope. Hence, other characters, or a combination of characteristics excluding or in addition to color must be employed to make a choice in the key. Suggestions are given in appropriate places for making certain tests to help differentiate genera on the basis of color. Although it is a combination of characters which differentiates algae in the final analysis, the key can select these characters one by one only.

HOW AND WHERE
TO COLLECT FRESH-WATER ALGAE

ILAMENTOUS algae can be collected from mass growths by hand, and representative tufts placed in vials or collecting jars. Less conspicuous forms may be found as fuzzy films on submersed grasses, old rush culms, and sticks. Using the fingers these growths can be lifted away or pulled from their attachment, or short sections of stems of aquatic plants and grass leaves can be placed in vials and the algae removed with scraping tools in the laboratory. A dropping pipette and a pair of tweezers are useful for collecting minute forms.

Using the back of the thumb nail, or a dull-edged knife will serve, greenish coatings on rocks and submersed wood can be scraped away. Such an instrument is useful for removing samples of green or brown feltlike or mucilaginous growths from wet stones about waterfalls, from dripping cliffs and rocky outcrops.

Submersed glass, shells, and bits of crockery in the water furnish substrates for many algae which occur as minute, green discs or tufts. Old, rotting wood may be perforated with algae which lie so far below the surface that they are scarcely visible, but wood that appears at all greenish from the exterior should be examined.

Feel under the rim of dams or along the edges of stones in flowing water. Many blue-green and also some of the more rare fresh-water red algae occur in such habitats.

On and in damp soil are to be found numerous species of Cyanophyta and Diatoms. Sometimes algae occur in pure 'stands' and sheets or films of a single species may be lifted or scraped from soil, wet boards, and from the face of moist cliffs.

On beaches near the high water line, but back far enough where the sand lies unmolested most of the time, the upper dry layer of sand may be removed to disclose a densely green stratum of algae. The green sand can be scraped into a container and rinsed, and then when the water is poured off in the laboratory an interesting mixture of algae will be found, together with a variety of microscopic animals (protozoans, rotifers, copepods, *etc.*). This biotic cosmos is known as *psammon* and includes many organisms that normally occur in sandy beaches although not necessarily in the open water of a nearby lake or stream.

In *Nitella* (one of the larger green algae), in *Lemna trisulca* (one of the duckweeds), in *Ricciocarpus natans* and *Riccia fluitans* (floating liverworts) occur various green and blue-green, endophytic algae. Small portions of these aquatic plants, and others as well, may be allowed to age and to become discolored in laboratory dishes. The endophytes (and some epiphytes too) will then appear more clearly and can be dissected away for study.

In humid climates trunks of trees and surfaces of leaves may have epiphytic and endophytic (semi-parasitic) algae such as *Trentepohlia*, and *Cephaleuros*. *Arisaema* (Indian Turnip, Jack-in-the-pulpit) leaves invariably contain the parasitic alga *Phyllosiphon* which causes yellow or red spots in host tissue.

The habitats of fresh-water algae are diverse, some living in hot springs at 77° C.; others in snow fields at high altitudes, whereas others live in animals, or on them such as *Basicladia* on the snapping turtle.

One interesting habitat is the back of snapping turles where the coarse, wiry filamentous alga *Basicladia* is found invariably. Other algae may be associated with *Basicladia* on the 'mossy' backs of turtles, whereas alligators are sometimes veritable algal gardens and offer a variety of species for the less timid collector. In the rainforests of the tropics, Central America, *e.g.*, the three-toed sloth harbors among its hair scales a minute red alga, *Cyanoderma bradypodis*, and a filamentous green alga, *Trichophilus Welcheri*.

In alpine and subalpine regions where there are banks of permanent snow, red streaks will be found in the snow fields, or foot prints will turn red as the snow is compacted. The color is produced by unicellular green algae, especially *Chlamydomonas nivalis,* which contain a red carotenoid pigment (haematochrome) developed in many organisms exposed to intense illumination. Although such cells contain chlorophyll the green is masked by the more prevalent haematochrome. Occasionally green and yellow snow banks are found. A small quantity of red or 'bloody' snow when allowed to melt in a jar may yield a surprising quantity of such genera as *Scotiella, Ankistrodesmus, Raphidonema, Mycanthococcus* and certain dinoflagellates.

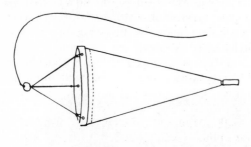

The Plankton Net

Specimens collected from the open water (plankton organisms) are best taken with a cone-shaped, silk, bolting cloth net (No. 20 mesh). Plankton nets are obtainable from biological supply houses, or may be made up by securing a yard of the silk from an importer or from a flour mill. The American Limnological and Oceanographic Society publishes periodically a list of commercial houses and firms where various kinds of collecting equipment may be obtained. A light-weight, brass (preferred) or thin galvanized iron ring (stout wire), or band may be used for the mouth of the net. A convenient size is a ring about 6 or 8 inches in diameter. Using a pattern (See Welch, P. S. 1948. Limnological Methods, Blakiston Co., p. 234-235) cut the silk so that when attached to the ring a cone about 14 inches long is formed. The silk should not be attached directly to the ring but sewed first to a band of stout muslin which then can be sewed over the ring or metal band. If a flat band is used for the mouth of the net the edges should be filed smooth and rounded to eliminate as much cutting and fraying of the musline as possible. The net may be used as a closed cone in which instance it must be turned inside out and rinsed into a dish or jar after making a haul. More conveniently, the tip of the net may be cut off at a point about ½ in. or less from the end which will permit the insertion of a small homeopathic vial (4 to 6 dram capacity) which can be tied around its neck into the apex of the net. Thus the sample will become concentrated in the vial and when the net is reversed the collected material can be poured into a sample bottle, and the net then rinsed before another sample is taken. Of course the vial at the end of the net can be untied with each use and another inserted. Better still, a small metal (aluminum) band, threaded to receive a 6- or 8-dram screw cap vial can be sewed into the tip of the net. Then the vial can be unscrewed and a fresh one inserted conveniently after each use. Muslin should be used at the neck of the net in which the aluminum, threaded ring is inserted. When comparative habitat studies are made much care should be used to see that the net is well-rinsed if it is to be used to collect from more than one habitat for critical studies; or a separate net should be used for each habitat.

The net should have 3 leaders of equal length attached to the ring at regularly spaced points. The leaders should be tied to a small ring to which the tow cord is also attached. Use a heavy line such as a sash cord for the towing or casting line. The leaders may be heavy wire or nylon cord. Braided copper wire is sometimes used for the leaders but these become worn quickly at points of attachment and snap with resultant loss of equipment.

Utricularia, an under-water animal-trapping plant, is a veritable Christmas tree loaded with miscellaneous algae which are caught among the leaves, in the bladders, and held in the mucilage that envelopes the plant.

Microscopic forms of algae may be obtained in great numbers from the squeezing of *Sphagnum* (and other mosses), especially when the plants feel slippery or slimy. Overhanging grasses and sedges, and exposed plant roots in *Sphganum* bog pools and seeps abound in many species of algae, especially desmids. Squeezings from such situations may be collected directly in a wide-mouth bottle (or vial) or it is often found desirable to collect the squeezings in a plankton net and so obtain a rich concentration of algae. *Utricularia* (bladderwort), especially when such plants occur in soft or acid lakes, is a veritable net itself. Handfuls of this plant can be squeezed into a plankton net with very fruitful results. The bladders of *Utricularia* sometimes contain an interesting assortment of small algae, especially desmids.

Specimens collected from the field should be put in receptacles with just enough water to cover them, leaving ample space for air, especially if the sample is to be stoppered for some time before arriving at the laboratory. Clots of larger filamentous algae may have the excess water gently squeezed from them, rolled in wet and then dry paper (newspaper highly satisfactory) and so kept in good condition. An efficient and inexpensive container for field collecting is a cellophane bag. A pack of sandwich bags can be taken into the field and used for individual collections, placing a small label or code number in the bag with a minimum amount of water.

Immediately upon returning from the field, vials or packets of material should be opened and poured into wide, shallow dishes so that they may be well-aerated using just enough water to cover the specimens. If the collection is not too crowded in a dish of water the plants may be kept alive and in good condition almost indefinitely, especially if the dishes are stored in a cool place with reduced illumination such as a north-facing window. Some kinds of algae will remain in satisfactory condition for study (even though additional growth may not occur) when stored in a refrigerator kept at ordinary temperatures used in food storage.

Some collectors prefer to spread algae on cards or stiff paper to dry, and then make herbarium specimens of them. In working with such specimens later, a few drops of water placed on the dried plants will soak up the material well enough that it can be lifted away for mounting on a slide. Specimens so treated, however, are not satisfactory unless one has had a long experience in examining algae and is familiar with their appearance in the undried condition.

If it is desirable to keep a record of the location from which separate field collections are made, it is obviously necessary to give samples a code number or label at the time they are taken. One satisfactory way of doing this is to carry 3- x 5-inch cards, all but cut through into narrow strips which will fit into collecting vials. A number then can be written on a slip which is torn off from the card and inserted. Information bearing the same code number can be written into a field notebook for future reference. In the laboratory a permanent number can be assigned to the vials and written on the cork or label if the material is to be saved for subsequent studies.

LABORATORY PROCEDURE

Preserving

IF samples are to be preserved an amount of 6-3-1 preservative equal to the volume of the specimens (and its water medium) may be added to the vial. This preservative is composed of 6 parts water, 3 parts 95% alcohol, and 1 part commercial formalin. If 5 cc. of glycerin are added to each 100 cc. of the preservative, a medium is produced which protects the specimen against total loss should the preservative evaporate. Cork-stoppered vials, as a rule, are much more serviceable than screw-cap vials which permit a greater amount of evaporation of the liquid because the tops loosen (especially with some types of screw-caps) upon standing for a time.

Formalin-acetic acid-alcohol (FAA) makes an excellent preservative as well as a killing agent if material is later to be prepared for staining or cytological work. To 50 cc. of 95% alcohol add 5 cc. of glacial acetic acid, 10 cc. of commercial formalin, and 35 cc. of water. Proprionic acid may be substituted for the glacial acetic. This preservative is useless for Dinoflagellates with wall plates, however, because the acid causes plates to dissociate.

For general and incidental preserving, ordinary 3% formalin may be used if the above ingredients are not available. (Add 3 cc. of commercial formalin to 37 cc. of water.)

Preparing Mount

For a study of most fresh-water algae a compound microscope is needed which has a 10X ocular and 10X and 43X objectives. A 20X ocular is necessary if camera lucida (see glossary) drawings are to be made. Larger forms of algae such as the Characeae are best studied with a binocular dissecting microscope. Best illumination for the microscope is obtained from daylight because colors of the algal pigments appear more naturally. In lieu of good daylight (light from a northern window preferred), artificial light from a microscope lamp fitted with a daylight blue bulb is used, or a lamp which has a blue filter. Naturally, all optical parts of the microscope should be kept free of dust, moisture, and finger prints, using rice lens paper for cleaning. It is difficult enough to see micro-organisms clearly when optical conditions are perfect.

An eye-piece micrometer and a stage micrometer for microscope calibration are essential if measurements are to be made.

In preparing mounts for the study of algae *small* amounts of material should be used, and spread out evenly in a thin layer. Dense clumps and opaque masses of algae in a microscope mount produce only disappointment, eye strain and headaches.

For the study of Diatoms it is necessary to have a clear and unobstructed view of the wall and its markings, and of the details of internal wall structures, free from the chloroplasts and othei cell contents. There are several methods for cleaning and clearing Diatom cells (frustules), some of which are rather complex, involving boiling in acid, *etc.* A simple procedure which is satisfactory for generic determination is to spread a bit of material in a generous drop of water on a microscope slide. The slide is held over a flame and the water brought to a boil. The smear is steamed thus for a few seconds, after which a drop of water or 5% glycerin can be used for a study slide.

For diatom techniques see Burke (1937) and Fleming (1949). Also see Patrick and Reimer (1966) for an excellent description of collecting and clearing techniques. If semi-permanent microscope mounts are desired, specimens may be placed on a slide, evenly spread out in a large drop of 5% glycerin. The slide should be set away under a dust-proof cover. Once or twice a day for 2 or 3 days other drops of the glycerin solution are added until, through evaporation of the water, approximately 100% glycerin remains about the specimens. To this a small drop of melted glycerin jelly is added and the cover slip put in place. Care should be used to add just enough jelly to fill out the area under the cover slip so as not to allow leakage from beneath it. The cover slip may be ringed then with a sealing materials such as balsam, colorless fingernail polish, Bismark Black, or Gold Size. (See catalogues of biological supply houses which list these and other mounting and sealing materials.

A useful reagent to demonstrate the presence of starch ($C_6H_{10}O_5$ of the Chlorophyta) is I-KI. Commonly employed solutions are: 1) Iodine, 2 gs., Potassium Iodide, 1 g., Water, 200 cc.; 2) Lugol's Iodine, Iodine, 1 gr., Potassium Iodide, 2 gs., Water, 300 cc. A killing and fixing solution may be prepared by adding to 200 cc. of water, 10 gs. of Iodine, 200 gs. of Potassium Iodide, and 20 cc. of Glacial Acetic Acid. Starch becomes dark, purplish-blue to black when stained with Iodine.

A depression slide may be used if specimens are to be examined over an extended period, for a study of motility, reproductive processes, *etc.* Rub a smear of vaseline around the margin of the depression. Place a drop of water or culture medium containing the specimen in the center of a coverglass. Then invert the cover-glass with the drop suspended in the slide depression. Press down the margins of the coverglass in the vaseline film to seal the chamber. In such a chamber the supply of oxygen is limited of course. A similar and often more efficient type of mount is to seal a low, plastic or glass collar to a slide (in a film of vaseline). Smear the top edge of the collar with vaseline and invert a hanging drop in the collar, pressing down the edges of the coverglass into the film of vaseline so as to seal the chamber. Such a mount can be used for low magnification study.

THE PHYLA OF ALGAE

HE organisms which constitute what are commonly known as "algae" are extremely diverse in form, color, habit, and in their habitats. Actually there are as many as 8 separate phyla or divisions of the plant kingdom included under "algae," (9 if Cryptophyceae, of uncertain position, are given a phylum status). Hence to write descriptively of algae one is confronted with almost as great a task as if he were treating all the phyla of land plants, fungi, mosses, ferns and seed plants, plus 3 or 4 additional groups. To be sure, all the phyla of algae do not include as many families and genera as do some of the higher plants, but the green algae alone include some 15 to 20 thousand species, distributed among about 400 genera.

The 3 major phyla of algae (those which are the most common) are the Chlorophyta (green), Cyanophyta (blue-green) and Chrysophyta (yellow- or brown-green). It is suggested that to facilitate the differentiation of these 3 groups and to become acquainted with the colors that characterize them, a known green alga (*Spirogyra*), a blue-green (*Anabaena*) and a Diatom be mounted side by side on the same slide. This will permit the ready comparison of the colors and also a comparison of the wall features, cell contents, *etc*. Then a series of illustrations depicting these 3 groups should be examined so that gross morphology can become associated with the respective pigmentations.

The phyla of fresh-water algae herein recognized are as follows:

1 Chlorophyta (Green Algae).

Plants unicellular, colonial, or filamentous; floating, swimming or attached and stationary; cells containing plastids (chloroplasts) in which chlorophyll (grass-green) is predominant, and in which there is usually a shiny, starch-storing body, the pyrenoid; pigments are 2 chlorophylls (-a and -b), 2 (possibly 3) carotenes, as many as 6, possibly 10 xanthophylls, and with red carotenoids (haematochrome) sometimes present; starch test with iodine positive (in almost every instance); nucleus definite (although often small and inconspicuous); cell wall (rarely lacking) composed of cellulose and pectose; swimming cells or motile reproductive elements furnished with 2 (usually), 4, or rarely as many as 8 flagella of equal length and attached in the anterior end; sexual reproduction by iso- aniso- and by heterogametes.

2   Cyanophyta (Blue-Green Algae).

Plants unicellular, colonial, or in simple or branched (sometimes falsely branched) filaments; chloroplasts lacking, the pigments seemingly distributed throughout the entire protoplast (or nearly so, often more dense in the peripheral region of the cell); pigments are chlorophyll-a, 3 carotenes, 2 or possibly as many as 15 xanthophylls (not necessarily present in all forms), phycoerythrin, phycocyanin; cell wall thin, a membrane which usually has a gelatinous outer sheath; contents often with false (pseudo) vacuoles which refract light and obscure the true color of the cells which may be green, blue-green, gray-green, violet, tan, brown or purple; definite nucleus lacking but occurring as a cluster of chromatic granules in the midregion (central body) of the cell; motile cells and sexual reproduction wanting; reproduction by cell division (fission) or by spores (endospores; akinetes); food storage questionably glycogen, possibly floridean starch; iodine test for starch negative.

3   Chrysophyta (Yellow-Green, or Yellow-Brown Algae).

Plants unicellular or colonial, rarely filamentous; pigments contained in chloroplasts in which yellow, brown or golden-brown usually predominate; pigments are: 3 chlorophylls, 3 carotenes, as many as 7 (possibly 16) xanthophylls (not necessarily present in all forms); food storage in the form of oil or leucosin, the latter often giving the cell a metallic lustre; starch test with iodine negative; wall relatively thick, pectin, often silicified, or with siliceous scales, and often in 2 sections which adjoin or overlap in the midregion; motile cells and swimming reproductive elements furnished with 2 flagella of unequal length (or with 1 flagellum); rhizopodial (pseudopodial and amoeboid) extensions of the cell not uncommon in some families.

4   Euglenophyta (Euglenoids).

Cells solitary, swimming by 1 evident (usually) or by 2 (rarely 3) flagella; a gullet present in the anterior end of the cell in many members, as is also a red eye-spot; chloroplasts few to many, variously shaped bodies (a number of genera colorless); pigments are: chlorophyll-a, -b, 4 carotenes, possibly 5 xanthophylls, and often red carotenoid (haematochrome); pyrenoids usually present, either on or in the chloroplasts, or free in the cell; food reserve in the form of an insoluble starch, paramylum, which is negative to the iodine test, and fatty substances; nucleus large and centrally located; cell membrane in the form of a pellicle, rigid or plastic, frequently striated; sexual reproduction (in the strict sense) lacking; vegetative reproduction by longitudinal cell division, and by encystment followed by multiplication of the cell.

5 Cryptophyta (Cryptophyceae of some authors) (Cryptomonads).

Cells solitary (rarely colonial), mostly swimming, protozoanlike organisms with 2, often laterally inserted or subapical flagella unequal in length; chloroplasts few and large, brown, blue, or red with pyrenoids commonly present; pigments are: 2 chlorophylls, 2 carotenes, 4 xanthophylls, phycocyanin and phycoerythrin (in some); food reserve in the form of solid starch or starchlike substances, the iodine test sometimes positive; cell membrane a firm periplast; a gullet commonly present in the anterior end; rarely trichocysts; reproduction by longitudinal cell division; sexual reproduction unknown.

6 Pyrrhophyta (Dinoflagellates).

Cells solitary (rarely filamentous in a few marine genera); mostly swimming by 2 flagella of approximately equal length and usually lateral in attachment (apical in one family), 1 flagellum wound about the cell in a transverse furrow, and 1 extended posteriorly from their point of attachment in a longitudinal furrow; cells mostly dorsiventrally flattened and differentiated, the longitudinal furrow extending along the ventral surface; cell wall (rarely absent) firm and simple, or formed of regularly arranged, polygonal plates (as in the so-called armored or thecate Dinoflagellates); pigments in chloroplasts include: chlorophyll-a, 2 carotenes, 4, possibly 6 xanthophylls, (with peridinin and dinoxanthin being the most abundant), phycopyrrin often giving the cells (especially when in mass) a reddish color; food reserve starch, starchlike substances and oil; a pigment-spot (possibly an eye-spot) commonly present; reproduction by longitudinal division; sexual reproduction lacking (except in 1 genus, as far as known); asexual zoospores formed in some genera.

7 Rhodophyta (Red Algae).

Plants simple or branched filaments (unicellular in 1 questionable genus); pigments contained in chloroplasts including; chlorophyll-a and -d, 2 carotenes, 3 (possibly as many as 14) xanthophylls, phycoerythrin and phycocyanin (in fresh-water genera phycoerythrin is reduced and the plants are commonly gray-green, violet-green or tan-colored); food reserve in the form of floridean starch which is iodine-negative; walls relatively thick, often containing pores with intercellular connections, highly mucilaginous; sexual reproduction by heterogametes, the egg contained in a carpogonium, the antherozoids as non-motile elements cut off from the tips of special branches; asexual reproduction by monospores and by tetraspores (in some genera); motility of vegetative and reproductive cells lacking; thalli often macroscopic in size.

8 Chloromonadophyta (Chloromonads).

An obscure and little-understood group composed of but a few genera and species; cells solitary, swimming by 1 or 2 flagella, apically attached; chloroplasts (when present) greenish with xanthophylls predominating over the chlorophyll, pigments including chlorophyll-a, 2 carotenes and at least 3 xanthophylls; food reserve in the form of oils or fat; contractile vacuoles and a reservoir at the anterior end of the cell; cell contents with trichocysts radiately arranged just within the cell membrane or clustered near the anterior end; reproduction by cell division; sexual reproduction unknown.

9 Phaeophyta (Brown Algae).

A phylum almost entirely marine, including the brown sea weeds (kelps); essentially filamentous (some microscopic) but mostly macroscopic and stout and leathery; pigments in chloroplasts, including: chlorophyll-a and -c, carotene-B and 7 xanthophylls (especially fucoxanthins), food reserve in the form of laminarin or soluble carbohydrates including alcohol (mannitol); pyrenoids sometimes present; reproduction vegetative by fragmentation, asexual by kidney-shaped, biflagellate zoospores with lateral attachment, or sexual by iso- aniso- and heterogametes.

SYNOPSIS OF THE ALGAL PHYLA

OST phyla of the algae are present in both marine and fresh water, although some occur more abundantly in one or the other of the two habitats. The Phaeophyta, for example are almost entirely marine, the Euglenophyta almost all fresh-water in distribution. The following general key is presented to characterize the phyla and to facilitate a comparison.

1 Cells without chloroplasts, pigments blue-green, olive-green, or purplish, distributed throughout the entire protoplast (although cells may be somewhat less colored in the central region); wall usually thin (often showing as a membrane only) and generally with a mucilaginous sheath (wide or narrow, watery or firm and definite); food reserve in the form of glycogen or a starchlike substance); iodine test for starch negative; no motile cells; no sexual reproduction; no definite nucleus, constituting the Akaryonta..................Blue-Green Algae........................*Cyanophyta*

1 Cells with chloroplasts, the pigments not distributed throughout the protoplast; cell wall clearly evident (with rare exceptions, *Pyramimonas*, e.g., Fig. 56); stored food in the form of starch, oils or leucosin; starch test for starch positive or negative; nucleus present (Eukaryonta)..2

2 Cells with grass-green chloroplasts (but see some species of *Euglena*, Fig. 13, or the filamentous alga *Trentepohlia*, Fig. 7 which although possessing chlorophyll, have the green color masked by an abundance of a red carotenoid pigment (haematochrome) 3

2 Cells with chloroplasts some other color, gray-green, brown, violet-green, yellow-green or sometimes purplish.....................5

3 Free-swimming, unicellular with numerous ovoid, star-shaped, or platelike chloroplasts which are grass-green; food storage as clearly evident grains of insoluble paramylum (sticks or plates); iodine test for starch negative; 1 (showing) or 2 (rarely 3) coarse flagella attached at the apex in a gullet; eye-spot usually evident ....*Euglenophyta*

3 Organisms not as above...4

4 Unicellular, without an eye-spot; chloroplasts numerous discs usually radially directed at the periphery of the cells; motile

19

by means of 2 flagella inserted in an apical reservoir; trichocyst organelles usually present just within the cell membrane (sometimes scattered); food reserve oil. Chloromonads............................
....*Chloromonadophyta*

4 Unicellular, colonial, or filamentous; swimming or not (often free-floating); when swimming using 2 to 4 fine flagella attached at the apex of the cell in a colorless reservoir; chloroplasts 1 to several; usually with a conspicuous pyrenoid (starch-storing granule); iodine test for starch positive........................Green Algae
....*Chlorophyta*

5 Chloroplasts light olive-brown to dark brown; nearly all marine; essentially filamentous but occurring mostly as thalli of macroscopic size (complexes of filaments) stored food in the form of laminarin and alcohol; starch test with iodine negative; motile cells with 2 laterally attached flagella.................................
Brown Algae..*Phaeophyta*

5 Plants marine or fresh-water, but not occurring as brown thalli of macroscopic size...6

6 Chloroplasts yellow-green to yellow- or golden-brown; food in the form of leucosin or oil; starch test with iodine negative; plants unicellular, colonial, or filamentous; sometimes swimming with apically attached flagella of unequal length, or with 1 flagellum; many form especially Diatoms) with siliceous walls; wall often in 2 adjoining or overlapping sections............................
Yellow-Green Algae..*Chrysophyta*

6 Chloroplasts not yellow-green or pale green, but dark golden-brown, gray-green, violet-green (rarely blue or red); food in the form of oil or starchlike carbohydrates; iodine test for starch usually negative...7

7 Unicellular with dark, golden-brown chloroplasts; swimming by 2 laterally attached flagella; a conspicuous red (eye-?) spot usually present; many forms with the wall composed of polygonal plates; cell with a transverse and a longitudinal furrow; reserve food in the form of starch or oil.........Dinoflagellates............*Pyrrhophyta*

7 Organisms unicellular or filamentous, not motile or if so, swimming by apical or subapical, flagella (rarely lateral); chloroplasts red brown, greenish, bluish, violet-green or gray-green..............8

8 Plants non-motile; chloroplasts violet or gray-green, sometimes bluish-green in fresh water, red in marine forms; occurring as filamentous thalli of macroscopic (sometimes microscopic) size; food reserve starchlike carbohydrates; starch test with iodine negative........................Red Algae............................*Rhodophyta*

8 Organisms mostly motile and unicellular; chloroplasts 1 or 2 golden-brown (rarely blue or red bodies; organisms unicellular

(rarely colonial); swimming by sub-apically attached flagella; food reserve starchlike carbohydrates: iodine test for starch positive in some..................Cryptomonads...................*Cryptophyta* (This class of the algae has several characteristics in common with the Dinoflagellates and in some systems of classification they are included with the Pyrrhophyta.)

A Selected List of Books and Major Papers Dealing with the Classification of Fresh-water Algae

Atkinson, G. F. 1890. Monograph of the Lemaneaceae of the United States. Ann. Bot., 4: 177-229. Pls. 7-9.

Bourrelly, P. 1966. Les algues d'eau douce. Algues vertes. Boubée & Cie, Paris.

Bourrelly, P. 1968. Les algues d'eau douce. Algues jaunes et brunes. Boubée & Cie, Paris.

Boyer, C. S. 1916. Diatomaceae of Philadelphia and Vicinity. Philadelphia.

Brunnthaler, J. 1915. Protococcales. In: A. Pascher. Die Süsswasserflora Deutschlands, Osterreichs und der Schweiz. Heft 5. Chlorophyceae 2; 52-205. Jena.

Burke, J. F. 1937. Collecting recent diatoms. Preparing recent diatoms. Mounting recent diatoms. New York Microsc. Soc. Bull., 1(3): 9-12; 1(4): 13-16; 1(5): 17-20.

Chapman, V. J. 1952. The Algae. Macmillan Co., New York.

Collins, F. S. (1909) 1928. The Green Algae of North America. Tufts College Studies, Sci. Ser., 2(1909): 79-480. Pls. 1-18. Reprinted with supplements 1 and 2 by G. E. Stechert Co., New York.

Copeland, J. J. 1936. Yellowstone Thermal Myxophyceae. Ann. New York Acad. Sci., 36: 1-232. 73 Figs.

Drouet, F. 1968. Revision of the Classification of the Oscillatoriaceae. Academy of Natural Sciences of Philadelphia.

Drouet, F. and Daily, William A. 1952. A Revision of the Coccoid Myxophyceae. Butler Univ. Bot. Stud., 12: 1-218.

Eddy, Samuel. 1930. The fresh-water armored or thecate Dinoflagellates. Trans. Amer. Microsc. Soc., 49: 277-321.

Elmore, C. J. 1921. The Diatoms (Bacillarioideae) of Nebraska. Univ. Nebr. Stud., 21(1/4): 1-214. 23 Pls.

Fleming, W. D. 1949. Cleaning and preparation of diatoms for mounting. Bull. Amer. Soc. Amateur Microscopists, 5(3): 40-43.

Flint, L. H. 1947. Studies on fresh-water red algae. Amer. Jour. Bot., 35(7): 427-433.

Flint, L. H. 1948. Studies of fresh-water red algae. Amer. Jour. Bot., 35(7): 428-433.

Flint, L. H. 1949. Studies of fresh-water red algae. Amer. Jour. Bot., 35(7): 428-433.

Fritsch, F. E.   1935, 1945.   The Structure and Reproduction of the Algae. Vols. I, II. Cambridge University Press.

Geitler, L.   1930-1931.   Cyanophyceae. In: L. Rabenhorst. Kryptogamen-Flora von Deutschland, Osterreich und der Schweiz. 14 Lf. 1(1930): 1-288; Lf. 2(1931): 289-464. Figs. 1-131. Leipzig.

Gojdics, Mary.   1953.   The Genus *Euglena*. Univ. Wisconsin Press, Madison.

Heering, W.   1914.   Ulotrichales, Microsporales, Oedogoniales. In: A. Pascher. Die Süsswasserflora Deutschlands, Osterreich und der Schweiz. Heft 6. Chlorophyceae 3: 1-250. Figs. 1-384. Jena.

Huber-Pestalozzi, G.   1955.   Die Binnengewässer. Das Phytoplankton des Süsswassers. 4 Teil. Euglenophyceen. Stuttgart.

Huber-Pestalozzi, G.   1961.   Die Binnengewässer. Das Phytoplankton des Süsswassers. 5 Teil. Chlorophyceae (Grünalgen). Ordnung: Volvocales. Stuttgart.

Hustedt, F.   1930.   Die Kieselalgen. In: L. Rabenhorst. Kryptogamen-Flora von Deutschland, Osterreich und der Schweiz. 7. Leipzig.

Irenée-Marie, Fr. 1939. Flore desmidiale de la region du Montréal. La Prairie, Canada.

Jaques, H. E.   1948.   Plant Families—How to Know Them. Wm. C. Brown Co., Dubuque, Iowa.

Krieger, W.   1933-1939.   Die Desmidiaceen. In: L. Rabenhorst. Kryptogamen-Flora von Deutschland, Osterreich, und der Schweiz. 13 Abt. 1: 1-712. Pls. 1-96. Abt. 1, Teil 2; 1-117. Pls. 97-142. Leipzig.

Krieger, W. and Gerloff, J.   1962, 1965.   Die Gattung *Cosmarium*. Lief. 1: 1-112. Taf. 1-19; Lief. 2: 113-240. Taf. 23-42. J. Cramer. Weinheim.

Lemmermann, E.   1913.   Euglenineae. Flagellatae 2. In: A. Pascher. Die Süsswasserflora Deutschlands, Osterreich, und der Schweiz. Heft 2: 115-174. Figs 181-377. Jena.

Pascher, A.   1927.   Volvocales-Phytomonadinae. In: Die Süsswasserflora Deutschlands, Osterreich, und der Schweiz, Heft 4: 1-508. Figs. 1-451. Jena.

Pascher, A.   1937-1939.   Heterokonten. In: L. Rabenhorst. Kryptogamen-Flora von Deutschland. Osterreich, und der Schweiz. XI: 1-1097. Figs. 1-912. Leipzig.

Patrick, Ruth and Reimer, C. W.   1966.   The Diatoms of the United States. Vol. I. Academy of Natural Sciences of Philadelphia.

Prescott, G. W.   1962.   Algae of the Western Great Lakes Area. IInd Ed. Wm. C. Brown Co., Dubuque, Iowa.

Prescott, G. W.   1968.   The Algae: a Review. Houghton Mifflin Co., Boston.

Printz, H. 1964. Die Chaetophoraien der Binnengewässer. W. Junk. Den Haag.

Round, F. E. 1965. The Biology of the Algae. St. Martin's Press, New York.

Schiller, J. 1933-1937. Dinoflagellatae. In: L. Rabenhorst. Kryptogamen-Flora von Deutschland, Osterreich, und der Schweiz. X (1933). Teil 1: 1-617; Teil 2, Lf. 1(1935): 1-160; Lf. 2(1935): 161-320; Lf. 3(1937): 321-480; Lf. 4(1937): 481-590. Leipzig.

Smith, G. M. 1920, 1924. Phytoplankton of the Inland Lakes of Wisconsin. I, II. Wis. Geol. and Nat. Hist. Surv. Bull. 57. Madison.

Smith, G. M. 1950. Freshwater Algae of the United States. IInd Ed. McGraw-Hill Book Co., New York.

Tiffany, L. H. 1937. Oedogoniales, Oedogoniaceae. North American Flora, 11, Part 1. New York Botanical Garden.

Tiffany, L. H. and Britton, M. E. 1952. The Algae of Illinois. Univ. of Chicago Press.

Tilden, Josephine E. 1910. Minnesota Algae. I. University of Minnesota Press, Minneapolis.

Tilden, Josephine E. 1935. The Algae and Their Life Relations. University of Minnesota Press, Minneapolis.

Ward, H. B. and Whipple, G. C. 1959. W. T. Edmondson, Ed. Fresh-Water Biology. Willey. London.

West, W. and West, G. S. 1904-1912. A Monograph of the British Desmidiaceae. Vols. I-IV. Ray Society, London. -and Carter, Nellie, 1924. Vol. V. Ray Society, London.

Whitford, L. A. and Schumacher, G. J. 1969. A Manual of the fresh-water algae in North Carolina. North Carolina Agric. Exper. Sta., Bull. 188.

Wolle, F. 1887. Freshwater Algae of the United States. Vols. I, II. Bethlehem, Pa.

Wolle, F. 1892. Desmids of the United States and List of American Pediastrums. Bethlehem, Pa.

Wood, R. D. and Imahori, K. 1964-1965. A Revision of the Characeae. Vols. I, II.

PICTURED-KEY TO THE COMMON GENERA
OF FRESH-WATER ALGAE

1a Plants macroscopic, up to 40 or more cm. high, growing erect, with stemlike axes bearing whorls of branches and forked, cylindrical 'leaves' clearly visible to the unaided eye. Figs. 1-3. Stoneworts. Characeae...2

1b Plants microscopic, or if macroscopic with cellular structures and branches not visible to the unaided eye; without whorls of branches clearly visible...4

2a Branching unsymmetrical, with dense heads and whorls of short branches and scraggly longer ones; microscopically showing globular male organs (globules or 'antheridia') lateral beside the oval female organs (nucules or 'oogonia'); plants usually gray-green. Fig. 1...*Tolypella*

There are about 10 species of this genus reported from the United States, but only 3 seem to be at all common. *Tolypella* species are widely distributed throughout the world but are more common in the southern hemisphere. In general these plants appear as scraggly *Chara* (Fig. 2), but they grow singly rather than in dense beds. Like that genus also *Tolypella* species prefer hard water lakes (or slowly flowing streams) and seem to be confined to rather shallow water. The Characeae is composed of 2 Tribes, Chareae and Nitelleae. The former has an investment of 5 cells around the female organ (oogonium or nucule), forming a 5-celled coronula at the apex. In the latter the investing cells are delimited by a cross wall at the base of the coronula and these cells are also divided. *Tolypella* shows

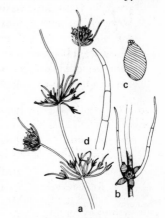

Fig. 1. *Tolypella intricata* (Trentep.) v. Leonh. (a) portion of plant showing habit of branching and the heads of short branches in which reproductive organs are located; (b) a node showing 4 "oogonia" or nucules and 1 "antheridium" or globule; (c) an oogonium showing the crown cells (10 in number); (d) tip of branch.

its relationship to *Nitella* by having also 10 cells. The sex organs are borne in the dense heads of short branches which characterize the genus; other branches being very long and fingerlike. The plants are usually gray-green but are not coated with lime as is *Chara*.

25

2b Branching symmetrical with rather evenly spaced whorls of equal-length branches at stem nodes; globules ('antheridia') above or below the nucules ('oogonia')....................................3

3a Plants coarse and usually rough to the touch with lime; gray-green; ill-smelling (garlic or skunk odor); microscopically showing globules ('antheridia') lateral on the axis and below the oval nucules ('oogonia'), (although some species are dioecious); coronula of oogonium composed of 5 cells; internodes of the main axis and branches in the whorls enclosed by columnar, corticating cells. Fig. 2..*Chara**

(*Chara coronata* and *C. Braunii* have no corticating cells. They may be identified by the habit of branching, by the location of the sex organs, and by the presence of 5 cells in the coronula.)

Fig. 2. (a) *Chara canescens* Lois.-Des., portion of a plant in which thornlike cells arising from the corticating elements give a spiny appearance; (b) *C. excelsa* Allen, showing the oval nucule ("oogonium") above and the globule ("antheridium") below.

Most of the species, of which at least 42 have been reported from the United States, are world-wide in their distribution. Many, however, are endemic in Japan, Australia, South Africa, *etc.* They vary in length from 5 cm. to a meter or more in length. They are to be found usually in hard-water or alkaline lakes and slow-flowing streams in which calcium is abundant in the form of carbonates or bicarbonates and may be dredged from as deep as 20 meters. In their physiology the plants cause lime to become deposited on stems and 'leaves,' sometimes to the detriment of the plant which may sink under the weight. The encrustation is responsible for the common name "stonewort." Marl and other kinds of calcareous deposits may be formed largely by *Chara* over long periods of time.

3b Plants delicate, or if relatively stout never roughened with lime; dark green, not ill-smelling; microscopically with globules terminal on a short pedicel within a cluster of branches and slightly above the lateral nucule; axis and branches never cor-

---

Lamprothamnus and *Lychnothamnus* are 2 uncommon genera related to *Chara*. The former has the oogonium below the antheridium (except in 1 species) whereas the latter has the oogonium with an antheridium on either side, all produced from separate nodal cells.

ticated; coronula of 10 cells, the tips of the cells which envelope the oogonium being divided into 2 cells. Fig. 3.................*Nitella*

Species of *Nitella* are not seen as often as are charas because they usually grow more deeply, thriving in soft water or acid lakes rather than in hard water situations. Some species occur in bog lakes that are darkly stained with humic and tannic acids and are collected only by dredging with a plant hook. Species like *N. tenuissima,* however, are to be found in shallow water. The plants are greener than *Chara* because they are not encrusted with lime; are not ill-smelling; often have a glistening or translucent appearance.

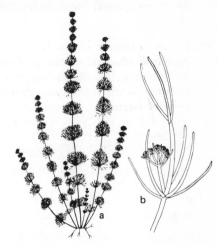

Fig. 3. (a) *Nitella tenuissima* (Desv.) Kuetz., habit; (b) *N. flexilis* (L.) C. A. Agardh, portion of plant showing habit of branching.

4a (1) Cells *containing* chloroplasts with green predominating; or with other pigments predominating, yellow-green, brown, reddish or blue..5**

4b Cells *without* chloroplasts, with pigments seemingly distributed and diffused throughout the cell (or nearly so). Blue-Green Algae. Cyanophyta...560

5a Plants grass-green or leaf-green;* *or* gray- to violet-green to tawny-green. (Mostly Chlorophyta, Euglenophyta and the violet-green Rhodophyta.) But see *Botrydium* (Fig. 320) and *Vaucheria* (299) which although densely green belong to the non-starch-producing Chrysophyta that are yellow or golden-brown........25

**See *Polytoma* (Fig. 32), one of several colorless members of the Chlamydomonadaceae; *Euglenomorpha* (Fig. 28) a colorless endozoophyte; *Dinobryon* (Fig. 359) which usually appears as empty cone-shaped loricas; *Peridinium, Ceratium* and other members of the dinoflagellates (Figs. 382, 387) which often occur as dead and empty cells which do not show the brown chloroplasts which characterize this flagellated Phylum, species and genera being differentiated by details of wall structures; *Trachelomonas,* Fig. 27, usually appearing as brown empty loricas of various shapes.

*Use the iodine test to identify and differentiate the Chlorophyta from all other groups (except that some dinoflagellates (Pyrrhophyta) show a positive starch test.

5b Plants not grass-green or gray-green but yellowish or golden-brown; *or* reddish, either because of a chloroplast pigment or because of carotenoid haematochrome; *or* rarely with bluish chloroplasts..6

6a Plants red (with phycoerythrin), or orange-red with carotenoid pigments (haematochrome) which partly or completely mask the green of the chloroplast. (See *Ancylonema* (Fig. 224), a filamentous form sometimes greenish but more often violet or purplish.)..7

6b Plants not red, but yellow-green, golden-brown, brownish or with bluish chloroplasts or protoplasts....................................416

7a Plants filamentous, erect or prostrate..8

7b Plants solitary cells, or forming colonies invested by a common mucilage..11

8a Thallus composed of closely adjoined, prostrate filaments forming an epiphytic disc on the leaves of land plants. Fig. 4...........
....*Phycopeltis*

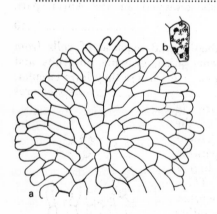

In this genus most species grow as a disclike layer of cells on the surface of leaves of higher plants. The thallus is rather regular in outline, produced by laterally oppressed, branching filaments of rectangular cells (the branching habit often obscure). The cell contents are often orange or yellowish from carotenoid pigments (haematochrome) although actually there are green chloroplasts. Gametangial cells are sessile on the thallus whereas zoosporangia are stalked. Species are most common in humid subtropical and tropical situations. Thus far the genus has not been reported from the United States but is to be expected in the Gulf states.

Fig. 4. *Phycopeltis arundinacea* (Mont.) de Toni. (a) habit of disclike thallus; (b) single cell showing parietal, fenestrate chloroplast. (Chloroplasts sometimes aappear as separate, irregularly shaped platelets.)

8b Thallus with erect filaments, sometimes arising from a basal, pseudoparenchymatous expanse or cushion of cells. (See *Kyliniella*, Fig. 242 sometimes reddish)..9

9a Filaments erect, growing from a lobed, subepidermal cell in the
    stomatal chambers of leaves of higher plants, the erect stalks
    bearing a sporangium. Fig 5...................................*Stomatochroon*

The thallus in this genus is
much reduced, consisting of
an enlarged, lobed cell within the stomatal cavities of
higher plant leaves, from
which an erect stalk arises.
The stalk or branch bears one
or more sporangia. The plant
(stalk) is brick-red with carotenoids. The genus is found in
humid tropical and subtropical
regions, mostly on broad-
leaved evergreens, but is
known to occur on many kinds
of plants, usually preferring
sunny rather than densely
shaded habitats. The basal cell

Fig. 5. *Stomatochroon Lagerheimii*
Palm, showing upright branch from a
sub-epidermal cell. Sporangium terminal.
(Drawn from a specimen on a citrus leaf,
Ecuador.)

is green, with the chloroplasts crowded in the lower part.

9b Filaments otherwise..**10**

10a Thallus composed of a subepidermal expanse of cells from
    which erect, hairlike branches arise, growing on fruits and
    leaves of land plants (*Magnolia*, e.g.) where they form circular,
    gray discs. Fig. 6..*Cephaleuros*

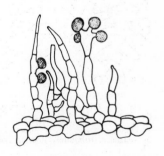

Cephaleuros virescens occurs in
tropical and subtropical parts of the
world (including southeastern United
States). The plant occurs as a parasite
or semiparasite on the leaves of higher
plants and fruits (*Magnolia, Thea,*
citrus fruits, *Rhododendron*. Because
of the discoloration and degeneration
of host tissue in the vicinity of the
parasite some damage is caused by
this alga and a certain amount of
economic loss results, especially to tea
growers. Although the parasitized areas
appear gray-green in color, individual
filaments of the cushionlike thallus of
the alga are usually reddish.

Fig. 6. *Cephaleuros virescens*
Kunze, diagram of a thallus as
it grows under epidermis of
host plant, with erect branches
protruding externally and bearing sporangia.

10b Filaments not growing from a subepidermal expanse but oc-
    curring on wood, tree-trunk and leaves, the walls of the cells

thick; apex of the filaments often capped with mucilage; un-branched or branched, with the branches arising at right angles to the main axis; sporangia terminal or lateral. (See also *Physolinum*, Fig. 277 which is usually reddish with carotenoids (haematochrome), sometimes included in *Trentepohlia*.) Fig. 7
....*Trentepohlia*

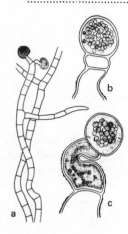

Fig. 7. *Trentepohlia lolithus* (L.) Wallroth. (a) filament with 2 terminal sporangia; (b), (c) sporangia in detail, mature and ready to be abscissed.

The species illustrated here and *T. aurea* Mart. are the 2 which are the most common of the 14 which have been reported from the United States. They grow on moist stones, dripping cliffs, and on the moist bark of trees and leaves. The characteristic orange color makes this plant conspicuous, especially when thalli form extensive patches, sometimes occurring as a felty-mat over large areas of rocky cliffs. In southern United States the moist sides of trees throughout extensive areas of the country side are colored orange by this alga. In humid situations of the tropics and subtropics the filaments become infested with a fungus to form the lichen *Coenogonium*, and in this condition the growth may be conspicuously fanlike on the sides of twigs and leaves. The carotenoid appears in the cell as a reaction to intense illumination. Reproduction in *Trentepohlia* is by isogametes produced in a specialized cell of the thallus, and by zoospores. Zoosporangia may be either lateral or terminal; are abscissed when mature and are carried by air current to germinate in a moist place by releasing biflagellate zoospores.

11a (7) Thallus a globular, tubular or amorphous, gelatinous matrix enclosing many cells (young colonies few-celled)................12

11b Plants unicellular or incidentally clustered and gregarious, not enclosed in a gelatinous matrix..16

12a Chloroplast axial with a central pyrenoid.................................13

12b Chloroplast parietal, a plate or cup, with or without a pyrenoid..14

13a Cells oval to elliptic in mucilaginous tubes or strands, together forming a gelatinous mass of macroscopic proportions,

color often more orange and yellowish than red. Fig. 8.........
(Not *Chroothece* as assigned to the Cyanophyta)......*Chroothece*

This member of the Rhodophyta (Bangiales) grows mostly on damp soil. Here it forms gelatinous masses involving tubes of mucilage in which there are oval or subcylindric cells. The stellate chloroplast is very striking. In mass the thallus is orange-colored or yellowish-brown. This is not to be confused with a discarded blue-green alga name now referred to the genus *Asterocystis*.

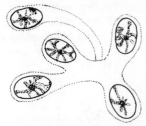

Fig. 8. *Chroothece mobilis* Pascher et Petrova, habit of portion of thallus showing cells with stellate chloroplasts within strands of mucilage.

13b Cells spherical or nearly so, with a sheath which becomes confluent with the colonial mucilage; inhabiting damp soil, often more purple in mass than red. Fig. 9.................*Porphyridium*

If this is a member of the Rhodophyta it is the only one known that is one-celled. Plants occur in gelatinous masses on damp soil, especially in greenhouses, or on wet walls. The growth is usually purple or wine-red. The cells have a stellate chloroplast.

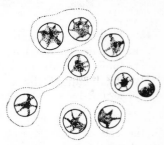

Fig. 9. *Porphyridium cruentum* Naeg.

14a (12) Cells in 2's and 4's at the periphery of a gelatinous matrix; chloroplast parietal but lobed, with a pyrenoid; pseudocilia and contractile vacuoles wanting. Fig. 10.........*Pseudotetraspora*

This genus occurs in both marine and fresh-water situations and in polar regions forms red or green snow. The colonial mass is an amorphous mucilage; usually macroscopic.

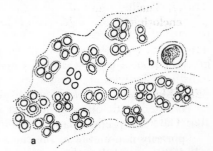

Fig. 10. *Pseudotetraspora Gainii* Wille. (a) habit of portion of thallus; (b) cell showing parietal chloroplast, usually lobed and with a single pyrenoid.

14b Cells not in 4's at the periphery of a colonial mucilage but distributed throughout the matrix..15

15a Thallus mostly aquatic and free-floating but sometimes attached; cells without individual sheaths apparent; with a lobed parietal chloroplast and 2 contractile vacuoles; cells green but resting stages are red with carotenoids (haematochrome). Fig. 11...*Palmellopsis*

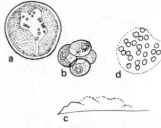

Fig. 11. *Palmellopsis gelatinosa* Korsch. (a) single cell (Redrawn from Korschikoff); (b) group of recently divided cells; (c) diagram of thallus on substrate; (d) colonial group of cells within mucilage.

The gelatinous colonies of this genus are amorphous, either planktonic or adherent to aquatic substrates. There is a cup-shaped chloroplast, a pyrenoid and 2 contractile vacuoles. The mucilage is not lamellate as in the similar genus *Palmella*. So far *Palmellopsis* is known only from Europe.

15b Thallus a gelatinous, amorphous mass on soil; cells solitary or in pairs enclosed in a thin, gelatinous sheath, the mucilage becoming confluent with the colonial matrix; chloroplast a parietal cup of the *Chlamydomonas* type, chlorophyll often obscured by a red pigment; contractile vacuoles lacking. Fig. 12 ....*Palmella*

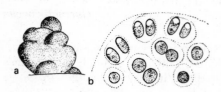

Fig. 12. *Palmella miniata* Liebl. (a) habit of colony; (b) portion of colony showing arrangement of cells and individual cell sheaths.

This plant forms lumpy, gelatinous nasses, 2 to 8 mm. in diameter on damp soil or on dripping rocks. The cells of *P. miniata* Leibl. are often red with (supposedly) carotenoids (haematochrome), whereas *P. mucosa Kuetz.* (without individual cellular sheaths) is always green. The oval cells, scattered throughout the mucilage may have indistinct, individual sheaths in many species. Like *Gloeocystis* (Fig. 85) which also has cup-shaped chloroplasts, *Palmella* may be confused with other gelatinous genera on soil.

16a (11) Cells predominantly motile, with many individuals temporarily non-motile in the same habitat...................................17

16b Cells predominantly non-motile, often encysted and stationary. Sometimes individuals emerge from the encysted condition and become motile in the same habitat.....................................21

17a Chloroplasts many oval or irregular platelike discs, or rarely diffused, the chlorophyll obscured by orange-red carotenoid (haematochrome); visible flagellum 1. Fig. 13.............Euglena*

There is a gullet at the anterior end of *Euglena* and 1 or more contractile vacuoles. The eye-spot is usually conspicuous. In some species. Although usually green, these elongate, slowly moving organisms sometimes are colored red because of carotenoids. A pond or slough may have bright red film produced by a *Euglena* 'bloom.' As is the situation with other red-colored green algae, the pigment is produced in response to intense light. *Euglena* species are often found in the psammon. About 60 species have been reported from the United States and many of these are world-wide in distribution. A few species of *Euglena* occur in marine waters.

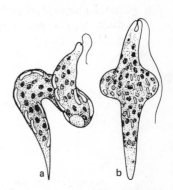

Fig. 13. (a) *Euglena convoluta* Korsch., showing lateral paramylum plates as seen on edge, one in flat view; (b) *E. elastica* Presc. Both of these are metabolic species, changing shape while swimming, whereas others are rigid and maintain a constant shape.

17b Chloroplasts 1 or 2 parietal plates or a cup; flagella 2..........18

18a Cells with a wide, sheathlike wall, the protoplast showing fine extensions to the wall margin; the green chloroplast obscured by orange-red carotenoid (haematochrome); plants of rock pools and cemented basins. Fig. 14.................Haematococcus

Although motile, this organism is more frequently found as a conspicuous coating of red cysts in the bottom of shallow rock pools and cemented basins. A common habitat is the garden bird-bath. In the swimming state it is readily identified by the fine fibrils which extend from the protoplast to the margin of the wide wall. The space between the wall and the protoplast is filled with colorless, watery mucilage. When not obscured by haematochrome the chloroplast can be

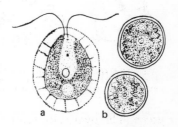

Fig. 14. *Haematococcus lacustris* (Girod.) Rostaf. (a) swimming cell showing protoplast with processes extending to the wall; (b) cysts (which are brick-red in color).

---

*One species of *Euglena* (*E. sanguinea*) has a diffuse blood-red color permanently; other species are brick-red when exposed to strong light, often forming powdery films on the water surface.

seen to be parietal with many pyrenoids. At times however, there are 2 chloroplasts, one posterior and one anterior, each plate with a pyrenoid *Haematococcus* and *Chlamydomonas* have been found by culture studies to be mutually antibiotic.

18b Cells without such a wide, sheathlike wall............................**19**
19a Cells oval or pear-shaped, with a longitudinal furrow bordered by trichocysts; 1 red chloroplast. Fig. 15..............*Rhodomonas*

The cells of this flagellate are usually somewhat obversely pyriform or broadly oval. The two flagella are of unequal length. Whereas the single, broad, platelike chloroplast may be olive-green, it is usually red. A distinctive character is a longitudinal sulcus or furrow bordered by trichocysts. *Rhodomonas*, a member of the Cryptophyta is known from Ohio and Michigan streams.

Fig. 15. *Rhodomonas lacustris* Pascher. (a) cell in 'front' view; (b) as seen from the side.

19b Cells otherwise..**20**
20a Cells oval or broadly rounded, or asymmetrical at the anterior end, with 2 (or 1) parietal, olive-green chloroplasts (which are often red); flagella 2, attached within an apical gullet. Fig. 16..*Cryptomonas*

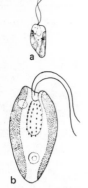

There are 8 species of this flagellate reported from the United States, but there probably are many more. The organisms seem never to occur many together; are easily overlooked in dense mixtures of algae; are fast-moving like species of *Chroomonas*. The cells are somewhat pyriform, being broader at the anterior end. There are 2 yellowish-green chloroplasts which, especially at certain times of the year, are red, and the 2 appear as 1 diffuse chloroplast. When the organisms are slowed in their movement and under proper optical conditions the characteristic gullet in the anterior end can be discerned, especially when the organism rotates on its axis. A somewhat similar-shaped flagellate is *Chilomonas* which has

Fig. 16. (a) *Cryptomonas erosa* Ehr.; (b) *C. splendida* Czosn. (Redrawn).

no chloroplasts but contains starch grains. See Fig. 308 also similar which has flagella of equal length and a blue-green chloroplast; the flagella of *Cryotomonas* are unequal.

20b Cells round, elliptic (to oval), with 1 parietal, cup-shaped chloroplast and 1 or more pyrenoids (rarely the chloroplast parietal H-shaped); flagella not attached to an apical gullet but arising from blepharoplasts; eye-spot usually evident; plants of snow fields, red when encysted especially. Fig. 17 ....*Chlamydomonas**

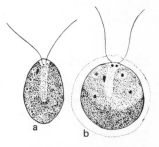

Fig. 17. (a) *Chlamydomonas polypyrenoideum* Presc.; (b) C. *sphagnicola* Fritsch et Takeda, a species with bipapillate protrusions at the anterior end of the sheath.

Whereas this common genus is represented by approximately 507 described species it is doubtful that they are all distinct. Unless specimens are given careful study (sometimes involving culture) they may be confused with other biflagellated genera, or with the motile reproductive cells of other algae. The species of this genus are encountered more frequently than any other members of the Volvocales and are to be found in a great variety of habitats; eu- and tychoplankton, in small rock pools, rain barrels, laboratory aquaria. A favorable habitat is the barnyard pool or watering trough. *C. nivalis* (Bauer) Wille produces red snow at high altitudes.

21a (16) Cells solitary, (rarely 2 together) mostly terrestrial and on dripping rocks, enclosed in a much lamellated gelatinous sheath, the cells lying eccentrically in the layers of mucilage. Fig 18...*Urococcus*

Although placed originally in the Tetrasporales this reddish-colored cell has been shown to be a stationary, non-flagellated member of the Pyrrhophyta (? Gloeodiniaceae). The cystlike cell apparently has many small, crowded chloroplasts, brown-orange in color, and globules of oil. In reproduction motile gymnodinoid zoospores are produced. The species other than *U. insignia* (Hass.) Kuetz. if shown not to be dinoflagellate will need to be transferred to another genus and renamed.

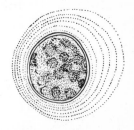

Fig. 18. *Urococcus insignis* (Hass.) Kuetz.

---

*Sphaerellocystis (Fig. 203) appears much like a non-motile *Chlamydomonas* in a wide, gelatinous sheath; has 2 contractile vacuoles but no eye-spot.

21b Cells otherwise..22

22a Cells epizoic in the hair scales of animals, especially the sloth; solitary or in clumps, gregarious. Fig. 19.............*Cyanoderma*

Fig. 19. *Cyanoderma bradypodis* Weber van Bosse. Cells in pseudofilamentous arrangement on hair scales of Panama sloth; and cell with chloroplasts.

Cyanoderma bradypodis Weber van Bosse is a unique member of the Rhodophyta which is epizoic among the hair scales of the 3-toed sloth. The cells are scattered or in patches in which there is a tendency to form filamentous arrangements. The hairs of the sloth may be pinkish because of the alga. In preserved specimens the chloroplasts seem to be several within the cell and disclike.

22b Cells otherwise..23

23a Cells inhabiting the tissues of higher plants, globular or flask-shaped with rhizoidal lobes and extensions. Figs. 20, 157........
....*Rhodochytrium*

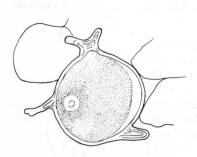

Fig. 20. *Rhodochytrium spilanthidis* Lag. in tissues of *Ambrosia* (Ragweed).

This curiously shaped, unicellular parasite, a member of the Chlorophyta, occurs on a greater variety of host plants than does the filamentous *Phyllosiphon* (Fig. 156), but seems to be most frequently found in ragweed, living within both stem and leaves. It is quickly identified by the red color and by the large number of starch grains. The chloroplast is massive and indefinite. Reproduction is by zoospores and isogametes.

23b Cells otherwise..24

24a Plants inhabiting snow fields and ice; cysts relatively small and smooth-walled; associated zygospores with thick, knobby walls. Fig. 17..*Chlamydomonas*

24b Plants inhabiting rock pools and cemented basins; cells relatively large (up to 50μ diam.), smooth-walled. Fig. 14............
....*Haematococcus*

25a (5) Organisms equipped with flagella, usually swimming in the vegetative state, solitary or colonial. (Preserved specimens should be examined for 2 or more minute protuberances at the anterior end of the cell which locate the position of flagella that may have been retracted or lost. Use 3-5% glycerine for mounting to slow down the movement of flagellated cells. (See Figs. 17, 38)...26

25b Organisms non-motile in the vegetative condition, (Check to be certain the organism is not a motile one at rest). See *Trachelomonas* (Fig. 27) which, although motile is commonly found as a non-motile brown shell (lorica) from which the flagellated protoplast has escaped); solitary or colonial, or filamentous forms...80

26a Cells solitary...27

26b Organisms colonial, 4 or more cells usually enclosed in a gelatinous sheath..67

27a Cells with a single flagellum, but housed in a vase-shaped lorica attached to filamentous algae or other substrates, the lorica open at the anterior end through which the flagellum protrudes; chloroplasts disclike. Fig. 21......................*Ascoglena*

This is a unique member of the Euglenophyta because of its stationary habit. The protoplast is enclosed by a brown lorica to which it is attached at the base by a protoplasmic strand. This and *Colacium* (Fig. 118) are the only euglenoids which, although provided with flagella, are nonmotile. Like *Trachelomonas* (Fig. 27) the cell divides within the lorica, one portion swimming away to establish itself in a new, sessile shell. Of the 2 known species, *Ascoglena vaginicola* Stein has been found in the United States, occurring in Ohio, Michigan and Montana.

Fig. 21. Ascoglena vaginicola Stein, cell in sedentary lorica.

27b Cells equipped with flagella, freely swimming........................28

28a Cells shining green, motile by 2 flagella, 1 trailing and 1 directed forward; cells with *apical reservoir* and with trichocysts (in most forms) arranged at the periphery or in the apical region; iodine test for starch negative; food reserve fats. Chloromonadophyta 29

28b Cells otherwise; grass-green or olive-green; flagella 1 to 4 but
     without 1 long, trailing flagellum; trichocysts lacking, or if
     present (*Cryptochryis*, Fig. 26) in rows on either side of a
     longitudinal furrow, not peripheral...31

29a Cells oval to pear-shaped, broadest at the posterior end; fla-
     gella apical; cells highly metabolic; trichocysts radially arranged
     just within the periphery; flattened as seen in end view.
     Fig. 22..*Vacuolaria*

29b Cells shaped otherwise...30

In this genus the pyriform cells are somewhat
flattened. In swimming the cells are highly metabolic (changing shape readily). Like other members of the Chloromonadophyta, one of the 2
flagella trails, the other directed forward. There
is a row of trichocysts immediately within the
periplast. There are numerous disclike chloroplasts but no eye-spot. Characteristically there is
an apical, contractile vacuole.

Fig. 22. Vac-
uolaria virescens
Cienk., showing
p e r i p heral
trichocysts, and
oval chloro-
plasts.

30a Cells round in cross section, in 'front' view oval, slightly nar-
     rowed posteriorly; trichocysts forming a cluster at the an-
     terior end; apical reservoir circular; flagella somewhat lateral
     in attachment. Fig. 23..*Merotrichia*

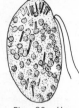

The cells in this genus are broadly ovate, usually somewhat larger anteriorly, with 2 long, laterally attached flagella. As is typical, 1 of the
flagella trails. The trichocysts are slender and
needlelike and somewhat scattered through the
cell but are definitely crowded and clustered
near the anterior end. Like most members of
the Chloromonadophyta this genus occurs in bogs
and swamps.

Fig. 23. Mero-
trichia c a p i tata
S k u j a (Redrawn
from Graffius).

30b Cells narrow or somewhat flattened as seen in end view; in
     'front' view oval or nearly circular but narrowed posteriorly,

sometimes forming a caudus; flagella apical; apical reservoir triangular; trichocyts radiately arranged at the periphery of the periplast. Fig. 24..*Gonyostomum*

Although rare, this genus is widely distributed, occurs more frequently than most other chloromonads, in acid lakes and bogs. Under the microscope it reminds one of a flat, green bottle; usually is quiet in the microscope field b u t moves with sudden, jerky motions for short distances.

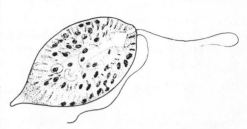

Fig. 24. Gonyostomum semen (Ehr.) Stein, showing the numerous ovoid chloroplasts (shaded) and the radiately arranged trichocysts (thread-casting organelles). It is normal for 1 flagellum to be directed forward, the other trailing.

Among the peripheral chloroplasts are slender trichocysts which throw out threads upon stimulation. The forward directed flagellum is at least twice the length of the cell. The apical gullet is pyramidate.

31a (28) Chloroplasts in the form of parietal, longitudinal plates (or sometimes diffuse); flagella 1 or 2. (See *Scherffelia*, Fig. 47, however which often shows longitudinal chloroplasts but 4 flagella.)..32

31b Cells with chloroplasts otherwise; 1 cup-shaped chloroplast, with 2 parietal chloroplasts, or with numerous disclike (rarely ribbonlike) chloroplasts; red eye-spot usually present............33

32a Cells cylindrical, with broadly rounded, truncate poles; 1 flagellum directed forward; with 2 laminate, longitudinal, grass-green chloroplasts. Fig. 25............................*Monomastix*

In this genus the cells are definitely cylindrical and truncate at both poles. The chloroplasts are 2 broad parietal plates with a single pyrenoid each. In the anterior end there is a contractile vacuole above which one, relatively long and forward-directed flagellum arises. In the posterior region is a cluster of elongate trichocysts. Confusingly the chloroplasts are usually grass-green rather than yellowish, although the genus belongs to the Cryptophyta.

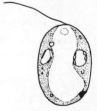

Fig. 25. Monomastix o p i s t h ostigma S c h e r f. (Redrawn from Belcher et Swale).

32b Cells oval in 'front' view, dorsiventrally flattened, often lobed and truncate at the anterior end, with a longitudinal furrow on either side of which is a row of circular trichocysts; flagella 2, of unequal length; chloroplasts 2 lateral plates, olive-green in color but sometimes brownish or yellow-brown. Fig. 26..*Cryptochrysis*

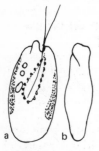

This biflagellate has 2 laminate chloroplasts which may be olive-colored or brownish. The flagella are relatively short and equal in length. The species known from Massachusetts has a bilobed anterior end with the flagella attached in a median depression.

Fig. 26. *Crypto-chrysis* c o m m *utata* Pascher. (a) 'front' view showing gullet and marginal tricho-cysts; (b) side view. (Redrawn from Pres-cott et Croasdale).

33a (31) Cells with numerous, disclike (rarely ribbonlike) chloro-plasts*; food reserve in the form of variously shaped, color-less (white) paramylum bodies (see Fig. 13) which do not stain blue-black with iodine; slow-moving by 1 (usually) or more stout flagella (see Fig. 31); a red eye-spot usually evident; cells mostly longer than wide, round in cross section (or sometimes somewhat flattened). Division Euglenophyta......34

33b Cells with 1 cup-shaped or star-shaped chloroplast, (but see *Polytoma,* Fig. 32, colorless), usually containing 1 or more conspicuous pyrenoids (doughnutlike, shiny bodies buried in the chloroplast or on its surface (rarely with 2 parietal chloro-plasts); food reserve starch, iodine test positive; lens-shaped eye-spot usually evident; actively swimming with fine, often obscure flagella, 1 to 8 in number. (Examine carefully for stublike flagellar remains. Add 5% glycerine to microscope mount to slow down organisms for observation. Motile Chloro-phyta (in part)..40

34a Cells enclosed in a lorica or shell with an apical opening through which the flagellum projects.....................................35

34b Cells not enclosed in a lorica.....................................36

35a Lorica vaselike, tubular, sessile on filamentous algae or other substrates, brownish because of iron deposits; enclosed cell

---

*The questionable euglenoid *Cryptoglena* has 2 parietal chloroplasts. See Smith, 1950, p. 355 for a description.

fusiform or elongate-elliptic, metabolic; flagellum 1. Fig. 21
....*Ascoglena*

35b Lorica of various shapes enclosing a flagellated cell, not ses-
    sile. (The loricas are more often than not found empty; brown
    or tan.) Fig. 27..*Trachelomonas*
    (The genus *Strombomonas* includes the *Trachelomonas*-like
    forms which have a colorless or pale tan lorica.)

There are several hundred species of
Trachelomonas, each showing a differently shaped shell or lorica and each having
its own special pattern or type of decoration. The amount of iron present in the
shell determines the intensity of color.
The species with colorless or yellowish
loricas have been transferred by some
students of the group to the genus *Strombomonas. Trachelomonas* species are
found intermingled among other algae
in shallow water of ditches and bogs, or
among aquatic weed beds near shores of
lakes.

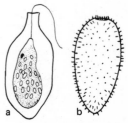

Fig. 27. (a) Trachelo-
monas ampulla Playf.; (b)
T. conica Playf.

36a (34) Cells with 3 flagella; endozoic in the digestive tracts of
    aquatic invertebrates. Fig. 28............................*Euglenamorpha*

This unusual euglenoid may be either
colorless or pigmented (in light); occurs
in the intestinal tract of frogs and tad-
poles. This is the only known tri-flagel-
lated member of the phylum. There are
many oval plastids and an eye-spot.

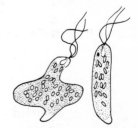

Fig. 28. Euglenamorpha
Hegneri Wenrich, two shapes.

36b Cells with 1 or 2 flagella; not endozoic.................................37

37a Cells nearly round or broadly fusiform in outline in 'front' view
    and appearing disclike, flattened when seen from the side
    but with a longitudinal ridge so that the cells are somewhat
    triangular in end view; cells usually twisted at the posterior
    end where there usually is a caudus (tail-piece); paramylum in
    the form of 1, few or several 'doughnut' rings or discs; periplast

usually longitudinally striated (sometimes spirally); flagellum 1. Fig. 29...*Phacus*

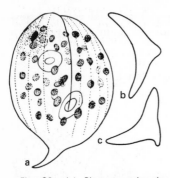

Fig. 29. (a) *Phacus curvicauda* Swir., 'front' or ventral view showing eye-spot, chloroplasts and 2 ring-shaped paramylum bodies (food reserve); (b), (c) *P. triqueter* (Ehr.) Duj. as seen in end view, the triangular shape being produced by a flange on the dorsal surface of the cell.

Although some species are spirally twisted and 'top'-shaped most are flat or at most only slightly saucer-shaped or pancakelike, with a long or short tail-piece. Although appearing flat in 'front' view they are somewhat triangular or 3-cornered when seen from the top because of a longitudinal flange. The rings of paramylum are usually very conspicuous, sometimes so large as to fill nearly the entire diameter of the cell. *Phacus* often appears in the same habitat with *Euglena* species.

37b Cells shaped differently, fusiform, subcylindric to pear-shaped; paramylum bodies not shaped as above; flagella 1 or 2........38

38a Cells highly metabolic (changeable in shape) but usually assuming an oval or pear shape, with a truncate apex; flagella 2; anterior gullet conspicuous; numerous disc-like chloroplasts. Fig. 30...*Eutreptia*

Fig. 30. *Eutreptia viridis* Perty. (Redrawn from Lemmermann).

The cells in this genus are fusiform when normally extended and bluntly truncate at the anterior end. Posteriorly they are abruptly narrowed into a caudal extension. There is an eye-spot and a gullet with small adjacent vacuoles in the anterior end. Under favorable conditions a granular swelling can be discerned at the base of each flagellum. The periplast, like many euglenoids, is spirally striated.

38b Flagellum 1; cells shaped otherwise......................................39

39a Cells round, oval or pear-shaped in 'front' view, round in end view; fixed in shape when swimming; paramylum in the form of 2 (or 4) lateral rings folded along the periplast; tail-piece, if present, in the form of a short, sharp projection from the broadly rounded posterior end. Fig. 31............*Lepocinclis*

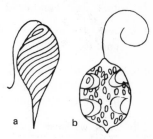

There are many species of this genus, world-wide in distribution, never forming pure growths but often intermingled with species of *Euglena* and *Phacus*. In optical section the cells are round and in many the periplast is spirally striated. On either side is a folded ring of paramylum; sometimes 2 such rings on each side. The cells swim more actively than *Euglena*.

Fig. 31. (a) *Lepocinclis acuta* Presc., showing spiral markings on periplast; (b) *L. glabra* fa. *minor* Presc., showing 4 lateral bandlike paramylum bodies.

39b Cells elongate, fusiform or nearly cylindrical; round or (in a few species) somewhat flattened when seen in end view; fixed in shape when swimming, or metabolic; flagellum 1, forked at the base, each portion arising from a blepharoplast; chloroplasts oval plates, or diffuse (rarely ribbon-like); paramylum bodies in the form of 1 or 2 large, or several small rods or sticks; tail-piece sometimes present, formed by the gradual narrowing of the cell. Fig. 13..*Euglena*

40a (33) Cells colorless (similar to *Chlamydomonas*). Fig. 32......
....*Polytoma**

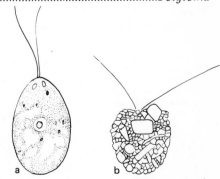

This colorless chlamydomonad often has an eyespot. There are 2 contractile vacuoles in the anterior end and there is the same neuromotor apparatus that is found in *Chlamydomonas*. Species in the genus are favorite subjects for physiological studies, especially in reference to saprophytic nutrition.

Fig. 32. (a) *Polytoma obtusum* Pascher; (b) *P. granulifera* Lackey. (Redrawn from Lackey).

*One dubious species, *P. granuliferum* Lackey is dark, almost black; has an investment to which sand grains are attached (Fig. 32a).

40b Cells with chloroplasts, pigmented; starch test positive..........41

41a Protoplasts at a considerable distance within the cell wall and connected to it by fine, radiating processes; before encysting cells green but often with a mass of red pigment (haematochrome) that partly obscures the green color; organisms often encysted, forming rust-colored growths in rock pools and cemented basins. Fig. 14...............*Haematococcus*

41b Cells not as above; free-swimming, not colored red by carotenoids..........42

42a Cells with a definite, cellulose wall (sometimes thin); in some with a gelatinous sheath, or with a lorica (a shell exterior to the cell or protoplast)..........43

42b Cells without a definite cellulose wall, (focus carefully) with a cell membrane only; lorica lacking..........59

43a Cells with 4 flagella..........56

43b Cells with 2 flagella..........44

44a Cells enclosed in a shell-like lorica which in some forms is externally roughened..........45

44b Cells not enclosed in a lorica, but often enclosed by a gelatinous sheath..........52

45a Lorica smooth or punctate..........46

45b Lorica externally granulate..........48

46a Lorica colorless, rectangular in 'front' view, with the corners produced into horns. Fig. 33..........*Pteromonas*

Fig. 33. *Pteromonas aculeata* Lemm. Other species are truncately oval or quadrangular in shape as seen in 'front' view.

This genus takes its name from the winged appearance of the envelope. Although there are about 7 species known, the most common is perhaps *P. aculeata* Lemm., recognizable by the rectangular appearance in 'front' view. Like *Phacotus* (Fig. 38) *Pteromonas* commonly occurs in the plankton of rivers. See *Scotiella* (Fig. 202) a genus which has been regarded by Pascher as belonging to *Pteromonas*, even though not flagellated in the vegetative condition.

47a Lorica globular, not granular but punctate and often appearing rough or granular (focus sharply); the enclosed cell a different shape. Fig. 34...*Dysmorphococcus*

This genus has a broadly oval lorica which is different in shape from the enclosed protoplast that lies some distance within the shell. The lorica has numerous small pores, giving a dotted appearance and there are 2 separate pores through which the flagella extend. An eye-spot is present, and 1 or more pyrenoids in the parietal, cup-shaped chloroplast.

Fig. 34. *Dysmorphococcus variabilis* Takeda, showing a sample of the markings on the lorica.

47b Lorica obversely pyriform and 3-lobed when seen in 'front' view, compressed when seen from the side, in end view oval but with 2 lateral protuberances; the cell closely fitting the shape of the lorica. Fig. 35...................................*Cephalomonas*

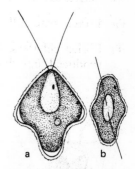

These cells have a colorless lorica which is close-fitting. The anterior end is broadly rounded, the posterior narrowed. The flagella are diagonally widely divergent.

a   b

Fig. 35. *Cephalomonas granulata* Higin. (a) 'front' view showing eye-spot and pyrenoid; (b) apical view. (Redrawn from Higinbotham).

48a (45) Lorica cordate in 'front' view, irregularly granular, not dark-colored, somewhat quadrate when seen from the side, with a lobe at each angle and a fifth, median posterior lobe; the cell elliptic within the lorica. Fig. 36............*Wislouchiella*

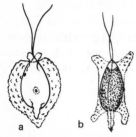

Fig. 36. *Wislouchiella planc-tonica* Skvor. (a) 'front' view showing shape of cell within lorica; (b) side view.

Named for the biologist Wislouch, this biflagellated organism is identified readily by the oddly-shaped lobes or processes of the wall which extend in several planes. The lorica is conspicuously granular. Species are rare but widely distributed in the United States.

48b Lorica shaped and decorated otherwise................................49
49a Lorica irregularly lobed, lumpy, with low irregularly arranged granules, the lorica usually 4-lobed in end view; enclosed protoplast broadly oval to elliptic and about the same shape as the lorica. Fig. 37...*Thoracomonas*

Fig. 37. *Thora-comonas Feldmannii* Bourr. (Redrawn).

These cells have a transparent, gelatinous lorica that has brown lumps because of knotted, iron deposits. The cytology of the cell within is much like that of *Chlamydomonas* but there may be many pyrenoids; the eye-spot is median in the cell.

49b Lorica shaped and decorated otherwise................................50
50a Lorica and its cell approximately the same shape as seen in 'front' view, often brown, bivalved and the seam showing as a suture in side view; irregularly granular. Fig. 38........*Phacotus*

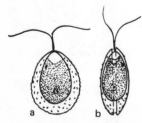

Fig. 38. *Phacotus lenticular-is* (Ehr.) Stein. (a) 'front' view showing cell within lorica, the eye-spot and pyrenoid; (b) side view showing the bivalve structure of the lorica.

This genus is relatively rare, but is often abundant in collections from habitats where it occurs. It is both euplanktonic and tychoplanktonic and may occur in rivers as well as lakes. The lorica and the protoplast are both egg-shaped in 'front' view, much narrowed when seen from the side when the bivalve nature of the lorica can be seen. There is a distinct space between the cell and the lorica. Three species have been reported from the United States.

50b Lorica shaped and decorated otherwise..................................**51**

51a Lorica thin, without an obvious apical pore, with spirally arranged granules, the protoplast the same shape as the lorica. Fig. 39...*Granulochloris*

This genus is well-named because of the highly granular nature of the lorica. The organisms are distinctive with the spiral arrangement of the granules. The protoplast is similar to *Chlamydomonas*. There are about 13 species known from the United States.

Fig. 39. *Granulo-chloris seriata* Pascher et Jahoda. (Redrawn from Pascher et Jahoda).

51b Lorica relatively thick, with a broad apical pore, ornamented with prominent calcium granules; the lorica globular, the protoplast obversely pear-shaped. Fig. 40............*Coccomonas*

The lorica is thick-walled and has calcareous and iron impregnations and granules which are irregularly arranged. The protoplast is decidedly narrowed (usually) at the anterior end. Upon cell division the lorica splits and the 2 daughter cells are liberated. There are at least 11 species known.

Fig. 40. *Coccomonas orbicularis* Stein, showing granular lorica containing an elliptic cell with eye-spot and pyrenoid in a cup-shaped c h l o r oplast. (Redrawn from Conrad).

52a (44) Cells fusiform, sometimes elongate and narrowly pointed at the apices, without an external sheath. Fig. 41.................
....*Chlorogonium*

The cells in this genus are all more elongate than any other members of the Volvocales. Usually found in swamps and shallow ponds, they sometimes appear abundantly in laboratory aquaria. Of the 30 known species, 4 have been reported from the United States.

Fig. 41.
C h lorogo-
nium elon-
g a t u m
Dangeard.

52b Cells shaped otherwise, oval, elliptic, often with a smooth or lobed sheath (not a shell or lorica)..53

53a Cells with a lobed sheath or with a sheath bearing extensions 54

53b Cells with a smooth sheath; protoplast smooth-walled...........55

54a Cells with 4 reflexed, pointed lobes (3 in view); quadrate in end view. Fig. 42..*Brachiomonas*

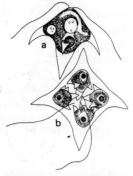

This genus is marine but often occurs in brackish water and tide pools. The 2 flagella arise from the narrow anterior end of a cell which is 4-lobed (quadrate when seen in end view) and which has an extended, conelike posterior. About 6 species are known.

Fig. 42. *Brachiomonas Westiana* Pascher. (a) vegetative cell; (b) zoospore-formation. (Redrawn from West).

**54b Cells with an irregularly lobed and lumpy sheath, the proto-
plast often withdrawn from the wall. Fig. 43...........*Lobomonas***

The irregular, lumpy appearance of this genus is
one of its chief characteristics. The organisms appear
in the same habitat with *Haematococcus* (Fig. 14), i.e.
temporary rain water pools and cement basins. There
are 10 species but apparently only 1 has been reported from the U.S.

Fig. 43.
L o bomo-
nas rostra-
ta Hazen.

**55a (53) Protoplast with an envelope decidedly narrowed anterior-
ly, not the same shape as the envelope. Fig. 44..*Sphaerellopsis***

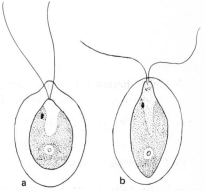

This genus probably
should be classified under
Chlamydomonas (Fig. 17)
although specialists separate its 20 species on the
basis of the very wide gelatinous sheath being different in shape from that of
the protoplast. It occurs in
the tychoplankton of lakes
and ponds. See also *Smithsonimonas* (Fig. 45) occurring mostly as red cysts in
snow.

Fig. 44.   (a) *Sphaerellopsis gloeocystiformis*
(Diel) Gerlof.; (b) *S. fluviatilis* Pascher.

**55b Protoplast not decidedly narrowed anteriorly,
the protoplast the same shape as the gelatinous
sheath, or without an evident sheath. Fig. 17
....*Chlamydomonas***

F i g. 45.
S m i t hsoni-
monas Abbotii
Kol. (Redrawn
from Kol).

56a (43) Cell enclosed in a yellowish lorica which is ornamented with prominent granules or other markings; lorica strongly flattened and sometimes pear-shaped in lateral view. Fig. 46 ....*Pedinopera*

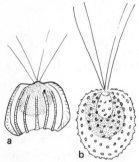

The pores and granules which ornament the wide, yellowish sheath help to identify this genus. Sometimes there are longitudinal ridges. There are 5 species, differentiated on the basis of lorica markings, only 1 of which has been reported from the United States.

Fig. 46. (a) *Pedinopera rugulosa* (Playf.) Pascher; (b) *P. granulosa* (Playf.) Pascher. (Redrawn from Pascher).

56b Cells without a lorica...57

57a Cells oval in 'front' view, strongly flattened when seen from the side; sheath with 2 flaring, winglike lateral processes apically; chloroplasts 2, lateral and parietal. Fig. 47..................
....*Scherffelia*

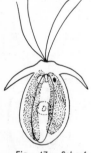

This genus is distinct because of the lateral wings which arise near the apex of the cell. There are some 12 species differentiated primarily by the form of the wings. It is to be expected in the United States but thus far is known only from Europe.

Fig. 47. *Scherffelia cornuta* Conrad. (Redrawn from Conrad).

57b Cells shaped otherwise, with a single chloroplast...................58

58a Cells broadly oval to somewhat cordate, with a slightly depressed apex, decidedly compressed as seen in end view; the 4 flagella arising in 2 separate pairs apically. Fig. 48................
....*Tetraselmis (Platymonas)*

Although usually found in brackish water, this genus contains at least 1 species that appears in fresh water. To make identification the cells should be seen from the top or side to determine whether they are flattened. The eye-spot may be anterior or median. It is thought by some that this name is synonymous with *Platymonas*, a genus which occurs in both fresh and salt water.

Fig. 48.
P l atymonas
elliptica G.
M. Smith.

58b Cells ovate or cordate, round in end view, the flagella all arising from one point. Fig. 49...*Carteria*
(*Tetrablepharis* is very similar but is colorless.)

Like *Polytoma* (Fig. 32) this genus is characterized by having 4 flagella, but the cells are round when seen in end view. The chloroplast is variable in shape and may not appear as shown in the illustration. It may be a thin plate along the wall, cup-shaped and covering most of the wall except at the anterior end, or H-shaped. This is a large genus of some 70 species, separated into 5 subgenera on the basis of the chloroplast form and presence or absence of pyrenoid. One study has indicated that *Carteria ovata* is a diploid phase of a *Chlamydomonas*.

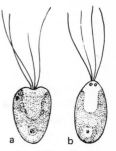

Fig. 49. (a) Carteria cordiformis (Carter) Dies.; (b) C. Klebsii Dill.

59a (42) Cells with a single flagellum directed posteriorly. Fig. 50
....*Pedinomonas*

Cells in this genus have no wall. They are circular or oval and possess a single flagellum which is directed posteriorly so that the organism swims backward. The chloroplast lies basally and along one side. There is a pyrenoid but no eyespot. There may be 4 species of this genus but only 1 has been reported from the United States, Ohio and Montana.

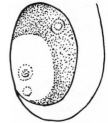

Fig. 50. Pedinomonas rotunda Korsch. (Redrawn from Korschikoff).

59b Cells with 2 to 8 flagella...60

60a Cells with 2 flagella...61

60b Cells with 4 or 8 flagella...64

61a Cells obversely pear-shaped or oval, broadly rounded anteriorly, but with longitudinal folds, 4- to 6-lobed or stellate when seen in end view. Fig. 51.....................................*Stephanoptera*

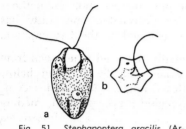

Fig. 51. *Stephanoptera gracilis* (Artari) G. M. Smith. (a) 'front' view; (b) end view showing point of flagella attachment.

These pyriform motile cells without a wall have longitudinal folds (wings) and when seen from the end are 6-radiate and starlike. The chloroplast also has longitudinal flanges which extend into the folds of the membrane. The eye-spot is rod-like. One species has been found in the United States, occurring in saline water.

61b Cells not obversely pear-shaped, without longitudinal folds; not stellate in end view...62

62a Cells narrowed anteriorly, egg-shaped or pear-shaped in 'front' view, round in end view; cells often reddish with haematochrome; species of brackish or saline waters. Fig. 52...............
....*Dunaliella*

Fig. 52. *Dunaliella salina* Teodor. Two differently shaped individuals.

This species and 2 others are apparently the only ones described for the genus thus far, but they are widely distributed in saline and brackish inland waters. The chloroplast of these pyriform cells lies in the posterior, broader part. *Dunaliella* belongs to a family which is characterized by the lack of a true cell wall, having only a cell membrane.

62b Cells shaped otherwise; not inhabiting brackish or saline waters...63

63a Cells transversely reniform (bean-shaped) with flagella of decidedly different length, attached apically but both trail-

ing; eye-spot black, anterior; chloroplasts sometimes brownish
or bluish green. Fig. 53................(*Nephroselmis Heteromastix*)

This name now includes in
synonymy the genus *Nephroselmis*. The cells are transversely,
angularly oval with the chloroplast lying along the posterior
wall. The 2 flagella are unequal in
length, a feature difficult of determination. There is a large, con-

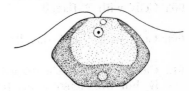

Fig. 53.   *Heteromastix a n g u l a t a*
Korsch.

spicuous pyrenoid and a less conspicuous eye-spot (sometimes
lacking). Although classified in the Volvocales, one study has
indicated that this genus should be assigned to the Cryptophyta.

**63b Cells irregularly spheroid, decidedly flattened when seen from
the side, with an apical depression; flagella attached below
the apex and directed at a deflexed angle; chloroplast a complete, parietal band with 2 pyrenoids; eye-spot red, median
rather than anterior. Fig. 54......................................*Mesostigma***

Cells in this genus are broadly oval to
nearly circular in outline but are much
flattened when seen from the side. The
chloroplast completely encircles the cell.
There are 2 conspicuous pyrenoids. The
flagella are attached in a subapical depression. Characteristic of the Polyblepharidaceae there is no cellulose wall. Apparently only 2 species are known.

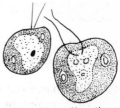

Fig.   54.   *Mesostigma
viridis*   Lauterborn.   (Diagrammed from Bourrelly.)

**64a (60) Cells oval in 'front' view, round in end view, with 8 apical
flagella and 2 or 4 contractile vacuoles; chloroplast cup-shaped
with a large basal pyrenoid. Fig. 55...............*Polyblepharides***

This genus is identified by having a veritable tuft
of flagella (usually 8) which are relatively short.
There are several contractile vacuoles at the anterior
end. If there is an eye-spot it lies lateral about midway
in the cell. There may or may not be a pyrenoid.
Thus far only 2 species have been reported from
the United States, occurring along the Atlantic sea-
board.

F i g.   55.
P o l y ble-
p h a rides
f r a gariifor-
mis   Hazen,
showing 3 of
the contrac-
tile vacuoles
at the an-
terior   end.
(R e d rawn
f r o m   Ha-
zen).

64b Cells with 4 flagella...65

65a Cells pear-shaped or elliptic, with an apical depression and with longitudinal folds; 4-lobed when seen in end view, the flagella attached one in each depression betweeen the lobes. Fig. 56...*Pyramimonas*

Fig. 56. *Pyramimonas tetrarhynchus* S c h m a r. (a) 'front' view; (b) end view showing points of flagella attachment.

This is *Pyramidomonas* of some authors, including about 25 species, all of which are 4-lobed when seen in end view. There is a flagellum attached in each of the 4 depressions between the lobes. The eye-spot is variable in position. The 4 species reported from the United States have a wide distribution and are to be expected in ponds, pools and roadside ditches.

65b Cells shaped otherwise, without longitudinal folds..............66

66a Cells curved, bean-shaped or wormlike, with 4 long flagella directed posteriorly; chloroplast an elongated plate. Fig. 57 ....*Spermatozoopsis*

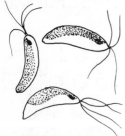

Fig. 57. *Spermatozoopsis exultans* Korsch., three cell shapes.

These cells are curved or crescent-shaped, with 4 flagella, but sometimes only 2. The chloroplast is a parietal plate without a pyrenoid; the eye-spot is relatively large and conspicuous. Of the 2 known species 1 has been reported from the United States.

66b Cells broadly oval and broadly rounded anteriorly, round in end view, with 4 flagella arising from one point; chloroplast

cup-shaped with a basal pyrenoid. Fig. 58................................
....*Quadrichloris (Tetrachloris)*

This name is synonymous with *Tetrachloris*. The cells are very similar to *Pyramimonas* in one view but are round in cross section. The membrane is not rigid and the organisms change shape while swimming. There are 5 species known but thus far none has been reported from the United States.

F i g. 58. *Q u adrichloris c a r terioides* (P a s c her et Jahoda) Fott. (R e d r a w n from Fott).

67a (26) Cells arranged in a plane, forming a flat or twisted plate 68

67b Cells arranged within a spherical, spheroidal, oval or somewhat cubical colony..69

68a Colony horseshoe-shaped, flat or twisted, the colonial sheath with 2 or 3 posterior lobes. Fig. 59.........................*Platydorina*

Although rare and seldom seen this genus can be readily identified by the flattened, slightly twisted and horeshoe-shaped colony. It is to be found in the same habitats as favor other members of the Volvocales. Originally found in Illinois *P. caudata* Kofoid has appeared in 8 other states but never outside of this country.

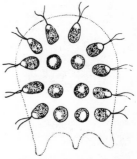

Fig. 59. *Platydorina caudatum* Kofoid. The flagella of the organisms in the center of the colony are directed vertically to the colony surface.

68b Colony a circular or subquadrangular plate. Fig. 60....Gonium

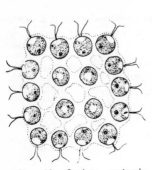

The number of cells in this disclike colony may vary according to species, from 4 to 32 or 64. The rectangular plates tumble over and over in motion. The flagella of the inner cells are directed at right angles to the colony plane; those of the lateral cells are directed outward in the colony plane. Eight species are known from the United States. In sexual reproduction each cell becomes metamorphosed to act as an isogamete. Apparently some species are homothallic and others heterothallic (plus and minus gametes formed in different strains or clones.

Fig. 60. *Gonium pectorale* Muell., an 18-celled colony.

69a (67) Colony globular or pyriform, or quadrangular, without an investing colonial mucilage..**70**

69b Colony globular or ovoid; cells enclosed by a mucilaginous sheath..**74**

70a Colony pyriform, narrowly tapering; cells radiately arranged. Fig. 61..*Raciborskiella*

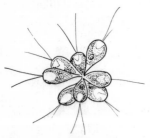

This genus with 2 species is distinct because of the colonial arrangement of the radiating cells that taper to a fine point posteriorly. Only 1 species is known from fresh water.

Fig. 61. *Raciborskiella uroglenoides* Swir. (Redrawn from Swirenko).

70b Colony otherwise, composed of oblong, elliptic or pyriform cells, not radiately arranged..**71**

71a Colony small, composed of 2 or 4 cells arranged with long
   axes parallel and all directed the same. Fig. 62.......................
   ....*Pascherina (Pascheriella)*

This name is synonymous with *Pascheriella.* The
organism is rare; occurs in rain water pools and catch
basins of temporary duration. Unlike most members of
this group of the algae the chloroplast is a laminate,
parietal plate rather than being cup-shaped. *Pascherina*
apparently has been found in only one station in
the United States, in California.

Fig. 62.
*Pascherina
tetras*
(K o rsch.)
Silva, cells
s h o wing
t h e sub-
f l a gellar
vacuoles.

71b Colonies of more numerous cells, 8 to 16, with long axes not
   parallel..72

72a Cells with 4 flagella arising from a protuberance at the broad
   anterior end; cells compactly clustered in tiers of 4, with the
   anterior ends directed the same way. Fig. 63.............................
   ....*Spondylomorum*

In this genus the cells have a 'huddled' appearance with the broad anterior ends all directed the same way.
The cells have a tendency to arrange
themselves in tiers. The eye-spot is posterior rather than anterior. Whereas the
flagella are conspicuous it is difficult
to determine that there are 4 on each
cell. It has been suggested that this
genus should be united with *Uva.*
(Fig. 65).

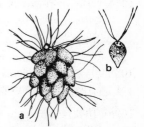

Fig. 63. *Spondylomorum
quaternarium* Ehr. (a) colony;
(b) single organism showing
posterior eye-spot and sub-
flagellar vacuoles.

72b Cells with 2 flagella; cells not in tiers of 4............................73

73a Cells pyriform to rhomboid, with narrow anterior ends and long flagella all directed the same; quadrately arranged in 2 tiers of 4 each, one tier above the other and interconnected by gelatinous strands. Fig. 64...*Corone*

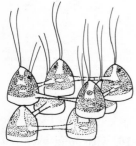

This is an 8-celled colony with 4 cells in two tiers, one above the other. The anterior ends are all directed the same way; bear 2 very long flagella. Thus far only one species is known, from Czechoslovakia.

Fig. 64. *Corone bohemica* Fott. (Diagrammed from Fott).

73b Cells huddled in a cluster with anterior ends and flagella all directed the same. Fig. 65..............................*Uva (Pyrobotrys)*

Pyrobotrys is a synonymous name for this genus as well as for *Chlamydobotrys*. Like *Spondylomorum* the cells of this colonial organism are closely grouped; have their anterior ends all directed the same way. There are 2 long flagella and a conspicuous eye-spot, anterior or posterior. The chloroplast is somewhat massive and is without a pyrenoid. Three species have been reported from the United States

Fig. 65. *Uva gracilis* (Korsch.) Bourr., a colony of individuals in which the eye-spot is posterior.

74a (69) Colonial spheroidal or oval; cells crowded, somewhat pyriform, with the broad ends all directed outwardly. Fig. 66 ....*Pandorina*

This is a tumbling and rolling colony which is usually more oval than spherical, with the cells rather compactly arranged. The flagella extend from the broad anterior end of the pyriform cells in a more or less parallel fashion and then flare widely emerging from the colonial sheath. Often colonies are found in which each cell has undergone cleavage to form daughter colonies. *Pandorina morum* Bory is worldwide in distribution, whereas *P. charkowiensis* Korsch., also found in the United States is relatively rare. The cells of the latter are compressed-spheroid; have a chloroplast with longitudinal ridges.

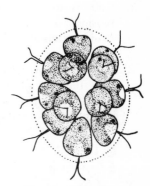

Fig. 66. *Pandorina morum* Bory. Cells are pyriform and often are more compactly arranged than shown in the illustration.

74b Colony globular or broadly ovoid; cells not crowded but evenly spaced..75

75a Colonies large, up to 1 mm. in diameter and containing as many as 50,000 cells. Fig. 67..*Volvox*

This globular colony contains thousands of individuals and usually can be seen with the unaided eye. It occurs in water that is rich in nitrogenous matter (frequently) and sometimes produces "blooms" of short duration during summer months. It is often accompanied by *Pleodorina* (Fig. 71) and *Eudorina* (Fig. 70). Reproduction is oogamous and when colonies are mature they may contain several, much enlarged eggs and packets (plakea) of motile sperm. Some species, however, are heterothallic and produce either one or the other of the gametes. Fre-

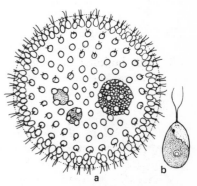

Fig. 67. *Volvox tertius* Meyen. (a) colony showing 1 daughter colony and 2 eggs; (b) cell showing parietal chloroplast and eye-spot.

quently the colonies will be found to have 1 to several daughter colonies produced by the cleavage of selected vegetative cells.

75b Colonies composed of from 8 to 128 cells..............................**76**

76a Cells fusiform, with sharply pointed lateral processes or extensions of the protoplast, arranged in a circle within an ovoid, gelatinous sheath. Fig. 68........................*Stephanosphaera*

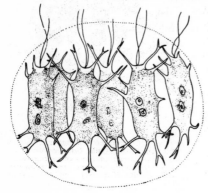

Like *Pascherina* (Fig. 62) this organism occurs in small, temporary pools in rocks, sometimes at high altitudes. The cells are all directed one way, lying in an equatorial belt within the oval gelatinous sheath, with flagella all directed forward.

Fig. 68. *Stephanosphaera pluvialis* Cohn. Oval colony with organisms forming a median band. The cells commonly show 2 pyrenoids.

76b Cells round or ovoid, without lateral processes........................**77**

77a Cells arranged at the equator of a spheroidal or oval gelatinous sheath; cells in 2 tiers, 8 or 16 in number. Fig. 69......
....*Stephanoon*

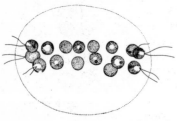

This genus is a clear, oblate, gelatinous sphere with 1 or 2 series of spherical cells encircling it at the equator. The cells are very similar to other volvocoids but possess 2 flagella of unusual length. Each cell may form a daughter colony as in *Pandorina* (Fig. 66).

Fig. 69. *Stephanoon Askenasyii* Schew.

77b Cells not arranged at the equator of a gelatinous sphere, but distributed throughout..**78**

78a Cells all the same size within the colony, arranged within the periphery of the colonial mucilage but showing a tendency to occur in tiers. Fig. 70..*Eudorina*

Unlike *Pandorina* (Fig. 66) the cells are round or slightly oval and are rather evenly spaced within the globular, colonial mucilage. The cells usually show a distinct tiered arrangement. *Eudorina elegans* Ehr., the most common species with world-wide distribution occurs with other colonial Volvocales, in both eu- and tychoplankton. *E. unicocca* G. M. Smith is known also from the United States and from Panama. It is differentiated by the colony showing a more definite polarity, with the sheath forming lobes at the posterior end.

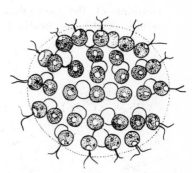

Fig. 70. *Eudorina elegans* Ehr. In this species the cells have a tendency to be arranged in transverse bands or tiers. It occurs in the same habitats with *volvox* (Fig. 67) and *Pleodorina* (Fig. 71).

78b Cells of two sizes within the same colony, the smaller located in one sector or at one pole..79

79a Colony globular, composed of from 32 to 132 cells; larger reproductive cells at the anterior sector, and with from 4 to 12 smaller vegetative cells at the opposite pole; cells not enclosed by individual sheaths. Fig. 71......................*Pleodorina*

This colony usually consists of 132 or 164 cells; is globular and the cells are spherical. The two distinct sizes of cells, the smaller confined to the posterior pole, identifies this genus. In reproduction *Pleodorina* is oogamous like *Volvox*. The genus is commonly found in the same habitats with *Volvox* and *Eudorina* but never seems to form blooms. The two common species are widely distributed in the United States.

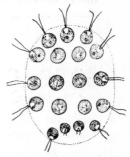

Fig. 71. *Pleodorina illinoisensis* Kofoid. Another common species, *P. californica* Shaw has about half of the cells larger (reproductive cells), the smaller cells being strictly vegetative.

79b Colony spheroidal, of from 16 to 124 cells, somewhat flattened where 2 or 4 smaller vegetative cells are located, each cell enclosed by an individual sheath. Fig. 72..........*Astrephomene*

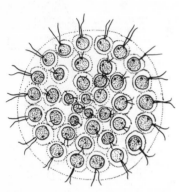

This is a globular colony of 128 or 164 spherical cells, each individual being enclosed by its own sheath. There is a cup-shaped chloroplast but no pyrenoid; an eye-spot; two apical flagella which arise separately. The colony is distinctive by being somewhat flattened at the 'posterior' pole where there is a group of 4 (or several) smaller cells with their flagella so directed that they produce what is called a rudder. There is but one species, originally described from South Africa.

Fig. 72. *Astrephomene gubernaculifera* Pocock, posterior view showing the smaller "rudder" cells.

80a (25) Plant a *filament* (cells in continuous or interrupted series), with or without branches; *or* a flat, horizontal expanse; *or* an attached cushion with the branches closely appressed laterally so that the filamentous plan is not clearly evident (see *Apatococcus*, Fig. 120A); *or* a branched, tubular, threadlike thallus without cross walls (coenocytic)...................................290

80b Plant *not* filamentous, not as above, but solitary cells; *or* a colony of 2 or more cells (often enclosed by mucilage or by old mother-cell walls (see *Oocystis*, Fig. 143); *or* cells variously adjoined to one another (see *Scenedesmus*, Fig. 75; *Pediastrum*, Fig. 124)...81

81a Cells solitary or gregarious but not forming colonies of adjoined cells.................................182

81b Cells adjoined to form a colony; *or* arranged within a colonial sheath or copious mucilage.......................82

82a Colony composed of 2 cells adjoined along the entire length of one wall...................................83

82b Colony composed otherwise...................................85

83a Colony composed of 2 trapezoidal cells adjoined along their bases. Fig. 73..*Euastropsis*

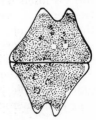

There is but one species of this unique genus in which the colony is always composed of but 2 trapezoidal cells which are similar in shape to many species of *Pediastrum*. The genus is rather rare but widely distributed; common in arctic Alaska.

Fig. 73. Euas-tropsis R i c h t e r i (Schmid.) Lag.

83b Colony composed otherwise...84
84a Cells oval, the wall beset with needle-like spines with thickened bases. Fig. 74..*Dicellula*

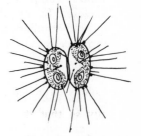

Cells in this genus occur in pairs, side by side. The walls in 1 species are beset with slender needles which have a buttonlike base. Only 2 species are known but as yet not reported from the United States.

Fig. 74. Dicellula planc-tonica Swir. (Redrawn from Korschikoff).

84b Cells oval or fusiform; walls smooth or with 1 or 2 curved spines not thickened at the base, or with teeth (colony usually composed of from 4 to 12 cells adjoined in a linear series, Fig. 75..*Scenedesmus*

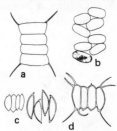

There are numerous species and varieties of this genus, occurring in both tycho- and euplankton. The cells are oval, fusiform, or crescent-shaped according to species. In some there are two forms of cells in the same colony (coenobe), the individuals at the outside of the row often being lunate, and different in the form of spines. Although usually in a row of 4, some species

Fig. 75. (a) Scenedes-mus quadricauda (Turp.) de Bréb.; (b) S. bijuga var. alternans (Reinsch) Hansg.; (c) S. incrassa-tulus var. mononae G. M. Smith. (Redrawn from Tiffany). (d) S. opolien-sis P. Richter.

have cells in a double, alternating series; or there may be a single row of 12 cells. *Scenedesmus* species invariably appear in laboratory cultures and aquaria, often coloring the water green; are frequently found in the psammon. Under unnatural conditions the plants may appear as single cells and show all manner of variability in respect to cell shape and presence or absence of spines. Also under culture conditions *Scenedesmus* may adopt a zoospore method of reproduction rather than by the normal autospores. Perhaps the most common species is *S. quadricauda* and its numerous varieties.

85a (82) **Colony composed of cells invested by a common mucilage (but see** *Oocystis,* **Fig. 143 with the cells enclosed by old mother-cell walls, not by mucilage)**......................................86

85b **Colony composed of an aggregate of cells often adjoined, not enclosed by mucilage but may be enclosed by or attached by old mother-cell walls or fragments of them. (In some forms cells may be solitary, e.g.** *Chaetosphaeridium,* **Fig. 115).** 132

86a **Colony attached or adherent, sometimes on soil, mosses or in snow**..87

86b **Colony free-floating, sometimes entangled among other algae but not growing attached. (Frequently algae which are normally attached become separated from their substrates. Look for attaching stalk, discs or other evidence of the organisms having been attached**..99

87a **Colony a number of gelatinous stalks arising from an attaching disc; cells fusiform, in 2's or 4's at the ends of the strands. Fig. 76**..*Tetracladus*

Fig. 76. *Tetracladus mirabilis* Swir., cells at the ends of branching gelatinous strands. (Diagrammed from Swirenko).

In this genus cells occur in 4's (sometimes in 2's) at the end of thick, branched, gelatinous stalks which arise from an attaching base. There is 1 parietal chloroplast with a pyrenoid. Autospore-formation is the only known method of reproduction. *T. mirabilis* is the only species described thus far.

88a Colony in the form of compact packets of angular cells enclosed in a close, gelatinous sheath; commonly found among
epidermal cells of aquatic plants, but sometimes found free-
living. Fig. 77..*Chlorosarcina*

The cells are usually angular from
mutual compression and ordinarily are
enclosed by a gelatinous sheath. There
are 5 species but only 1, *C. consociata*
(Klebs) G. M. Smith seems to be
common in the United States; found
in duckweed thalli (*Lemna.*). Old,
colorless plants of *L. trisulca* often
show the green flecks of this and
other endophytic algae such as *Chlorochytrium Lemnae.* (Fig. 158).

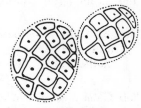

Fig. 77. *Chlorosarcina consociata* (Klebs) G. M. Smith.

88b Colony otherwise, not endophytic in the tissues of aquatic
plants..89

89a Colonial mucilage saclike or balloon-shaped, sometimes intestiniform; macroscopic..90

89b Colony microscopic; pyriform (pear-shaped) or composed of
gelatinous strands..91

90a Colonies amorphous, on moist soil, dripping rocks (rarely
under water); colonial mucilage forming lumpy (usually macroscopic) masses; enclosed cells round or oval, each enclosed
by an individual sheath (often in concentric layers). Fig. 12
....*Palmella*

90b Thallus gelatinous, balloonlike, saccate or intestiniform (macroscopic); cells in 2's and 4's at the periphery and often show-

ing pseudocilia (long, hairlike, false flagella). Fig. 78...................
....*Tetraspora*

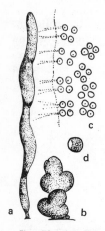

Fig. 78. (a) Tet-
raspora c y l i n drica
(Wahl.) C. A. Agardh,
habit of colony; (b)
T. gelatinosa (vauch.)
Desvaux, habit of
colony; (c) enlarge-
ment of *Tetraspora*
cells with pseudo-
cilia; (d) single cell
showing cup-shaped
chloroplast.

Early in the spring, or throughout the summer in cold, running water, gelatinous, balloonlike or intestiniform strands of *Tetraspora* may
be found attached to submersed substrates.
At times thalli 2 or 3 feet long develop. Most
of the dozen or so recognized species are
macroscopic, but a few appear as microscopic,
floating colonial clumps. Especially when the
plants are young, favorable optical conditions
will disclose long, fine, shadowy pseudocilia
which extend through the colonial mucilage.
Compare *Tetraspora* with *Gloeocystis* (Fig. 85)
which has larger and fewer cells in a gelatinous
matrix; no pseudocilia.

**91a (89) Colony pyriform, microscopic, attached at the narrow
end to filamentous algae or aquatic plants; cells in pairs or
in 4's, with clearly evident pseudocilia. Fig. 79............*Apiocystis***

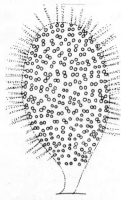

Fig. 79. Apiocystis Brau-
niana Naeg. Diagram of a
colony showing cell arrangement and pseudocilia.

This plant is always in the form of a
microscopic, balloonlike sac growing attached to filamentous algae or to aquatic
plant stems. The cells are arranged somewhat irregularly in 2's and 4's. The
pseudocilia are usually conspicuous
throughout the life of the colony. *Apiocystis Brauniana* is relatively common and
widely distributed, but in the Alaskan
Arctic there is a rare species in which the
gelatinous sac has a very thick and lamellated sheath and the thallus grows to
almost macroscopic size.

91b Colony formed otherwise..92

92a Thallus consisting of branched, gelatinous strands which are freely anastomosing, enclosing spherical cells, sparce in number, in linear pairs; (the thallus faintly colored); macroscopic. Fig. 80..*Gloeodendron* (*Schizodictyon*)

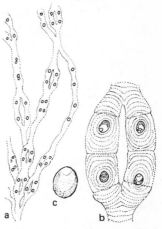

The anastomosing, gelatinous tube which comprises the thallus of this genus is conspicuously transversely lamellate. The oval or globular cells are in linear pairs, sparsely distributed throughout the length of the tube. *Schizodictyon* is synonymous with this genus. There are 2 species.

Fig. 80 *Gloeodendron catenatum* (Thomp.) Bourr. (a) habit of thallus; (b) portion of thallus enlarged to show lamellate sheaths. (Diagrammed from Thompson); (c) single cell.

92b Colony otherwise..93

93a Mucilaginous matrix indefinite in shape, without a bounding sheath, intermingled in mosses or on dripping rocks; cells cylindrical or subcylindric, relatively large with showy chloroplasts and conspicuous pyrenoids (See *Cylindrocystis*, Fig. 81)........94

93b Mucilaginous masses with a definite boundary; cells elongate and subcylindric, relatively small and numerous within the colony. (See *Gloeocystis*, Fig. 85)..95

94a Cells cylindrical, sometimes slightly constricted in the midregion; chloroplasts 2, axial, stellate. Fig. 81..........*Cylindrocystis* (Some species have been transferred to *Actinotaenium*).

Although some of the half-dozen species of this Saccoderm desmid have very slightly constricted cells, they are mostly unconstricted and have a wall composed of 1 piece; no wall pores which are characteristics of the Placoderm desmids

Fig. 81.   *Cylindrocystis Brebissonii* Menegh.

(See Fig. 179). There is a star-shaped chloroplast with a large pyrenoid in each half (or end) of the cell. The genus is not confined to acid habitats as is true for most of the desmids, but may occur in alkaline bogs, among wet mosses or on stones, especially in alpine regions. Some species have been transferred to *Actinotaenium* (not treated herein).

94b Cells oval, watermelon-shaped, with a single parietal chloroplast, not constricted in the midregion (some species with narrowly cylindrical cells); contents purplish with phycobilins. Fig. 82..*Mesotaenium*

Fig. 82. Mesotaenium de Greyii Turner Fa., showing variation in cell shape, and the lamellate chloroplast.

These are oval or oblong cells; have an axial, platelike chloroplast and a wall that is all in 1 piece (Saccoderm desmids). Although some of the 14 species occurring in this country are freefloating, others such as *M. macrococcum* (Kuetz.) Roy et Biss. usually occur among mosses and in gelatinous masses on rocky seeps, often at high altitudes.

95a (93) Cells cylindrical or elongate-oval, numerous, scattered throughout an amorphous but evident mucilage (rarely freefloating), the cells often with their long axes parallel. Fig. 83..*Coccomyxa*

Fig. 83. Coccomyxa dispar Schmidle. The end of a gelatinous strand showing oval or bacilliform cells, each with a parietal chloroplast.

There are 24 recorded species of this genus; only 1 seems to have been reported from the United States, forming gelatinous masses of varying extent on damp soil, on wet wood, on old fungal sporophores; rarely is free-floating. It has been found also attached to wooden flumes of swiftly flowing water. In subaerial habitats they are often intermingled and closely associated with either unicellular and colonial algae; often show a great variation of size within the same colony.

95b Cells shaped or arranged otherwise..**96**

96a Cells elliptical or nearly spherical, arranged in 2's and 4's within an amorphous mucilage; mother-cell wall often enclosing
   a family of cells, all within a common mucilaginous sheath;
   cells with a parietal, cup-shaped chloroplast and an eye-spot;
   colonies may be microscopic but also appear as gelatinous
   masses on subaerial substrates, moist soil, *etc.* Fig. 84...............
   ....*Palmella Stage Chlamydomonas*

Chlamydomonas (Fig. 17) often becomes quiescent under unfavorable
conditions, or as a normal stage in
the life history. The cells adhere to a
substrate, lose the flagella, but continue to divide, enclosing themselves
in mucilage, and form extensive gelatinous masses. The cells are arranged
in 2's and 4's, surrounded by mucilaginous sheaths, thus somewhat resembling *Palmella* (Fig. 12). In this form

Fig. 84. *Palmella* stage of
Chlamydomonas.

Chlamydomonas is often mistaken for *Gloeocystis* (Fig. 85).
Laboratory aquaria often contain *Chlamydomonas* in this palmelloid stage. The cells may become actively motile again by developing new flagella.

96b Cells spherical (oval in some species), scattered throughout
   the colonial mucilage or in groups of 4; orange-colored oil
   globules sometimes present; eye-spot lacking...........................97

97a Cells enclosed by distinct concentric sheaths of mucilage,
   scattered, single or in 2's and 4's within amorphous, colonial
   mucilage (often free-floating); chloroplast a parietal cup.
   Fig. 85...*Gloeocystis*

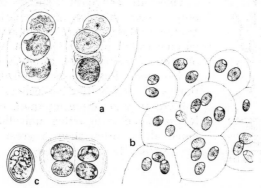

Fig. 85. (a) *Gloeocystis gigas* (Kuetz.) Lag.; (b) *G. ampla* (Kuetz.) Lag.; (c)
G. major Gerneck, showing dense, cup-shaped chloroplast.

There are several species of *Gloeocystis* and all are very common. They are not very distinctive plants and therefore many small, round or oval green cells, especially when enclosed in mucilage, belonging to other genera may be mistaken for this genus. The concentric layers of mucilage about the cells provide a helpful character for identification. *Gloeocystis ampla* (Kuetz.) Lag. does not always have mucilage in layers, however; but this free-floating species is identified by its oblong or oval cells.

97b Cells with or without evident individual sheaths; mucilage not in concentric layers...98

98a Chloroplast cup-shaped, not covering the entire wall; cells all the same size within the colonial mucilage which is lumpy and usually macroscopic; cells with individual sheaths; on soil. Fig. 12...*Palmella*

98b Colonial mucilage scant and sometimes not evident; cells of variable sizes; gregarious, in or on soil; chloroplast covering almost the entire wall. Fig. 86.........................*Chlorococcum**

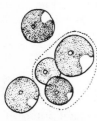

Although this plant occurs on soil it reproduces by swimming reproductive cells (zoospores). Another species, *Chlorococcum infusionum* (Schrank) Menegh. is aquatic and is differentiated from *C. humicola* (Naeg.) Rab. by the fact that its cells are all uniform in size and shape. Old, wet bones and rocks under dripping water are favorable places for both species. Unless it is *Desmococcus* (*Pleurococcus*) (Fig. 120) *C. humicola* is probably the most widely distributed alga species in the world.

Fig. 86. *Chlorococcum humicola* (Naeg.) Rab. Cells occasionally are seen to be enclosed in a mucilaginous sheath.

99a (86) Colonial sheath fusiform, definite in shape (margin lacey in some species); cells fusiform, rarely solitary, usually in 4's. Fig. 87...*Elakatothrix*

In this genus the cells are somewhat 'cigar'-shaped and occur end to end in pairs or side by side in a fusiform, gelatinous sheath. *Elakatothrix gelatinosa* Wille has both ends of the cell pointed, whereas other species have the adjoined poles truncate. In 1 of the 5 species found in the United States, *E. americana* Wille the gelatinous, colonial sheath is irregularly lacy or fringed.

Fig. 87. *Elakatothrix viridis* (Snow) Printz.

*See Appendix for other unicellular green algae.

99b Colony not fusiform but globular, globular-quadrate, cubical or elongate and threadlike...100

100a Colony regularly spherical or oval, *or* a rectangular plate....116

100b Colony shaped otherwise; irregular strand-like or cubical (some young *Tetraspora*,Fig. 78 may be somewhat spherical in colony shape)..101

101a Colony of 4 cells or multiples of 4 in one plane, interconnected by gelatinous strands, the cells bearing a scalelike fragment of the old mother-cell wall. Fig. 88.......*Coronastrum*

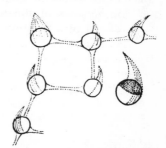

This is a very rare alga and only 1 of the 3 known species has been reported from the United States. The arrangement of the cells and their distinctive winglike scale make identification certain.

Fig. 88. *Coronastrum aestivale* Thompson. (Redrawn from Thompson).

101b Colony formed otherwise...102

102a Colony of 8 egg-shaped cells, the narrow anterior ends all directed the same, arranged in 4's in 2 tiers and interconnected by narrow gelatinous strands (cells equipped with flagella which may be lost or retracted and not evident). Fig. 64..*Corone*

102b Colony formed otherwise...103

103a Colony a hollow cube of 8 round cells arranged one at each corner and interconnected by stout, gelatinous strands. Fig. 89..*Pectodictyon*

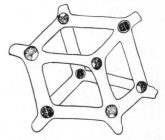

There are 2 species known for this genus. Since its original discovery in Ohio by Taft, *P. cubicum* has appeared in several midwest and western states. It appears in the euplankton of lakes as well as in the tychoplankton of small ponds.

Fig. 89. *Pectodictyon cubicum* Taft. (Redrawn from Taft).

103b Colony formed otherwise...104

104a Cells spherical, arranged in a linear series within long, gelatinous, pseudofilamentous strands which often branch and anastomose. Fig. 238................................*Palmodictyon*

104b Cells arranged otherwise...105

105a Cells cylindrical, elongate-ellipsoid or elliptical.................106

105b Cells other shapes...109

106a Cells elliptical, grouped in 2's and 4's and partly enclosed in remains of the mother-cell wall; multiples of 4 all enclosed in a gelatinous matrix; 1 parietal chloroplast. Fig. 90 ....*Lobocystis*

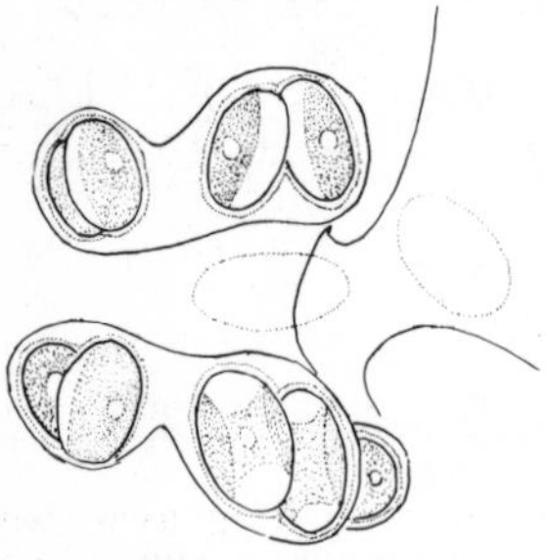

Cells in this colonial genus are arranged in pairs, enclosed by a sheath and occurring at the ends of dichotomous or V-shaped strands. The entire colony is usually found enclosed by a gelatinous sheath. There is 1 parietal chloroplast (or 2), each with a pyrenoid. *L. dichotoma* Thompson has been found only in Kansas.

Fig. 90. *Lobocystis dichotoma* Thompson. (Redrawn from Thompson).

106b Cells shaped or arranged otherwise.................................107

107a Cells oval or watermelon-shaped with an axial, platelike chloroplast; cells few within a watery, amorphous mucilage. Fig. 82...*Mesotaenium*

107b Cells shaped otherwise, or with different chloroplasts.......108

108a Cells cylindrical, rarely slightly constricted in the midregion, with 2 stellate, axial chloroplasts; enclosed in a watery, inconspicuous mucilage; (cells more often than not solitary). Fig. 81...*Cylindrocystis*

108b Cells bacilliform or elongate-elliptic, many within a copious mucilage; chloroplast a parietal plate. Fig. 83........*Coccomyxa*

109a (105) Colony forming stringy, intestiniform strands, sometimes branched and anastomosing; cells in 2's and 4's. Fig. 78 ....*Tetraspora*

109b Colony shaped otherwise...110

110a Colony composed of a few (2 to 4) oval cells, with 1 parietal chloroplast, enclosed in an irregularly shaped, lamellate, gelatinous sheath. Fig. 91.......................................*Dactylothece*

Cells in this genus are shaped as in *Mesotaenium* (Fig. 54) but are much smaller (not more than 3-4 *u* in diameter) and have a laminate, parietal chloroplast. The cells are enclosed in mucilage (rather formless) and form thin, expanded masses on moist rocks. *Dactylothece confluens* (Kuetz.) Hansg. is the only species reported from North America. The species can be identified by the few number of cells involved in a colony.

Fig. 91. *Dactylothece confluens* (Kuetz.) Lag.

110b Colony composed of round, pyriform or oval cells; gelatinous sheath not stratified..**111**

111a Semicircular fragments of old mother-cell walls partly enclosing daughter cells, or lying about in the mucilage; cells often showing pseudocilia. Fig. 92...............................*Schizochlamys*
(*S. gelatinosa* is held to be synonymous with *Placosphaera*)

At times the free-floating, gelatinous masses of this plant may be of macroscopic proportions, and so abundant that they may be scooped from the surface of the water by hand. More frequently the growths are less extensive and small aggregates of cells occur intermingled with other algae in shallow water situations. The fragments of old mother-cell walls scattered about the cells help in the identification. Under favorable

Fig. 92. *Schizochlamys gelatinosa* A. Braun.

optical conditions a tuft of long, fine pseudopodia are discernible, 4 to 8 from each cell. The cells (often oblate-spheroid) have 1 or 2 platelike chloroplasts, parietal, but may appear massive and indistinct. This is an anomalous plant, placed in the Tetrasporales because of the gelatinous colony, with indefinitely arranged cells and because of the pseudocilia. The presence of oil rather than starch as a reserve food and the method of cell division raise a question as to its true affinity.

111b Semicircular fragments of old mother-cell walls not present
....**112**

112a Colonies saclike or irregularly globose; cells arranged in 4's. Fig. 78...*Tetraspora*

112b Colonies shaped otherwise; cells not arranged in 4's............113

113a Cells ovoid, compactly arranged in semi-opaque mucilage which is often brown or yellow and so obscures the cells; colonies frequently compounded by interconnecting strands of tough mucilage between clusters of cells. Fig. 93.................
....*Botryococcus*

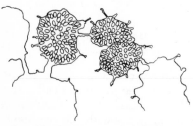

Specimens of this genus, especially *Botryococcus Braunii* Kuetz. can be identified by the golden-brown, a m o r p h o u s lumps of mucilage, with cells in the colony scarcely visible. The gelatinous material contains an oil which obscures the cells, especially when the colonies are older. The individual cells have a yellowish sheath, are oval and are usually somewhat radiately arranged. The colonies often have rubbery strands of mucilage which interconnect with other colonies to form a complex. Occasionally *B. Braunii* Kuetz. develops growths of 'bloom' proportions. This genus is considered to be responsible for a curious type of coal in Scotland.

Fig. 93. *Botryococcus Braunii* Kuetz., showing an expression in which a colonial complex is formed by interconnecting strands of tough mucilage. Colonies frequently appear solitary and as a yellow-brown lump in which individual cells can scarcely be seen, if at all. The color of the colony occurs in the mucilage. The species often forms blooms, especially in hard-water lakes.

113b Cells round, oval or pyriform, not arranged in semi-opaque mucilage; (mucilage of juvenile *Botryococcus* (Fig. 93) is colorless, however)..114

114a Cells round or oval, in 2's and 4's within gelatinous, lamellate sheaths; cells with individual sheaths in some species; colonies solitary or aggregated. Fig. 85.................................*Gloeocystis*

114b Cells shaped and arranged differently.................................115

115a Gelatinous colony globular; cells wedged-shaped, in radiating clusters; 1 parietal chloroplast without a pyrenoid. Fig. 94
....*Gloeoactinium*

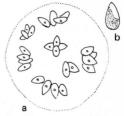

The colonial sheath is wide and ample, enclosing clusters of elliptic or wedge-shaped cells that are mostly grouped in 4's. There is but 1 species.

F i g. 94. *Gloeoactinium limneticum* G. M. Smith. (a) colony; (b) single cell.

115b Colony irregular; cells pyriform, sharply pointed posteriorly, radiately arranged. Fig. 95...*Askenasyella*

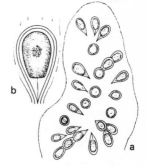

The gelatinous matrix which encloses the pyriform cells may be nearly globular, but often is irregular in outline. The cells are arranged in a radiate fashion, with the narrow end directed inwardly. The parietal chloroplast is in the broad anterior end. A fine protoplasmic thread extends from the posterior end of the cell to the chloroplast. Plants are either tychoplanktonic or attached.

F i g. 95. *Askenasyella chlamydopus* Schm. (a) colony; (b) single cell. (Redrawn from Schmidle).

116a (100) Cells incised or constricted in the midregion to form semicells (cell halves), the cells often interconnected by fine, gelatinous strands. Fig. 96...*Cosmocladium*

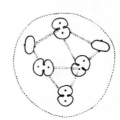

This species has every appearance of a tiny *Cosmarium*-like desmid in which the cells are enveloped by a colorless, gelatinous sheath. *Cosmocladium* belongs to the Placoderm desmids, those which have the wall in 2 sections that adjoin in the midregion where there usually is an incision (sinus) forming an isthmus between 2 semicells. There are but few species in the genus. Like the majority of desmids it occurs in soft or

Fig. 96. *Cosmocladium tuberculatum* Presc.

acid-water bogs. Under properly reduced illumination the fine, often double, gelatinous strands interconnecting the cells can be determined.

116b Cells not constricted to form semicells...................................117

117a Chloroplast star-shaped, the radiating processes with their outer ends flattened against the wall. Fig. 97...... ...*Asterococcus*

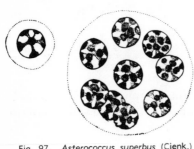

Two species of this genus are known to occur in North America *Asterococcus superbus* (Cienk.) Scherf. may occur singly or in small colonies of 2 or 8 relatively large cells and shows the star-shaped chloroplast more clearly than does *A. limneticus* G. M. Smith. The latter has smaller cells, larger in number within the colony. This species, as the name indicates, occurs in the euplankton.

Fig. 97.   *Asterococcus superbus* (Cienk.) Scherf.

117b Chloroplast not axial and star-shaped...................................118

118a Cells arranged in groups of 4 at the ends of branching and somewhat radiate, mucilaginous strands (focus carefully into the colony. (See Fig. 99)...119

118b Cells not arranged at the ends of branching strands............120

119a Cells appearing both reniform (bean-shaped) and ovoid in the same colony. Fig. 98...................................*Dimorphococcus*

In this plant the cells are in clusters of 4, 2 of which when seen in 'top' view appear oval, whereas 2, as seen from the side are reniform or somewhat crescent-shaped, hence the genus name. *Dimorphococcus lunatus* A. Braun is often abundant in soft-water lakes, whereas the other species known from this country, *D. cordatus* Wolle is less frequently found. Both species may occur in open-water plankton or in the tychoplankton near shore. A character that is helpful in identification is a negative one, the absence of a conspicuous gelatinous sheath enclosing the colony.

Fig. 98.   *Dimorphococcus lunatus* A. Braun.

119b Cells spherical or broadly oval, all the same shape within the colony. Fig. 99...*Dictyosphaerium*

Cells are in clusters of 4 as in *Dimorphococcus* (Fig. 98), but all the same shape, round or oval. The interconnecting fibers, the remains of old mother-cell walls are finer than in that genus. Sometimes an indefinite gelatinous envelope is seen. The chloroplast is a cup-shaped, parietal layer covering most of the wall.

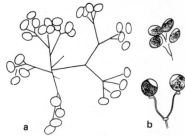

Fig. 99. *Dictyosphaerium pulchellum* Wood. (a) habit of colony; (b) individual cells at ends of strands.

120a Cells globular...**121**

120b Cells other shapes, ovoid, fusiform, crescent-shaped, or bean-shaped..**126**

121a Cells spherical, in 2's and 4's at the periphery of amorphous mucilage; cells with 1 parietal chloroplast with a pyrenoid, often forming red or green snow. Fig. 10...*Pseudotetraspora*

121b Cells arranged otherwise...**122**

122a Cells with a distinct sheath; colonial mucilage lamellate. Fig. 85...*Gloeocystis*

122b Cells without distinct sheaths; colonial mucilage not lamellate...**123**

123a Colony spherical, the mucilage including radiating fibrils; cells in packets of 4 distributed throughout the mucilage. Fig. 100...*Radiococcus*

The cells are cruciately arranged in clusters of 4. The colony sheath is ample and nearly always shows fine, radiating fibrils from the cell-clumps toward the periphery of the envelope.

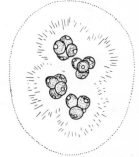

Fig. 100. *Radiococcus nimbatus* (de Wild.) Schm. (Redrawn from Thompson).

123b Colony without radiating fibrils...124

124a Colony a clear globe of mucilage, with cells in 4's arranged
at or near the periphery. Fig. 101......................*Eutetramorus*

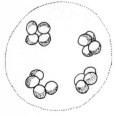

In this genus the cells are in quartets but not cruciately arranged as in *Radiococcus* (Fig. 100). The gelatinous sheath is very wide and homogeneous. There is but 1 species.

Fig. 101. *Eutetramorus globosus* Walton.

124b Cells arranged otherwise...125

125a Colony of 32 to 64 cells scattered through the colonial mucilage, ordinarily with several daughter colonies of small cells
intermingled; chloroplasts cup-shaped. Fig. 102....................
....*Sphaerocystis (Palmellocystis)*

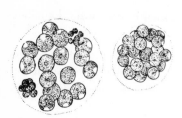

This plant, of which there is only 1 species in North American records, should be compared with *Planktosphaeria* (Fig. 103). There is 1, cup-shaped chloroplast, and the colony almost invariably shows clusters of small cells formed by the cleavage of a parent cell into 4 or 8 daughters. There is a wide gelatinous sheath but the individual cells do not show the lamellate envelope of *Gloeocystis* (Fig. 85), a genus which may be confused with *Sphaerocystis*. Young cells of *Planktosphaeria* may have 1 cup-shaped chloroplast but as the cells mature several, angular chloroplasts characterize the genus.

Fig. 102. *Sphaerocystis Schroeteri* Chod.

125b Colony of 8 to 16 cells, with polygonal chloroplasts, each
with a pyrenoid; colony not containing clusters of daughter

cells. (Young cells have only 1 or 2 chloroplasts.) Fig. 103
....*Planktosphaeria**

This plant, only 1 species known, occurs
mostly in the typchoplankton among other
algae, but occasionally is collected in open
water. Unless care is used this plant may
be confused with *Gloeocystis* (Fig. 85),
Sphaerocystis (Fig. 102) or other spherical
algal cells within a mucilaginous sheath.
When mature the cells are recognizable
by their angular, 5-sided chloroplasts, each
of which contains a pyrenoid. The colonial
sheath is often very thin and difficult of
determination.

F i g. 103. *Plankto-
sphaeria gelatinosa* G.
M. Smith.

126a (120) Cells lunate or sickle-shaped, tapered and pointed at
the apices...127

126b Cells bean-shaped, oval, or spindle-shaped, the apices sometimes tapered but rounded or blunt at the poles.................128

127a Cells decidedly curved, with the 2 poles nearly touching one
another in some species, arranged irregularly in groups of
4 with the convex walls apposed within a gelatinous sheath.
Fig. 104... ....*Kirchneriella*

The crescent-shaped or arcuate
cells of this genus are enclosed in
a mucilage which sometimes is
indistinct. *Kirchneriella*, of which
there are 6 species in the United
States, usually occurs in open-
water plankton. The species are
differentiated by degrees of curvature and variations in stoutness.
The cells are mostly so sharply
curved that their apices nearly
touch, whereas in *Selenastrum*
(Fig. 121), with which *Kirchneriella* should be compared, the
cells are symmetrically crescent-
shaped and they are not enclosed
by a gelatinous sheath.

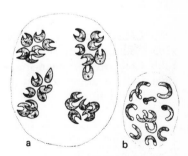

Fig. 104. (a) *Kirchneriella lunaris*
(Kirch.) Moebius; (b) *K. obesa* var.
major (Ber.) G. M. Smith.

*Follicularia is 1-celled or colonial, the cells eccentrically arranged in a
gelatinous, lamellate sheath; has chloroplasts similar to *Planktosphaeria*.

127b Cells symetrically crescent-shaped, in groups of 4, 2 of which face one another (concave margins apposed); colonial sheath usually not evident. Fig. 105.....................................*Tetrallantos*

Fig. 105. *Tetrallantos Lagerheimii Teiling.*

Tetrallantos Lagerheimii Teil. is a rare species, the only one known for the genus, but is widely distributed. The characteristic arrangement of the cells is determined at the time that they are formed in groups of 4 within the mother-cell. After the mother-cell wall breaks down to release the daughter cells fragments of the wall may persist as interconnecting or radiating threads within the colonial mucilage which is often very thin and difficult of determination.

128a (126) Cells curved, sausage-shaped with rounded ends, adjoined to one another by fine threads; gelatinous sheath wide. Fig. 106...*Tomaculum*

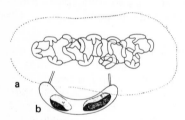

Fig. 106. *Tomaculum catenatum* Whitford. (a) colony; (b) single cell. (Redrawn from Whitford).

These sausage-shaped cells, sometimes with lateral, lobelike extensions, are interconnected by threadlike strands. Upward of 20 such joined cells are enclosed in a hyaline, gelatinous sheath to form free-floaing colonies. There are 1 or 2 parietal chloroplasts, each with a pyrenoid. The single species has been found only in North Carolina.

128b Cells shaped or arranged otherwise.......................................**129**
129a Cells fusiform or spindle-shaped...**131**
129b Cells ovate, bean-shaped or oblong.......................................**130**
130a Cells oval, somewhat irregularly arranged in 4's, forming a flat plate. Fig. 107...*Dispora*

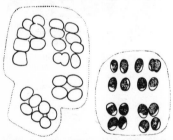

Fig. 107. *Dispora crucigenioides* Printz.

There is only 1 species of *Dispora* in the United States and apparently is rare; 2 others have been reported from Europe. It is sometimes difficult to differentiate these flat, platelike colonies from some species of *Crucigenia* (Fig. 126), especially *C. irregularis* Wille in which the cells are irregular in arrangement, although tending to occur in 4's.

130b Cells bean-shaped or oblong, reproducing by autospores which are retained within the enlarged mother-cell wall (the wall may gelatinize and appear as a mucilage sheath in some instances). Fig. 108.................................*Nephrocytium*

Most of the 8 species of this genus which occur in the United States are reniform or bean-shaped, often with 1 convex lateral wall and 1 flattened or slightly concave. They occur in mixtures of algae in the tychoplankton, although 2 species, *N. Agardhianum* Naeg. and *N. limneticum* G. M. Smith are usually found in the euplankton or relatively soft-water lakes. The former has elongate, almost vermiform cells which are sometimes curved or spirally twisted. *N. obesum* W. et W. has been transferred to *Oonephris obesa* (W. et W.) Fott. It has a massive, spongy chloroplast.

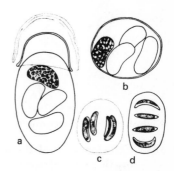

F i g. 108. (a) *Nephrocytium ecdysiscepanum* W. West; (b) *N. obesum* W. et W. (*Oonephris obesa* (W. et W.) Fott); (c) *N. limneticum* (G. M. Smith) G. M. Smith; (d) *N. lunatum* W. West.

131a (129) Cells in linear pairs, 1 or several pairs within a common mucilaginous investment (cells with long axes approximately parallel), sometimes solitary. Fig. 87.....................*Elakatothrix*

131b Cells arranged in parallel bundles, reproducing by autospores (daughter colonies forming within the mother-cell). Fig. 109 ....*Quadrigula*

There are 5 species found in the euplankton of lakes, all of which have elongate-fusiform or 'cigar'-shaped cells. The species illustrated has cells with bluntly rounded poles whereas the others have pointed apices. The cells occur in rather compact bundles of 4, all lying parallel in the colonial envelope.

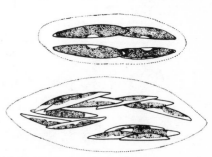

Fig. 109. *Quadrigula Chodatii* (Tanner-Fullman) G. M. Smith.

132a (85) Cells in compact packets of 4 or in multiples of 4, not enclosed by mucilage. Fig. 110......................*Chlorosarcinopsis*

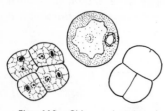

The 8 or 10 species in this genus may be either submersed or on moist subaerial habitats. Whereas cells may be solitary they normally form cubical packets of spheroidal individuals with some walls flattened by mutual compression. The chloroplast is parietal, covering most of the wall. Species must be differentiated by culturing.

Fig. 110. *Chlorosarcinopsis minor* (Gerneck) Herndon. (Redrawn from Herndon).

132b Cells not in compact packets of 4...133

133a Cells (or some of them in the colony) bearing long, gelatinous bristles or scales, or hairs. (See Fig. 115).............................134

133b Cells without gelatinous bristles, with or without spines which may be longer or shorter than the cell. (See Fig. 127) 139

134a Cells arranged in quadrate colonies of 4, interconnected by strands, each cell bearing a scalelike fragment of mother-cell wall. Fig. 88..*Coronastrum*

134b Colony formed otherwise...135

135a Cells in clusters of from 2 to 6 (rarely solitary), bearing more than 1 hair...136

135b Cells bearing but 1 hairlike bristle...138

136a Hairs with a gelatinous sheath at the base. Fig. 111...............
....*Conochaete*

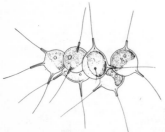

The globose cells of this genus are epiphytic and are enclosed by a gelatinous envelope from which 2 or 3 setae arise, the bases sheathed.

Fig. 111. *Conochaete comosa* Klebahn.

136b Hairs without a gelatinous sheath at the base.....................137

137a Cells several together (sometimes solitary) in a lamellate sheath, each cell with several long bristles. Fig. 112.................
....*Polychaetophora*

In this genus the cells are usually clumped or occur in a short, linear series, enclosed in a lamellate mucilaginous matrix which bears several gelatinous bristles. The chloroplast is a circular plate, apparently without a pyrenoid.

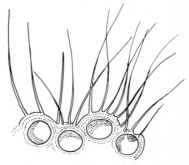

Fig. 112. *Polychaetophora lamellosa* W. et W.

137b Cells in a non-lamellate sheath, with 2 or 3 bristles (rarely 1). Fig. 113..*Oligochaetophora*

The epiphytic cells bear 2 or 3 simple, unbranched spinelike bristles. The cells occur solitary or in clumps of from 2 to 4 enclosed by a common gelatinous sheath. Compare with *Conochaete* (Fig. 111) and *Chaetosphaeridium* (Fig. 115).

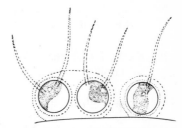

Fig. 113. *Oligochaetophora simplex* G. S. West.

138a (135) Cells forming an attached, compact cluster within the mother-cell wall which bears a branched hair that has no sheath. Fig. 114..*Dicranochaete*

Although this curious plant usually occurs as single cells, the individuals may be clustered as a result of recent cell division. It grows on filamentous algae and submersed aquatic plants; apparently is very rare. The unique branched setae on the sheath which arise from the lower side of the cell make identification certain.

Fig. 114. *Dicranochaete reniformis* Heiron.

138b Cells loosely arranged side by side in a cluster, each bearing an unbranched hair with a basal sheath. Fig. 115.................
....*Chaetosphaeridium*

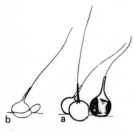

Fig. 115. *Chaetosphaeri-dium globosum* (N o r d s t.) Klebahn. (a) group of cells; (b) one cell showing tube-like utricle which may extend from one cell to another and so form a sort of colony.

The globular, hair-bearing cells of this genus occur either singly or in aggregates of from 2 to 8, living epiphytically on larger algae or aquatic plants. Frequently the cells are loosened from their substrate and are found floating free. This genus and *Dicranochaete* (Fig. 114) are anomalous members of the Coleochaetaceae. They are included there because of the type of sheathed bristle, in spite of the fact that they are not truly filamentous.

139a (133) Cells attached at the ends of branching, gelatinous stalks, or in elongate cups telescoping one another, formed from old mother-cell walls...**140**

139b Cells not at the ends of branching, gelatinous strands nor in cuplike sheaths...**142**

140a Cells oval, single or in pairs within cuplike remains of old mother-cell walls, the cups telescoping one another, forming branching chains. Fig. 116.......................................*Ecballocystis*

In this genus (monospecific) the oval cells are partly enclosed by cup-shaped remains of old mother-cell walls. The cups telescope others and several generations of walls are arranged to form branching chains. There are from 2 to 4 parietal chloroplasts, each with a pyrenoid.

Fig. 116. *Ecballocystis Frit-schii* Iyengar. (a) colony with cells enclosed in remains of old sheaths; (b) cell with auto-spores. (Redrawn in part from Iyengar).

**140b Cells shaped or arranged otherwise; growing epiphytically
on microcrustacea**..**141**

**141a Cells ellipsoid or somewhat fusiform; chloroplasts 1 or 2
longitudinal bands; stipes slender. Fig. 117**...............................
....*Chlorangiella (Chlorangium)*

According to some students, this genus is synonymous with the name *Chlorangium*. The organism
becomes attached, anterior end down, to small crustaceans and insect larvae by means of a gelatinous
stalk. Actually it is a swimming member of the
Tetrasporales which loses its flagella and becomes
sedentary. Sometimes the Chlorangiellaceae is included in the Volvocales. After attaching the cell
continues to divide, each new cell forming a stalk
so that a branched colony is produced. Some small
animals such as *Cyclops* may go swimming about
with a veritable plume of green cells on the anten-
nae and such hosts may appear green to the unaided eye because of the large number of attached
algae. The cells have 2 elongate, parietal chloroplasts. Compare *Chlorangium* with *Colacium* (Fig.
118), a member of the Euglenophyta.

Fig.   117.
C h lorangium
s t entorinum
(Ehr.) Stein.

**141b Cells ovate to oblong or ovoid; chloroplasts numerous, ovoid
discs; stalks relatively stout, branched, with a cell at the
apex of each branch. Fig. 118**......................................*Colacium*

Microscopic animals, especially
crustaceans, may appear green because of the large numbers of *Colacium* individuals attached to them,
either singly or in plumelike clusters. Like *Chlorangiella* (Fig. 117)
this organism is a motile, green cell
but belongs to the Euglenophyta.
There is a large number of disclike
chloroplasts and a conspicuous, red
eye-spot. The cells are attached to
branched stalks, anterior end downward. The rather specific association
of the algal cells with the animal
host invites speculation as to how
this relationship is established.

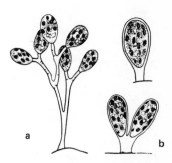

Fig.   118.   (a)   *Colacium arbuscula*   Stein;   (b)   *C.   vesiculosum*
Ehr.

142a (139) Cells ellipsoid or spindle-shaped, attached end to end, forming loose, branching chains. Fig. 119...........*Dactylococcus*

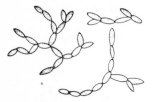

This anomalous genus is known from soil collections of algae. The characteristic chainlike arrangement of cells develops as the cells are cultivated whereas they are probably solitary in nature.

Fig. 119. *Dactylococcus infusionum* Naeg. (Redrawn from G. M. Smith).

142b Cells not arranged in branching chains..................................143

143a Cells globose or flattened along some sides from mutual compression; in packets or pseudofilaments; forming green films on moist substrates; chloroplast a parietal plate with pyrenoid indistinct. Fig. 120...
.................................*Desmococcus (Protococcus; Pleurococcus)*
See Fig. 120A, *Apatococcus*, similar to *Desmococcus* but without a pyrenoid.)

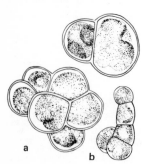

This genus like *Apatococcus* (Fig. 120A) has been and will continue to be confused with *Protococcus* and *Pleurococcus*. Honest attempts have been made to dissociate and clarify the taxonomic names. *Desmococcus* occurs on moist substrates (trees, boards, rocks) and is associated with *Apatococcus*. The cells occur in irregular packets but show a distinct tendency toward the formation of short filaments. The cells have a parietal chloroplast with a pyrenoid. Reproduction occurs readily by cell division and by aplanospores; is easily distributed by air currents, birds and insects. Trees with soft, spongy bark invariably have

Fig. 120. *Desmococcus viridis* (Ag.) Brand. (*Protococcus viridis* Ag.). (a) clump of cells; (b) filamentous tendency in cell arrangement.

Desmococcus as well as *Apatococcus,* especially on the north, more moist side. Conifers seldom have these algae occurring on them.

In this genus packets of cells are formed, the cells being angular from mutual compression. There is a broad, somewhat lobed to massive chloroplast without a pyrenoid. Cell division is carried on actively whereas aplanospore-formation is not uncommon. There is not a tendency toward filament-formation as in *Desmococcus* (Fig. 120). Plants occur in the same habitats as the latter. Synonymous with some *Pleurococcus* and *Protococcus* as reported in literature.

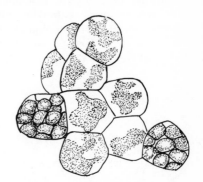

Fig. 120A. *Apatococcus lobatus* (Chod.) Boye-Petersen, clump of cells showing pseudofilamentous tendency; some cells forming aplanospores.

These gracefully curved cells occur in clusters of from 4 to 32, with a tendency to have the convex or 'outer' walls approximated. The curvature of the 'outer' and 'inner' walls of the crescent are more nearly equal than in the somewhat similarly shaped cells of *Kirchneriella* (Fig. 104), a genus which has cells irregularly arranged within a gelatinous envelope. Five species are commonly found in the United States,

Fig. 121. *Selenastrum gracile* Reinsch.

mostly differentiated by size of cell and degree of curvature. Mixtures of algae from shallow water often include *Selenastrum* but they may occur in the euplankton.

145b Cells straight, or acicular, or only slightly crescent-shaped, often loosely entangled about one another (frequently solitary rather than colonial). Fig. 122......................*Ankistrodesmus*
See also *Closteriopsis* (Fig. 122A) a long, slender needlelike cell with a chloroplast that has a row of pyrenoids.

Fig. 122. (a) *Ankistrodesmus falcatus* (Corda) Ralfs; (b) *A. convolutus* Corda; (c) *A. Braunii* (Naeg.) Brunn.; (d) *A. fractus* (W. et W.) Brunn.

Although there are about 12 species of this genus common in the United States, *Ankistrodesmus falcatus* (Corda) Ralfs is probably the one most frequently found. It occurs as solitary or loosely clustered needles or slightly fusiform cells intermingled with other algae. Sometimes this species forms almost pure growths in artificial pools or laboratory aquaria. One species, *A. spiralis* (Turn.) Lemm. has needle-shaped cells spirally twisted about one another to form bundles.

Fig. 122A. *Closteriopsis longissima* Lemm.

146a (144) Cells attached either along their side or end walls to form definite patterns, nets, plates, triangular clusters or short rows...**147**

146b Cells attached otherwise, if adjoined by lateral walls then not forming definite patterns..**166**

147a Cells cylindrical, 1 cell attached to 2 others at end walls
repeatedly to form a network. Fig. 123...........*Hydrodictyon*

This is the familiar "water net"
which often grows in such dense mats
in lakes and small ponds or irrigation
ditches as to become a troublesome
weed. This unique alga is able to reproduce very rapidly because each cell
of the net in turn produces a cylindrical net or a sheetlike expanse of
cells (depending upon species) within
it, which upon escape enlarges enor-
mously, each cells again forming a
daughter colony. The nets are of macroscopic size and there is a report of
one found more than 2 feet in length.
It is thought that the first written
record referring to a specific alga is of *Hydrodictyon* in ancient
Chinese literature.

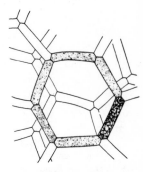

Fig. 123. *Hydrodictyon retic-
ulatum* (L.) Lagerheim.

147b Cells some other shape, not attached to form a network......148

148a Cells arranged to form flat, circular or rectangular plates....
....149

148b Cells not arranged to form flat plates...............................152

149a Cells forming circular plates (sometimes irregularly sub-circular), the marginal cells usually different in shape from those within. Fig. 124...*Pediastrum*

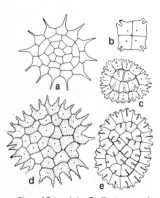

Fig. 124. (a) *Pediastrum sim-plex* (Meyen) Lemm.; (b) *P. tetras* (Ehr.) Ralfs; (c) *P. biradiatum* var. *emarginatum* fa. *convexum* Presc.; (d) *P. Boryanum* (Turp.) Menegh.; (e) *P. obtusum* Lucks.

Although there are many species of this genus the cells all have a great similarity, varying only slight-ly in shape and wall markings. They can be identified as *Pediastrum* by the platelike arrangement of the cells. In some species the plate is continuous whereas in others there are interstices and fenestrations. Commonly the cells at the margin differ in shape from those within. One species, *P. tetras* (Ehr.) Ralfs contains only 4 cells in the colony but there may be as many as 32 or 64 (always some multiple of 2). Rarely a 2-celled colony may be seen in which instance it might be mistaken for *Euastropsis* (Fig. 73).

Pediastrum cell walls are highly resistant to decay and many species are found in fossil or semifossil condition. The author knows of no instance in which *Pediastrum* cells have been found parasitized by aquatic fungi or bacteria. Colonies are often found in the psammon. Arctic lakes sometimes exhibit remarkable developments of *Pediastrum* species with colonies attaining huge proportions.

149b Cells not arranged to form circular plates.............................150

150a Cells triangular or ovoid, forming quadrangular plates and bearing 1 or more spines. Fig. 125............................*Tetrastrum*

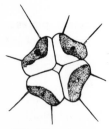

Fig. 125. *Tetrastrum heterocanthum* (Nordst.) Chodat.

There are 9 species of this genus reported from the United States, varying in cell shape and spine length. The thallus consists of a flat plate of 4 cells and bear from 1 to 4 slender spines each on the outer free walls. The cells are oval, heart-shaped or angular from mutual compression.

150b Cells rectangular or trapezoidal, or if oval never with spines
....151

151a Cells rectangular, oval or trapezoidal, the outer walls entire
(not incised); arranged in 4's to form quadrate plates, or in
multiples of 4. Fig. 126..*Crucigenia*

These cells (like *Tetrastrum*, Fig.
125) occur in 4's but usually form
multiple colonies or groups of rectangular plates. There are about 15
species in the United States, differentiated by the shape of the cells
which may be oval, triangular, or
elliptic in outline.

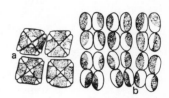

Fig. 126. (a) *Crucigenia tetra-*
pedia (Kirch.) W. et W.; (b) C.
rectangularis (A. Braun) Gay.

151b Cells trapezoidal, the outer free walls deeply incised, forming oval to somewhat angular plates (only 4 cells present in
plates of some species). Fig. 124.............................*Pediastrum*

152a (148) Cell wall with spines...153

152b Cell wall without spines...157

153a Cells ellipsoid or oval; spines numerous, needlelike............154

153b Cells ovoid or spherical; spines few (1 to 4); cells definitely
arranged and definite in numbers (usually more than 2)......155

154a Cells oval, side by side in pairs; the wall beset with numerous, slender spines with a thickened base. Fig. 74...............
....*Dicellula*

154b Cells ellipsoid, spines numerous and needlelike, the cells arranged side by side because of interlocking of spines (usually cells solitary). Fig. 127...*Franceia*
(See also *Bohlinia*, Fig. 128)

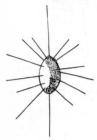

The species illustrated here and 2 others occur in the euplankton of lakes but rather rarely. The cells are solitary but they may be clustered from the interlocking of the needlelike spines which cover the wall. *Lagerheimia* (Fig. 192) has a similar shape, but with needlelike spines confined to the poles, or to the midregion of the cell. In *Franceia* the spines are uniformly distributed.

Fig. 127. *Franceia Droescheri* (L e m m.) G. M. Smith.

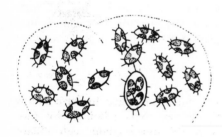

Although sometimes found solitary, cells in this genus are mostly embedded in an amorphous mucilage. The wall bears fine, short spines which are mostly more numerous near the poles of the ellipsoid cells than in the midregion. By some, *Bohlinia* is considered to be synonymous with *Franceia*, in which the spines are evenly distributed. Thus far only *Bohlinia echnidna* (Bohlin) Lemm. has been reported from this country.

Fig. 128. *Bohlinia echnida* (Bohlin) Lemm.

155a (153) Cells ovoid or fusiform, arranged side by side in 1 row or in 2 alternating rows; spines on the wall mostly short, arising from the poles of the cells, but sometimes from the face of the cells also. Fig. 75...................................*Scenedesmus*

155b Cells spherical, in groups of 4 or in multiples of 4 to form compound colonies; outer walls bearing long, slender spines
....**156**

156a Colony triangular; spines 1 to 7. Fig. 129............ ......*Micractinium*

This rare alga occurs in the euplankton, having clusters of 4 round cells arranged in the form of small pyramids. Each cell bears 1 to several long, tapering spines. Another species which is also seldom seen is *M. quadrisetum* (Lemm.) G. M. Smith, having oval or elliptic cells.

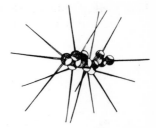

Fig. 129. *Micractinium pusillum* Fres.

156b Colony pyramidal, with the outer free walls of the cells bearing a single, stout spine. Fig. 130...... ....*Errerella*

Cells of this plant, of which there seems to be but a single species, are arranged to form a 3-dimensional pyramid. It is known only from the euplankton and apparently is very rare, although it has been reported from several parts of the United States.

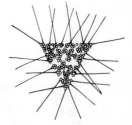

Fig. 130. *Errerella Bornhemiensis* Conrad.

157a (152) Cells spherical or polygonal, arranged to form hollow, spherical or many-sided colonies; cells adjoined by interconnecting protuberances of the mucilaginous cell sheaths. Fig. 131..*Coelastrum*

As the genus name suggests, cells of this plant are arranged to form a follow colony. In some species the cells are closely associated and the hollow feature is discerned with difficulty, whereas in others the cells are clearly separated in a peripheral layer and interconnected by prominent 'arms' of the mucilaginous sheath that encloses each

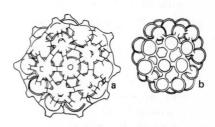

Fig. 131. (a) *Coelastrum cambricum* Archer. (Redrawn from G. M. Smith); (b) C. *microporum* Naegeli.

cell. There are about 14 species known from the United States. These differ in respect to the shape of the cell and the length of the processes of the sheath which in some species produce marginal protuberances. *Coelastrum microporum* Naeg. is especially common in both eu- and tychoplankton.

These 'cigar'-shaped cells are arranged in radiating colonies from a common center. The species illustrated is more common in the plankton than *A. gracillimum* G. M. Smith which has cells about as wide at the apices as in the midregion.

Fig. 132. *Actinastrum Hantzschii* Lag.

This plant resembles some *Scenedesmus* species (Fig. 75) but differs in having cells with their long axes parallel, quadrately arranged as a packet rather than in 1 plane. There are 3 species reported from the United States. *T. wisconsinense* G. M. Smith has trapezoidal cells.

Fig. 133. *Tetradesmus Smithii* Presc.

163a Cells crescent-shaped to somewhat triangular, the poles extended into horns, cruciately arranged with the convex margins apposed. Fig. 134....................................*Lauterborniella*

In this genus flattened, triangular-crescent cells are arranged about a common center with their concave walls outward. The outer angles are extended to form sharp poles. There is a parietal chloroplast and 1 pyrenoid.

Fig. 134. *Lauterborniella e l e g a n tissimum* Schm. (Redrawn from Schmidle).

163b Cells shaped or attached otherwise.......................................164

164a Cells oval, showing some polarity, the 'apical' more broadly rounded than the posterior, arranged in clusters of 4 with long axes parallel, but the cells somewhat staggered; walls often ribbed. Fig. 135...*Enallax*

This genus is very similar to *Scenedesmus* (Fig. 75) but is differentiated by the bunched or clustered arrangement, of the cells (not side by side in 1 plane). The cells are somewhat staggered or tiered in their arrangement.

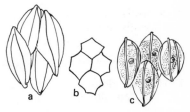

Fig. 135. (a) *Enallax* sp., habit of cell arrangement; (b) end view of colony (Redrawn from Pascher); (c) *E.* sp., showing chloroplasts and pyrenoids.

164b Cells shaped or arranged otherwise.......................................165

165a Cells crescent-shaped, in groups of 4, 2 with concave sides toward one another, the other 2 cells in another plane with the poles at one end only in juxtaposition. Fig. 105.................
....*Tetrallantos*

165b Cells sickle-shaped, fusiform or crescent-shaped, twisted about one another, or in bundles with long axes parallel. Fig. 122...*Ankistrodesmus*

166a (146) Cells adjoined by gelatinous strands or threads formed from remains of old mother-cell walls...............................167

166b Cells not adjoined by strandlike remains of old mother-cell walls...172

168a Cells spherical, at the corners of a hollow cube, formed by gelatinous tubes. Fig. 89..*Pectodictyon*

168b Cells globular or pyriform, in 4's, forming a square, interconnected by gelatinous strands, the cells bearing scalelike fragments of the old mother-cell wall. Fig. 88.....*Coronastrum*

169a (167) Cells spindle-shaped, in clusters of 4-8-16 at the ends of radiating, gelatinous strands. Fig. 136...............*Actidesmium*

Fig. 136. *Actidesmium*
Hookeri Reinsch.

This rare plant occurs in the tychoplankton of shallow pools; also found commonly in the Arctic. The star-shaped clusters of cells at the end of radiating (sometimes dichotomously branched) gelatinous strands render it certain of identification. The clusters of cells result from the fact that zoospores formed in the cells remain clustered at the tip of the mother-cell. The chloroplast is parietal or diffuse and does not contain a pyrenoid, as far as known.

169b Cells shaped or arranged otherwise......................................170

170a Cells globose, in clumps of 4-8, the groups held together by looplike fragments of the old mother-cell wall. Fig. 137........
....*Westella*

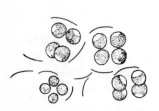

Fig. 137. *Westella botryoides*
(W. West) de Wild.

This plant should be compared with *Dictyosphaerium* (Fig. 99), which it may resemble superficially at times. *Westella* has no gelatinous envelope and although there are strands left by the old mother-cell wall they do not produce the regular, radiate structures as in *Dictyosphaerium*. Two species only are known from the United States.

170b Cells in 4's at the ends of fine, radiating strands which are the remains of old mother-cell walls.............................171

171a Cells globular or somewhat oval, in 4's at the ends of fine, dichotomously divided strands. Fig. 99.........*Dictyosphaerium*

171b Cells in 4's, both oval and reniform in the same cluster, at
the ends of (often indistinct) radiating (sometimes double)
gelatinous strands. Fig. 98............................*Dimorphococcus*

172a (166) Cells pyriform, bean-shaped or somewhat crescent-
shaped, the outer angles of the cells bearing horns; cells at
the ends of radiating, stout gelatinous strands, forming a
globular colony. Fig. 138...*Sorastrum*

There are only 4 species of this genus
reported from the United States, of which
Sorastrum spinulosum Naeg. is probably
the most common, occurring in euplankton. This species has relatively stout,
short spines at the angles of the cells, and
the basal pedicel is scarcely developed
so that the colony appears as a compact
cluster.

Fig. 138. *Sorastrum amer-
icanum* (Bohlin) Schmidle.

172b Cells other shapes, not so arranged, without horns, or with
spines different from above..173

173a Cells clustered, spherical or oval, in 2's and 4's, separated
from one another by semi-opaque masses of dark mucilage
which form X-shaped bands over the colony. Fig. 139........
....*Gloeotaenium*

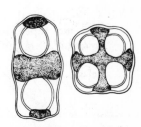

This monotypic genus is unique in appearance because of the dark bands of
mucilage that occur between the cells of
the colony, sometimes forming a cross-
shaped pattern. There are 2 or 4 cells
tightly enclosed within the mother-cell
wall. The chloroplast is dense, massive
and usually obscured by numerous starch
grains. *Gloeotaenium Loitelsbergerianum*
Hansg. is rare but widely distributed
over the world; occurs in the tychoplankton.

Fig. 139. *Gloeotaenium
Loitelsbergerianum* Hansg.

173b Cells not separated from one another by masses of dark
mucilage..174

174a Cells spherical, clustered (sometimes solitary), with thick walls which show refractive or refringent alveolae. Fig. 140 ....*Keriochlamys*

The globular or semi-globular cells in this genus are readily identified by the thick wall which has alveolae that refract light. Each cell has a parietal, platelike chloroplast and 1 pyrenoid. The genus is to be expected throughout the U. S. but thus far has been reported only from Kansas.

Fig. 140. *Keriochlamys styriaca* P a s c h e r. (Diagrammed from Pascher).

174b Cells arranged otherwise, without alveolar walls...............175
175a Cells with long, needlelike spines...176
175b Cells without long, needlelike spines..................................177
176a Cells spherical, with slender spines, needlelike throughout their length; colonial only because of entangling of spines; chloroplast a parietal plate with a large, distinctly bean-shaped pyrenoid. Fig. 141..*Golenkinia*

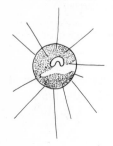

There are only 2 or 3 species of this genus reported, all of them common in tow samples from the open water of lakes. *Golenkinia radiata* (Chodat) has long, needlelike spines, 2 or 3 times the diameter of the cell in length, whereas *G. paucispina* West et West has more numerous spines that are about equal to the cell diameter. There is a parietal chloroplast with a distinctly curved or U-shaped pyrenoid.

Fig. 141. *Golenkinia radiata* Chodat.

176b Cells spherical, with spines that are thickened at the base or which taper from base to apex; chloroplast with a circular pyrenoid. Fig. 142..*Golenkiniopsis*

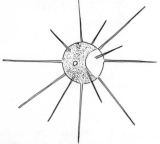

This genus (very similar to *Golenkina*) has been established on the basis of its circular (usual) type of pyrenoid, and by the fact that the spines are broader at the base, tapering to a fine point. (See Fig. 141).

Fig. 142. *Golenkiniopsis solitaria* Korsch.

177a (175) Cells enclosed by old mother-cell wall.......................178

177b Cells not enclosed by old mother-cell wall.......................179

178a Cells somewhat bean-shaped or kidney-shaped, or broadly
elliptic (old mother-cell wall often appearing as a mucilaginous sheath. (See note at 130b and Fig. 108). Fig. 108......
....*Nephrocytium*

178b Cells elliptic, lemon-shaped, or sometimes subcylindric, 1 or
more generations of mother-cell walls enclosing daughter
cells (autospores). Fig. 143...*Oocystis*
(See *Rayssiella*, Fig. 144 which has a unique way of liberat-
ing autospores; is similar in many respects to *Oocystis*.)

There are several species of
this genus common in both
euplankton and tychoplankton.
The various ones are dif-
ferentiated by the presence or
absence of nodules at the
poles, and by the number of
chloroplasts. Two or 3 generations of cell walls may be
enclosed within an original
mother-cell wall which enlarges so that it often appears
as a gelatinous sheath and
therefore may be misleading as
a generic character.

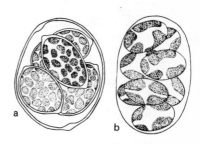

Fig. 143. (a) *Oocystis Eremosphaeria*
G. M. Smith; (b) *O. Borgei* Snow.

The autospores in this genus are
arranged at 2 poles in the mother-
cell. Upon release the mother-cell
wall forms loops which interconnect
the clusters of daughter cells. Only
1 species is known. *R. hemispherica*
Edel. et Presc.

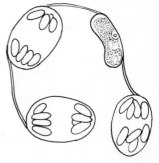

Fig. 144. *Rayssiella hemisphae-
rica* Edel. et Presc., one vegetative
cell and autospore-formation in
others.

179a (177) Cells spherical, occurring evenly distributed, often with interspersed clumps of small cells within the gelatinous sheath (sheath sometimes difficult to discern); chloroplasts several angular plates. Fig. 103....................................*Planktosphaeria*

179b Cells variously shaped but not with distributed clumps of daughter cells in the colony; often densely aggregated; chloroplast 1, parietal..180

180a Cells spherical or angular from mutual compression when occurring in clumps; subaerial..181

180b Cells fusiform or needle-shaped; aquatic. Fig. 122....................
....*Ankistrodesmus*

181a Cells spherical, gregarious but not adjoined, sometimes solitary. Fig. 86..*Chlorococcum**

181b Cells in dense clumps, forming a film or layer on moist substrates; cells spherical or angular from mutual compression, sometimes forming pseudofilaments. Fig. 120........................
............................*Desmococcus (Protococcus; Pleurococcus)***

182a (81) Cells attached, consisting of a euglenoid, flagellated organism enclosed in a brown, vase-shaped lorica with a wide, anterior opening. Fig. 21............................*Ascoglena*

182b Cells free-floating or attached, but without a sessile lorica
....183

183a Cells crescent-shaped or sickle-shaped, with sharply pointed or narrowly rounded and tapering apices.............................184

183b Cells some other shape..193

184a Cells with 2 axial chloroplasts, bearing longitudinal ridges, a chloroplast in each horn of the cell; pyrenoids conspicuous, usually in an axial row..185

184b Cells with 1 chloroplast, or with parietal chloroplasts not arranged as above..186

---

*See Appendix for other spherical unicells.
**See Bourrelly 1966.

185a Cells furnished with a stout spine at either pole. Fig. 145
....*Spinoclosterium*

Spinoclosterium, apparently with but
a single species (and a variety) is disjunct in its distribution throughout the
world, but is very rare. *S. curvatum* has
been found in southeast United States,
in the glaciated region of central North
America, and from the mountains of
the far west. It was originally reported
in the East Indies. Some authors include *Spinoclosterium* in *Closterium*,
but the distinctive polar spines would
seem to justify its separation, otherwise
the diagnosis of the genus *Closterium*
would need emendation. The chloro-

Fig. 145. *Spinoclosterium curvatum* Bernard.

plasts are prominently ridged and there are terminal vacuoles as
in *Closterium*. Zygospores never have been reported and it is
essential that reproduction in *Spinoclosterium* be learned to complete its diagnosis. Plants occur in sparse number in *Sphagnum*
bogs and soft water habitats. The variety *spinosum* Presc. with cells
inflated near the poles was described from Michigan.

**185b Cells crescent-shaped, variously bowed (sometimes nearly
straight), without apical spines. Fig. 146.. ....*Closterium***

This is one of the Placoderm
desmids in which there is no incision or sinus in the midregion.
The wall is in 2 sections, however, and the cell contents are arranged as 2 semicells, with a
chloroplast in each. Whereas
some species may be nearly
straight, *Closterium* is character-
stically bowed or crescent-shaped,
sometimes enlarged in the midregion, and sometimes with the
concave and convex margins
showing different degrees of

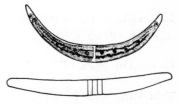

Fig. 146. *Closterium* spp. Two of
the many variations in curvature and
cell proportions in this genus. Some
species are almost straight or only
slightly bowed; others taper to relatively narrow apices; some are smooth-
walled, others striate.

curvature. The poles may be narrowed to fine points or may be
broadly rounded (sometimes slightly recurved). The two chloro-

plasts are often ridged with laciniate margins. Each contains from 1 to several pyrenoids. In the poles of the cell is a conspicuous vacuole in which there are from 1 to many vibrating granules of gypsum (showing Brownian movement). Cell division in some species leaves transverse bands or girdles. The wall may be smooth or striate; is often brownish because of iron deposits.

186a (184) **Cells only slightly crescent-shaped, usually straight or nearly so and sometimes S-shaped or sigmoid, with the poles drawn out into fine points**..**187**

186b **Cells definitely crescent-shaped, the poles abruptly sharp-pointed or drawn out into fine points; (but see** *Ankistrodesmus*). **Fig. 122**..**190**

187a **Cells attached by a slender stipe to other algae or to micro-fauna. Fig. 147**..*Characium*

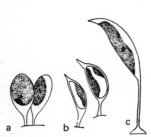

a   b   c

Fig. 147. (a) *Characium Debar-yanum* (Reinsch) De Toni; (b) C. *ornithocephalum* A. Braun; (c) C. *rostratum* Reinhard.

There are numerous species in this genus, differentiated by shape of cell and by length or stoutness of a stalk. Some are very minute and are easily overlooked, whereas others are larger and grow in associations so as to form patches on filamentous algae or on small animals. The genus *Characiopsis* (Fig. 324) contains species shaped like some of those in *Characium* and care should be used in determining the color of the chloroplast, the presence or absence of a pyrenoid, and the presence of starch as a reserve food. *Characiopsis* has a yellow pigment predominant and the starch test is negative; is a member of the Chrysophyta.

187b **Cells not attached by a stipe**..**188**

188a **Cells fusiform, the poles extended to form setalike spines**
....**189**

188b Tips of cells narrowed to fine points, not setalike but narrowly pointed or very narrowly rounded; chloroplast not extending the full length of the cell. Fig. 148.............*Ourococcus*

This rare plant might be confused easily with *Ankistrodesmus* spp. (Fig. 122) but the cells are usually stouter; are not nearly so needlelike. It is closely related to *Elakatothrix* (Fig. 87) in the Order Tetrasporales because the cells retain the ability to divide vegetatively to form new individuals, whereas in the Order Chlorococcales, which includes forms similar to *Ourococcus*, the cells cannot undergo division but must form new individuals within the wall of the parent cell.

Fig. 148. *Ourococcus bicaudatus* Grob. (Redrawn from G. M. Smith).

189a Cells fusiform, straight or slightly curved with each pole extended into a long, stout spine. Fig. 149.............*Schroederia*

The long, stout spine at the poles of straight (usually), fusiform cells differentiate this genus. There is a bandlike chloroplast that nearly covers the cell wall. The cell undergoes transverse cleavage prior to zoospore-formation. There is 1 species known for the U. S. Another species *S. Judayi* G. M. Smith hase been transferred to the genus *Ankyra* (Fig. 150).

Fig. 149. *Schroederia setigera* Lemm.

189b Cells fusiform or subcylindric, bent or curved, the apical
     pole extended into a long spine, the posterior with a stout,
     narrow extension which is forked or bifid at the tip; the cell
     wall separating medianly to release zoospores. Fig. 150........
     ....*Ankyra (Schroederia Judayi)*

In this genus somewhat curved, fusiform
cells have a long, straight spine at one pole
and a narrowed extension 'posteriorly' which
is forked at the tip. There is one parietal
chloroplast and a pyrenoid.

Fig. 150. *A n k y r a*
Judayi (G. M. Smith)
Fott.

190a (186) Cells slender, needlelike or sometimes fusiform (usually
     in clusters but may be solitary), often only slightly crescent-
     shaped; chloroplast parietal, the outline often discerned with
     difficulty). Fig. 122...*Ankistrodesmus*

190b Cells stouter, not needlelike; definitely crescent-shaped; the
     chloroplast parietal...191

191a Cells bearing a stout spine at either end. Fig. 151...................
     ....*Closteridium*

In this genus the cells are lunate or nearly
straight; are somewhat similar to some species of *Closterium* (Fig. 146) but can be
readily differentiated by the fact that there
is but a single, parietal chloroplast that nearly covers the cell wall, and by the absence
of terminal vacuoles with vibrating granules
characteristic of *Closterium*. There are 3
species reported for the United States.

Fig. 151. *Closteridium*
lunula Reinsch.

191b Cells without a stout spine at the poles...............................192

192a Cells enclosed in a mucilage (usually in clusters but some-
     times solitary); in some species the curvature is so great
     that the tips nearly touch. Fig. 104.........................*Kirchneriella*

192b Cells not enclosed in mucilage (rarely in mucilage, see Fig.
     121), usuually in clusters but sometimes solitary; curvature of
     the inner margin nearly that of the outer; tips of the cell not
     almost touching. Fig. 121...*Selenastrum*

Oophila Amblystomatis Lambert occupies the mucilage of frog and salamander eggs, often so abundantly as to give the egg masses a distinctly green color. It is a unicellular member of the Chlorococcales.

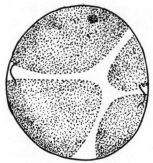

Fig. 152. *Oophila Amblystomatis* Lambert.

Cells in this genus are small, oval or spherical cells, occurring singly or gregarious, especially on soil and on moist subaerial substrates; whereas some species occur as inhabitors of Protozoa, *Hydra,* sponges and other aquatic microfauna. Fresh-water sponges are invariably green because of *Chlorella,* often referred

Fig. 153. (a) *Chlorella (Zoochlorella) parasitica* Brandt within *Ophyridium,* a colonial ciliate; (b) *C. (Zoochlorella) conductrix* Brandt, in *Hydra;* (c) *C. ellipsoidea* Gerneck, two cells enlarged to show parietal chloroplasts; (d) *C. vulgaris* Beij., cell with chloroplast; (e) cell with autospores.

*See Appendix for other unicellular green algae.

to as *Zoochlorella*. A few species are fairly well defined but mostly species must be cultured to make identification. Size, shape, number of pyrenoids are used to differentiate species. There is a thin, cup-shaped or platelike chloroplast. Like other members of the Chlorococcales, reproduction takes place by internal cells division, in this instance forming non-motile autospores. *Chlorella* is a genus which has been used widely in culture work for the study of photosynthesis, the production of protiens and in the production of an antibiotic, chlorellin. It lends itself well to mass culture and is investigated as a possible source of human food. *Palmellococcus* has been referred to *Chlorella* as a subgenus.

196a Cells globular or angular, with thick cyst walls, occurring in (or *on*, in the plasmodial state) the cells of *Sphagnum*; chloroplast massive and green although usually is colored yellow or golden, a member of the Xanthophyceae; encysted stage. Fig. 154..*Chlamydomyxa*

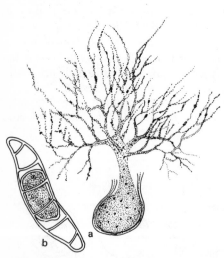

This curious organism (often greenish) occurs as a plasmodium over and in *Sphagnum* (mostly). The protoplast forms cysts within the empty, water-storage cells of *Sphagnum* leaves, which are thick-walled and usually yellow or golden-tan in color. The somewhat globular cysts have been shown to be multinucleate (as in the plasmodium). The cysts eventually form smaller, 2-nucleated cysts in which zoospores are formed. The organism is of uncertain position but is considered as a member of the Xanthophyceae.

Fig. 154. *Chlamydomyxa labrynthuloides* Archer. (Diagrammed from Archer). (a) vegetative thallus with pseudopodia; (b) cyst within a *Sphagnum* cell.

197a Plant a branched tube with globose swelling at the tips, growing on and among the cells of *Sphagnum.* **Fig. 155......**
....*Phyllobium*

The thallus of this genus consists of almost colorless, branched threads growing within and among the leaves of *Sphagnum.* The contents of the tubes accumulate at the tips of branches to form thick-walled akinetes. There are numerous ellipsoid chloroplasts, radiately arranged in the apical swellings.

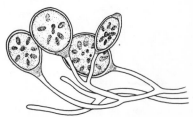

Fig. 155. *Phyllobium sphagnicola* G. S. West, a few colorless strands with terminal akinetes among cells of *Sphagnum* leaves.

197b Plant formed otherwise; not living in *Sphagnum* **...............198**

198a Plant a much-branched, coenocytic tube (multinucleate and without cross walls), growing in leaves of Araceae such as the Indian Turnip. Fig. 156... *Phyllosiphon*

This branched, tubular plant is non-cellular; forms green patches in the leaves of higher plants which become discolored. It may be more widely distributed than appears at present, but so far it is known only from northern and eastern sections in the United States,

Fig. 156. *Phyllosiphon Arisari* Kühn. (a) portion of thallus showing tangled threads; (b) habit of thallus in tissue of host. (Redrawn from Just).

but occurs in Europe and in tropical regions of high humidity. The coenocytic character and the lack of cross walls places *Phyllosiphon* in the Siphonales.

198b Plant not a branched, coenocytic tube................................199

199a An irregularly shaped, flasklike cell in the tissues of *Ambrosia* **(ragweed), and in other plants; cells usually red. Fig. 157, 20**
....*Rhodochytrium*

This curiously shaped, unicellular parasite occurs on a greater variety of hosts than does *Phyllosiphon* (Fig. 156), but seems to be most frequent in ragweed. It is readily identified by the red color and by the large number of starch grains. The chloroplast is massive and indefinite.

Fig. 157. *Rhodochytrium spilanthidis* Lag.

199b An irregularly oval, thick-walled cell in the tissues of *Lemna*
(Duckweed). Fig. 158..*Chlorochytrium*

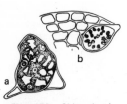

Fig. 158. *Chlorochytrium Lemnae* Cohn. (a) showing netlike chloroplast. (Redrawn from Bristol Roach); (b) cell in host tissue.

This genus occurs in both marine and freshwater hosts. In addition to the species illustrated there are 4 others known from inland waters of the United States, the most common being, however, *Chlorochytrium Lemnae* Cohn. Plants of *Lemna trisulca* when allowed to become colorless in the laboratory, frequently show green spots locating the position of the endophytic alga. The cell is diploid, the only haploid stages being the gametes which are produced within the encysted cells. The chloroplast is usually a parietal reticulum when the cells are mature, but is cup-shaped when young.

200a (193) Cells in the form of swollen vesicles on moist soil, with
colorless, subterranean, rhizoidlike extensions. Fig. 159........
....*Protosiphon*

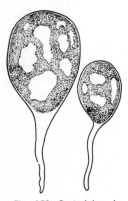

Fig. 159. *Protosiphon botryoides* (Kuetz.) Klebs, showing clathrate, parietal chloroplast.

Protosiphon is a 1-celled, coenocytic and bulbous plant inhabiting moist soil. Confusingly, it appears with *Botrydium* (Fig. 320) a member of the Xanthophyceae which is also balloonlike, but large; does not contain starch. There is a reticulate, sheetlike chloroplast (unlike the numerous disclike chloroplasts of *Botrydium*) which covers most of the wall. The sac has a colorless, rhizoidal extension that penetrates the soil. This genus is placed in its own family within the Siphonales.

200b Cells not as above..201
201a Cells attached, either sessile or on a stalk..........................202
201b Cells not attached, free-floating; or on moist soil, on snow,
  sometimes forming a green film...211
202a Cells bearing a seta or hair...203
202b Cells without setae..204
203a Setae simple (unbranched). Fig. 115.......*Chaetosphaeridium*

203b Setae branched. Fig. 114...*Dicranochaete*
204a (202) Cells on a slender stalk, or with the basal portion of the cell narrowed to form a stalk...................................209
204b Cells on a stout, thick stalk or a broad basal disc; cells globular, oval, or elgonate-elliptic...................................205
205a Cells globular or irregularly globose...................................206
205b Cells elongate, long-oval or somewhat fusiform...............207
206a Cells globular, sedentary, with anterior end downward (usually on *Cladophora*) on a broad, brown, short pedicel and enclosed in a brown sheath; protoplast filling the cell; chloroplast cup-shaped and located in the upper (posterior) portion of the cell, possessing a red eye-spot when young. Fig. 160 ....*Malleochloris*

This rare plant is to be sought on filamentous algae such as members of the Cladophoraceae. The sheath that encloses the cell is often reddish. Reproduction (similar to other Tretrasporales) is by swimming spores and by isogametes. There is a cup-shaped or urn-like chloroplast, a pyrenoid and 2 contractile vacuoles.

Fig. 160. Malleochloris sessilis Pascher. (Redrawn from Pascher).

206b Cells irregularly globular, sedentary on a broad attaching base, stalk practically wanting; with a thick, brown sheath enclosing a protoplast that does not fill it, the protoplast containing a cup-shaped chloroplast and an eye-spot as well as a contractile vacuole (giving the general appearance of a shelled zoospore). Fig. 161...............................*Chlorophysema*

The lorica of this genus is thick and brown. It is attached by a broad disc at the base of a very short (scarcely evident) pedicel. There are some 7 species, both epiphytic and epizoic.

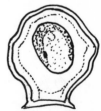

Fig. 161. Chlorophysema contractum Pascher. (Redrawn from Pascher).

207a (205) Cells oval, elongate, with 2 to several chloroplasts and enclosed in and attached by cup-shaped remains of old mother-cell walls, successive generations of cell walls forming branching chains, the cells 1 or 2 together in the extremeties. Fig. 116...................................*Ecballocystis*

207b Cells shaped and growing differently...........208

208a Cells oval to elongate-elliptic, attached by relatively broad, branching stalks to microcrustacea; chloroplasts many oval discs. Fig. 118 ....*Colacium*

208b Cells elongate-oval to fusiform, pointed anteriorly, narrowed posteriorly to a broad, attaching disc which is formed external to the cell wall; choloroplasts usually several to many narrow, parietal plates. Fig. 162. *Characiochloris*

In this genus the cells are similar to *Chlorangiella* (Fig. 117) but usually has many parietal choroplasts and 2 contractile vacuoles. There is no stalk but the cell (oval or fusiform) arises directly from a disc which is exterior to the cell wall.

Fig. 162
Characiochloris characioides
Pascher, showing scattered contractile vacuoles.

209a (204) Cells oblong or fusiform, gregarious (frequently solitary), on a slender attaching stipe which is often branched so that "plumes" are formed; epizoic on microcrustacea. Fig. 117...*Chlorangiella (Chlorangium)*

209b Cells shaped or growing differently.....................................210

210a Cells globular, attached by a slender, tapering stipe in the mucilage of other colonial algae (*Coelosphaerium, Anabaena*); chloroplast pariental, lying along the upper (outward) wall. Fig. 163..*Stylosphaeridium*

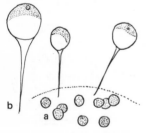

Fig. 163. *Stylosphaeridium stipitatum* (Bach.) Geitler et Gimesi. (a) cells in colony of *Aphanocapsa*; (b) single cell with chloroplast along apical wall.

This curious epiphyte is found in abundance when it occurs at all as minute 'hat pins' in the mucilage of colonial blue-green algae. Planktonic species of *Anabaena* and *Coelosphaerium* at certain times of the year, and usually when they are in 'bloom' condition are often densely beset with the epiphytes. There is a parietal chloroplast occupying the anterior wall.

210b Cells elongate-ovoid or fusiform (often curved), or if globular with the chloroplast parietal along the lateral walls; stalk as long as or shorter than the cell. Fig. 147...............*Characium*

211a (201) Cells elongate-fusiform, cylindrical or rod-shaped, crescent-shaped, slightly curved or straight; several to many times longer than their diameter..................................212

211b Cells oval, circular (or nearly so), pyramidal, trapezoidal, or star-shaped; isodiametrically angular, not more than 3 times the diameter in length..................................234

212a Cells with narrowed apices, sometimes sharply pointed......213

212b Cells with broadly rounded or truncate apices....................218

213a Chloroplasts 2, axial, one in either horn of a crescent-shaped cell which may be only slightly curved. Fig. 146....*Closterium* (See also *Spinoclosterium* Fig. 145)

213b Chloroplasts otherwise; cell not so shaped..........................214

214a Cells decidedly fusiform, one or both poles extended into setae or sharp points..................................215

214b Cells not broadly fusiform..................................217

215a Cells actually globular but enclosed in a fusiform sheath with longitudinal ridges. Fig. 164......................*Desmatractum*

This genus, with 2 species occurring in the United States, is rather rare, but widely distributed. It occurs in the euplankton of lakes and streams, often appearing as a minute seed pod with a single, globular seed. The wall is very wide and transparent and so forms a sheath-like envelope. There is a broad, parietal chloroplast and 1 pyrenoid. Both autospores and zoospores are used in reproduction.

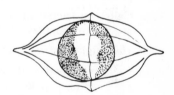

Fig. 164. *Desmatractum bipy-ramidatum* (Chod.) Pascher.

215b Cells themselves fusiform; without such a sheath............216

216a Setae formed by a narrowing of the cell to a fine point; chloroplast laminate (platelike), not extending the full length of the cell. Fig. 148......................*Ourococcus*

216b Setae formed by a fine spine on the wall, extending from the narrowed tips of the cell. Fig. 149...............*Schroederia* (See also *Ankyra*, Fig. 150).

217a (214) Cells many times (20 or more) longer than wide; the chloroplast with a row of pyrenoids. Fig. 122A......*Closteriopsis*

217b Cells less than 20 times the diameter long; slender or narrowly fusiform cells with 1 pyrenoid sometimes evident. Fig. 122..................................*Ankistrodesmus*

218a (212) With a notch in the apices of the cell. Fig. 165...............
..*Tetmemorus*

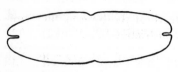

Fig. 165. *Tetmemorus laevis* (Kuetz.) Ralfs.

This genus belongs to the Placoderm desmids, having a wall in 2 sections that adjoin in the midregion. The median sinus is relatively shallow. The apical notch is prominent. Species that are found in the United States all seem to be confined to highly acid situations. Species are separated on the basis of semi-cell morphology, some tapering decidedly toward the apex; others more nearly cylindrical.

218b Without a notch in the ends of the cell................................219

219a Cells crescent-shaped, with an axial chloroplast bearing ridges in each horn. Fig. 146.....................................*Closterium*

(See also *Spinoclosterium,* Fig. 145)

219b Cells not crescent-shaped, or with other types of chloroplasts...220

220a Cells constricted in the midregion to form 2 semicells which are mirror images of one another.................................221

220b Cells not constricted in the midregion to form semicells......229

221a Cells furnished with whorls of protuberances which bear 1 or 2 spines; poles of the cell forked and spine-bearing. Fig. 166...*Triploceras*

Fig. 166. *Triploceras gracile* Bailey.

Cells of this Placoderm desmid are highly ornate, possessing whorls of spines. They are practically cylindrical in general shape but have slightly enlarged, lobed and spine-bearing apices. Like many other desmids *Triploceras* occurs in acid or soft waters, especially in *Sphagnum* bogs.

221b Cells not furnished with whorls of spiny protuberances......222

222a Cells 10 or more times longer than broad, usually cylindrical or nearly so, with margins smooth or undulate; in some with walls bearing rectangular raised areas................................223

222b Cells less than 10 times their diameter in length; cylindric, fusiform or tumid, usually straight but sometimes slightly curved (crooked)..**227**

223a Cells with a circle of folds or teeth at the base of the semicells where there is a shallow constriction..........................**224**

223b Cells without teeth or folds at the bases of the semicells....**225**

224a Cells cylindrical, approximately the same diameter throughout, the margins usually undulate; poles truncate and smooth. Fig. 167..*Docidium*

This genus is scarcely to be separated from *Pleurotaenium* (Fig. 169). In living cells the density of the chloroplast may obscure the characteristic creases in the

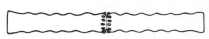

Fig. 167.   *Docidium undulatum* Bailey.

wall at the bases of the semicells. These folds form marginal teeth as seen at the periphery. Some species have undulate walls, others smooth. The poles are always abruptly truncate and not decorated.

224b Cells subcylindrical, curved, somewhat inflated at the base of the semicell, the margins not undulate; poles truncate but bearing spines at the angles, often with a median notch; a circle of prominent teeth at the bases of the semicells. Fig. 168 ....*Ichthyodontum*

This genus is practically cylindrical but the semicells are slightly enlarged at the base. The poles are abruptly truncate and in many instances (one species at least) show a dichotypical morphology; one pole is notched, with the angles spiniferous. There is a chloroplast in each semicell, longitudinally ridged and with a row of pyrenoids. The genus is known only from Java thus far.

Fig. 168.   *Ichthyodontum   S a c h l a n i i* Scott et Presc.

225a (223) Cells cylindrical or subcylindric, sometimes slightly narrowed at the poles which are truncate, but lobed and with spines or teeth...**226**

225b Cells cylindrical; poles truncate, smooth or with a circle of low granules or teeth, but not lobed; spineless; the margins smooth or undulate or with rectangular thickenings on the face of the semicells (one species with fine spines on the wall). Fig. 169...*Pleurotaenium*

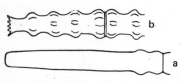

Fig. 169. (a) *Pleurotaenium trabecula* (Ehr.) Naegeli; (b) *P. nodosum* Bailey.

There are more species and a greater variety of shapes in this genus than in *Docidium* (Fig. 167) and they are more widely distributed. Although all of them are elongate and usually have subparallel margins, there is considerable variation in details of the wall decoration. In some species the walls are noded or undulate; one spiny. Usually there is a circle of granules around the poles of the cell. Some species are not so restricted in their distribution as most desmids and may occur in basic or slightly alkaline waters as well as in acid or soft waters.

226a Poles of cells tri-lobed, the lobes bearing teeth. Fig. 170..........
....*Triplastrum*

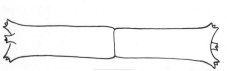

Fig. 170. *Triplastrum indicum* Iyengar et Ram. (Redrawn from Iyengar et Ramanathan).

The subcylindrical cells have a slight median constriction and truncate poles. At the apex are 3 short lobes, each bearing a pair of spines. The chloroplast is longitudinally ridged and there are 3 or 4 pyrenoids. The genus is known from India.

226b Poles bi-lobed, each with 1 spine. Fig. 171.........*Ichthyocercus*

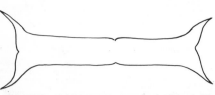

Fig. 171. *Ichthyocercus angolensis* W. et W.

This genus has subcylindrical cells and like *Triplastrum* (Fig. 170) is only slightly constricted in the midregion. The poles are distinctly enlarged, however and are slightly bilobed and each bears a sharp, awllike spine. There are 3 known species but they are rare. Conjugation in this genus has not been observed.

227a (222) **Cells with 2 star-shaped, axial chloroplasts, 1 in each semicell. Fig. 81**...*Cylindrocystis*
(Some species of *Cylindrocystis* have been transferred to *Actinotaenium*).

227b **Cells with other types of chloroplasts**....................................**228**

228a **Cells short cylindric, or subcylindrical; chloroplasts 1 in each semicell (rarely with 3 or 4 chloroplasts in each semicell forming transverse zones in the protoplast; no terminal vacuoles with moving granules. Fig. 172**.....................*Penium*

Some species of this genus are shaped somewhat like those in *Cylindrocystis* (Fig. 81), but *Penium* is a Placoderm desmid and has a wall in 2 sections that adjoin in the midregion. Also unlike

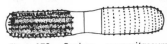

Fig. 172. *Penium margaritaceum* (Ehr.) Bréb.

Cylindrocystis, the walls may be punctate, poriferous or bear rows of granules. In general *Penium* is more cylindrical than the latter genus, and because new wall sections are formed when cells divide they may become as long as some small species of *Pleurotaenium* (Fig. 169).

228b **Cells slightly attenuated at the apices; chloroplasts with several pyrenoids; vacuoles with moving granules in the poles of the cell. Fig. 146**...*Closterium*

229a (220) **Chloroplasts in the form of spiral ribbons**..................**230**

229b **Chloroplasts some other shape**...**231**

230a **Cells 'cigar'-shaped, the poles rounded. Fig. 173**...................
....*Spirotaenia*

Fig. 173. *Spirotaenia condensata* Bréb.

The cylindrical cells in this genus may be slightly bent, but usually are straight and 'cigar'-like with broadly rounded poles. A few have the poles tapering slightly. The coiled, ribbonlike chloroplast aids in making identification. Usually there are many pyrenoids.

230b Cells cylindrical with truncate poles. Fig. 174...........*Genicularia*

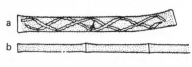

a

b

Fig. 174. *Genicularia elegans* West. (a) single cell; (b) filamentous arrangement.

In this genus the cylindrical cells may be solitary or adjoined end to end to form short, or relatively long filaments. Although the chloroplasts are spirally twisted and show a resemblance to *Spirogyra* (Fig. 227) this genus is usually identifiable by the cells being slightly enlarged at the poles, and also by the fact that the walls in most species are densely beset with short, sharp granules or short spines. *Genicularia* is a member of the Gonatozygaceae, closely related to the true desmids and found associated with them.

231a (229) Cells cylindrical, 10 or more times the diameter in length, the poles truncate; wall spiny or with sharp granules. Fig. 175..*Gonatozygon*

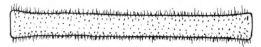

Fig. 175. *Gonatozygon aculeatum* Hastings.

This desmidlike genus, a member of the Gonatozygaceae, has solitary cells which are nearly always a bit crooked; have slightly enlarged, truncate poles. Most species have short and stout or long and fine spines. The chloroplast is a somewhat spiral or twisted ribbon that is axial rather than parietal as in *Genicularia* (Fig. 174). One system of classification places *Gonatozygon* in the Mesotaeniaceae.

231b Cells fusiform, short-cylindric, less than 10 times the diameter in length; wall smooth...232

232a Cells broadly fusiform or subcylindrical; 2 chloroplasts, 1 in each half of the cell, bearing longitudinal ridges and with notched margins. Fig. 176...*Netrium*

These are 'watermelon' or 'cucumber'-shaped cells which show the characteristics of the Saccoderm desmids. The wall is in one

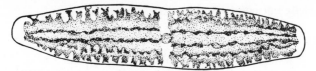

Fig. 176. *Netrium digitus* (Ehr.) Itz. et Roth.

piece and only rarely is there a slight median invagination. Like other members of the Mesotaeniaceae, the cell contents are divided into 2 portions, with two large, conspicuous and axial chloroplasts; the nucleus median. The chloroplasts are usually distinctly ridged with fimbriate margins. Usually there are several pyrenoids in each chloroplast.

232b Cells cylindrical or narrowly fusiform, with 1 chloroplast in each cell..233

233a Cells 'cigar'-shaped; chloroplast axial with 4 to 6 pyrenoids. Fig. 177...*Roya*

This rather rare Sacco-derm desmid has slightly curved, cylindrical cells in which there is but a single chloroplast that is notched in the midregion where the nucleus is located. There is a row of pyrenoids. *Roya* often occurs in subalpine regions; among wet mosses; also is found in mixtures of desmids from acid habitats. Two species have been reported from the United States.

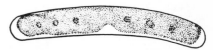

Fig. 177. *Roya obtusa* (Breb.) W. et W.

233b Cells elongate-ellipsoid or ovoid to subcylindrical; 1 parietal chloroplast; cell contents violet-colored. Fig. 82........................
....*Mesotaenium*

234a (211) Cells constricted in the midregion...........................235

235a Cells flat and nearly circular in proportions; starlike in 'front' view, the median incision very deep; semicells also deeply lobed or incised, in some species with secondary lobes and lobules. Fig. 178...*Micrasterias*

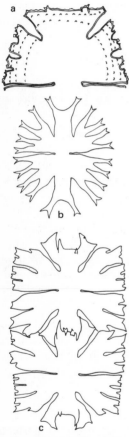

This genus is a member of the true or Placoderm desmids and includes some of the most beautiful of microscopic objects. Although the outline of the cell varies greatly among the 20 or more species reported from the United States, they can be identified by the flat, disclike shape. The sinus is deep and the semicells are variously lobed, sometimes with deep incisions so that arms are formed. The wall may be smooth or spiny and the lobes and lobules tipped with spines, or not. When seen from the top or side the cells are much compressed. One species, *Micrasterias foliacea* Bailey (Fig. 124c) has hooks on the polar lobes which enmesh with those of newly formed cells so that false filaments result. Most species are to be found in soft or acid-water ponds and *Sphganum* bogs.

Fig. 178. (a) *Micrasterias americana* var. *B o l d t i i* Gutw.; (b) *M. radiata* Hass. var.; (c) *M. foliacea* Bailey.

235b Cells not flat and disclike...236

236a Cells with shallow and broad, or a deep and narrow notch at the apex of the semicell. Fig. 179.........................Euastrum

There are numerous species of this Placoderm desmid, varying greatly in size, shape and type of wall ornamentation. Most of them, however, can be identified readily by the polar notch and by the protrusions or swellings on the face of the semicell. The cells are compressed when seen from the side, but show the facial swellings. The walls are often granular and, according to species, may have definite and conspicuous mucilage pores. The generic as well as specific features are best seen in empty cells. Like *Micrasterias* (Fig. 178) most species prefer acid habitats.

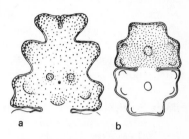

Fig. 179. (a) *Euastrum pinnatum* Ralfs; (b) *E. pectinatum* var. *inevolutum* W. et W.

236b Cells without a notch in the apex of the semicell..............237

237a Apex of the cell extended into 3 or more lobes or arms, radiately extended into 3 or more planes so that the cells are star-shaped or triangular to sexangular in top view..............238

237b Apex of semicell not extended into arms, or if with arms only 2, and not extending in more than 1 plane....................241

238a Semicells various, transversely oval, pyramidal or urn-shaped, the apex only slightly if at all elevated; semicells and arms either smooth or variously ornamented with spines and verrucae; the two poles of the cell similar in morphology and arm arrangement. Fig. 180......................................Staurastrum

This genus of Placoderm desmids includes more species perhaps than any other member of the Chlorophyta, although the desmid genus *Cosmarium* (Fig. 185) contains many hundreds of species also. There is a tremendous variation in shape, size and ornamentation. The most distinctive feature is the extension of the semicell into 3 or more planes (radiating arms, lobes and processes) so that the cells are seen to be triangular in end view or to have as many as 10 rays. In

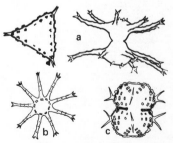

Fig. 180. (a) *Staurastrum rotula* Nordst., 'front' view; (b) end view; (c) *St. cornutum* Arch.; (d) end view.

one section of the genus the semicells have arms in one plane only (horizontal extensions of the semicell), but the shape of the arms and the type of spiny ornamentation identify such species with *Staurastrum*. Many species appear like *Cosmarium* (Fig. 185) when seen in 'front' view and one must focus carefully to see the arms or lobes of the semicell extending toward or away from the observer. Some species have long arms, especially among the euplanktonic forms. Most species are to be found in acid habitats, whereas a few are not selective and may occur in basic waters.

238b Semicells variously shaped and variously lobed, the apical lobe or apical region elevated, the two poles of the cell not always the same in morphology and arm arrangement........239

239a Semicells 3-lobed as seen in 'front' view, the apical lobe elevated or protruding, with the lateral margins subparallel, the cell from 3- to 8-lobed (rarely 10-lobed) as seen in end view which in outline is circular; poles of the cell similar in morphology; wall densely and uniformly granular. Fig. 181...*Euastridium*

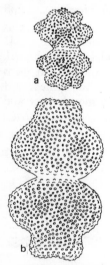

This genus of the desmids has features which resemble both *Euastrum* (Fig. 179) and *Staurastrum* (Fig. 180). The semicells are radiate, having lobes in several planes, and wall markings similar to *Euastrum*. The apex, however, is not notched as in the latter genus. There are only 2 or 3 species, widely distributed over the world, but especially in alpine regions.

Fig. 181. (a) *Euastridium verrucosum* Carter; (b) *E. Prainii* W. et W.

239b Cells shaped differently; wall not uniformly granular, the two poles of the cell different morphologically.........................240

240a Apex of one pole elevated and ornamented with a crown
of granules; the other pole convex, smooth; semicells elliptic
with 2 encircling series of long, spiny arms, one series near
the base and one near the apex; end view circular in outline
with 2 series of radiating arms, 10 in the lower series, 6 in
the upper. Fig. 182...*Amscottia mira*

This is another example of dichotypical morphology (See *Ichythyodon-
tum*, Fig. 168), one semicell being different from the other, especially in the
morphology of the polar lobe. The
semicells are radiate with at least 10
spiny arms as seen in end view. The
genus most nearly resembles *Staurastrum* (Fig. 180). Thus far only 1
species is known, from Africa, but it
may be expected in other tropical or
subtropical regions. The genus was
named for the recent Arthur M. Scott.

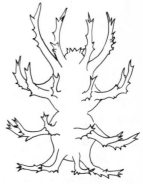

Fig. 182. *Amscottia mira*
Grönbl. et Kallio.

240b Semicells deeply 3-lobed, the apical lobe extended and
furnished with a circle of spines; the lateral lobes terminating
in spines; the two poles different in the arrangement of
spines, one pole being bilobed; in end view irregularly radiate with the lobes divided and spiniferous at their tips.
Fig. 183...*Allorgeia Valiae*

It is interesting that dichotypical desmids seem always to be collected from
tropical regions. *Allorgeia*, another African
genus is distinctly dichotypical, with one
semicell having lateral lobes at right angles
to the long axis of the cell, those of the
other semicell upwardly directed and bearing additional spines. The apical lobes of
the two semicells also are different. The
genus is named for the French phycologist
Allorge.

Fig. 183. *Allorgeia Va-
liae* Gauth.-Liev. (Redrawn
from Gauthier-Lievre).

241a (237) Semicells with 2 extended arms at their apices as seen in 'front' view, narrowly elliptic or fusiform when seen from the top. Fig. 184..*Staurastrum*

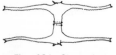

Fig. 184. *Staurastrum leptocladum* Nordst., a species with biradiate semicells.

The species illustrated is an example of those few members of the genus *Staurastrum* which have arms of the semicell directed in 1 plane only. Most such species are euplanktonic in soft-water lakes.

241b Cells without radiating arms; semicells compressed or rounded when seen from the top or side..242

242a Margin of semicells furnished with spines or processes......243

242b Margin of cell without spines although many species are granular, the granules sometimes sharp or conical. Fig. 185
....*Cosmarium*

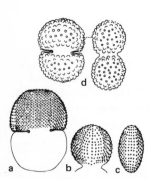

Fig. 185. (a) *Cosmarium panamense* Presc. (b) side view; (c) top view; (d) *C. margaritatum* (Lund.) Roy et Biss., 'front' and side views.

Like the genus *Staurastrum* (Fig. 180) *Cosmarium* includes several hundreds of species with considerable variation in shape, size, and wall ornamentation. The semicells appear flattened, however, when seen from the side or top; are usually oval or elliptic in outline; whereas a few are round in all views. The wall may be smooth or granular (sometimes with short, conical warts). In 'front' view the semicells may be oval, pyramidate, trapezoidal, semirectangular or even subcylindric. The sinus may be deep, or only a slight invagination. Like all members of the Conjugales, the chloroplasts are few, large and showy with conspicuous pyrenoids. One group of species is considered by some students to constitute the genus *Dysphinctium* (cells round in end view); others are grouped to form the genus *Actinotaenium* (round cells with axial, radiate chloroplasts).

243a Face of semicell with protuberances, or with the wall thickened in the midregion, sometimes with knobs, best seen when the cell is rolled to a lateral view position..................244

243b Face of semicell without swellings or protuberances. Fig. 186
....*Arthrodesmus*

This genus of Placoderm desmids has compressed cells like *Cosmarium* (Fig. 185), narrower in side or end view than in 'front' view. The angles of the semicells bear spines; the cell wall smooth, there being no granules, swellings or pits. Most species occur in acid habitats, intermingled with other desmids.

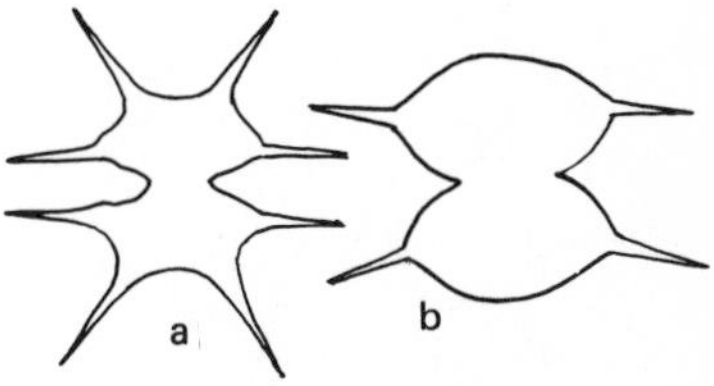

Fig. 186. (a) *Arthrodesmus octocornis* Ehr.; (b) A. *Fuellebornei* Schm.

244a Semicells with lateral, either simple or bifurcated processes and with a pair of spines on either side of the apical margin (at the upper angles of the semicell); the face of the semicell with a median protrusion that is often granular; the cells compressed in side or vertical view. Fig. 187.................
....*Spinocosmarium*

This genus was erected to include those plants which have a combination of both *Cosmarium* and *Arthrodesmus* features. The cells are flattened when seen from the top or side. The angles of the semicells bear spinelike extensions (as in *Arthrodesmus*, Fig. 186) and the walls have granules and verru-

Fig. 187. *Spinocosmarium quadridens* (Wood) Presc. et Scott, two forms.

cae similar to *Cosmarium* and *Staurastrum*. The type species. S. *quadridens* (Wood) Presc. et Scott was formerly referred to *Arthrodesmus*.

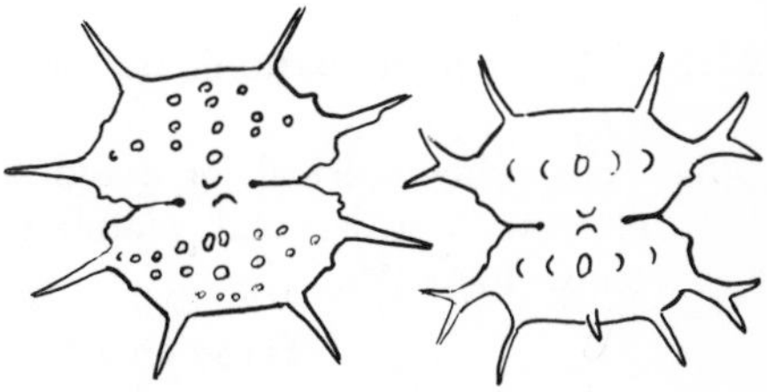

244b Cells otherwise, with a different type of ornamentation......245

245a Apex of semicell furnished with prominent spines; facial protuberances (if any) 1 large, low swelling, the wall thickened
here and often pitted or punctate. Fig. 188...........*Xanthidium*

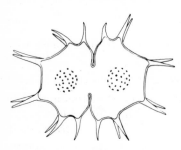

This genus, like *Arthrodesmus*
(Fig. 186) has cells which are
compressed (oval or elliptic in end
or side view). There is usually
a facialswelling of the semicell
which is often pitted. The angles of
the semicells bear 1 or a pair of
spines. There is less variation in
the shape of the semicell and wall
ornamentation in this genus than in
most of the other Placoderm desmids.

Fig. 188. *Xanthidium cris-
tatum* var. *uncinatum* Hass.

245b Apex without spines, or with a short, toothlike spine on
either side of the polar lobe. Fig. 179......................*Euastrum*

246a (234) Cells spherical, enclosed by a spindle-shaped envelope
which has longitudinal ridges. Fig. 164...........*Desmatractum*

246b Cells variously shaped but not enclosed in such an envelope
....247

247a Cells oval, ovoid, spherical or ellipsoid..............................248

247b Cells angular, pyramidal, trapeziform, or polygonal..........284

248a Cells subcylindrical, or ovoid, small, less than 4.5μ in diameter, with a parietal platelike chloroplast at one or both
ends. Fig. 189....................................*Diogenes (Nannochloris)*

These small, bacilliform or oval cells usually
occur in large numbers within a gelatinous
mass. The cells, individually or in pairs, are
enclosed by lamellate sheaths. The cells are
able to undergo cell division in vegetative reproduction and hence are assignable to the
Coccomyxaceae along with *Elakatothrix* (Fig.

Fig. 189. *Diogenes
bacillaris* (N a u m.)
Bourr.

87) and *Dactylothece* (Fig. 91). It is a
frequenter of laboratory cultures. The genus
name is regarded as being synonymous with
Nannochloris.

248b Cells different in size and shape, or with a different type of chloroplast..249

249a Cells bearing spines or ornamented with ridges, knobs or granules...250

249b Cells without spines or decorations.................................... 261

250a Cells oval, in pairs, bearing numerous, slender spines with thickened bases. Fig. 74...*Dicellula*

250b Cells otherwise, not so arranged or ornamented...............251

251a Cells spherical, solitary or in clusters, free-floating; wall thick and marked with refringent alveolae. Fig. 140...............
....*Keriochlamys*

251b Cells otherwise...252

252a Cells with spines greater in length than the diameter........253

252b Cells with spines shorter than the diameter of the cell; wall often decorated with a network of thickenings...................259

253a Spines not tapering from base to apex (with parallel margins, but pointed at the tip), long, and slender...................256

253b Spines tapering from base to apex (thornlike), long and slender or short and thick..254

254a Spines stout, broad at the base and tapering to a sharp point, evenly distributed over the cell wall. Fig. 190.............
....*Echinosphaerella*

This is a relatively rare plant from the euplankton. In making identification care should be used to distinguish the single parietal chloroplast by which the cell may be differentiated from some of the spiny zygospores of desmids (in which the cell content appears dark and massive, with no definitely shaped chloroplast distinguishable). Only 1 species is known, reported from several stations in the United States, including Alaska.

Fig. 190. *Echinosphaerella limnetica* G. M. Smith.

254b Spines long and slender thicker at the base and then abruptly narrowed..255

255a Cells oval, usually in pairs; spines numerous, needlelike but with a short section near the base thickened. Fig. 74.............
....*Dicellula*

255b Cells spherical, spines long and slender, with a distinct basal section thickened, then abruptly narrowed to a fine bristle. Fig. 191...Acanthosphaera

This plant can be distinguished from *Echinosphaerella* (Fig. 190) because the spines are somewhat needlelike, arising from a base which is decidedly thicker than in the apical section. There is a parietal, plate-like chloroplast. Euplanktonic.

Fig. 191. *Acantho-sphaera Zachariasii* Lemm.

256a (253) Cells round..257

256b Cells oval or ellipsoid...258

257a Chloroplast with a distinctly reniform pyrenoid. Fig. 141......
....Golenkinia

257b Chloroplast with a round pyrenoid. Fig. 142...........................
....Golenkiniopsis

258a (256) Spines at the poles or at the equator of the cell. Fig. 192
....Chodatella (Lagerheimia)

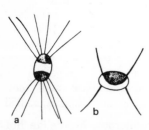

Unlike *Franceia* (Fig. 127) cells of this genus have long, needlelike spines confined to the poles, or to the poles and the equator. There are 13 species reported from the United States which are differentiated on the basis of cell shape and arrangement of spines. All are fairly common in the euplankton, and widely distributed. The genus should be compared with *Bohlinia* (Fig. 128).

Fig. 192. (a) *Lagerheimia longiseta* (Lemm.) Printz; (b) *L. quadriseta* (Lemm.) G. M. Smith.

258b Spines distributed over the cell wall. Fig. 127............*Franceia*

259a (252) Cells round...**260**

259b Cells oval. Fig. 128...*Bohlinia*

260a Cell with bluntly rounded protuberances when mature (smooth-walled when young), pale green (sometimes almost colorless), inhabiting snow fields. Fig. 193.... *Mycanthococcus*

This is one of several genera of unicellular algae which occur in banks of permanent snow. There is a light green, parietal chloroplast. The wall is smooth when the cells are young, but becomes thickened and bears blunt protuberances in age, thus showing a resemblance to certain species of *Trochiscia* (Fig. 194). The species illustrated here has been found in the snows of Yellowstone National Park and in the Olympic Mts. There are 3 or 4 species, one of which has been collected from caves in Europe.

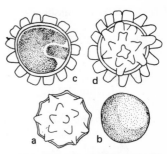

Fig. 193. *Mycanthococcus antarcticus* Wille. (a) cell showing thick, spiny, cystlike wall; (b) chloroplast; (c), (d) a species from the Olympic Mountain snowfields.

260b Cells decorated otherwise, with ridges, reticulations, sharp spines, or with rounded protuberances; chloroplast definite, green (some species occurring in snow). Fig. 194....................
....*Trochiscia*

In this genus spherical, unicellular plants have fairly thick walls that are variously decorated according to species; protuberances, reticulations, knobs or spines. It is a little-understood genus and some of the 25 species may be zygospores of other algae. In making identification one should observe the several, disclike chloroplasts. Some species of *Trochiscia* are found in red-snow fields.

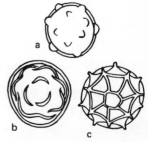

Fig. 194. (a) *Trochiscia granulata* (Reinsch) Hansg.; (b) *T. obtusa* (Reinsch) Hansg.; (c) *T. reticulata* (Reinsch) Hansg.

261a (249) Cells associated with fungi to form lichens. Fig. 195
....*Trebouxia*

Fig. 195. *Tre-bouxia Cladoniae* (Chod.) G. M. Smith.

The species illustrated is one of the most common forms associated with fungi to form lichens. The cells are spherical and contain an axial rather than a parietal chloroplast that is characteristic of most members of the Chlorococcales.

261b Cells not associated with fungi..262

262a Chloroplast 1, axial and central, sometimes with radiating lobes extending to the wall..263

262b Chloroplast not axial, or more than 1 in a cell, without radiating lobes..266

263a Cells egg-shaped, with a flotation cap at the narrow end; cells neustonic, floating beneath the surface film of water; chloroplast axial. Fig. 196..*Nautococcus*

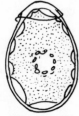

Fig. 196. *Nau-tococcus pirifor-mis* K o r s c h., showing flotation cap. (R e d r a w n from Starr).

This unusual genus is one of the few neustonic algae, floating and suspended from the surface film. The cells are adapted by having a flotation cap at the smaller end of the elliptic or pyriform cell. There is 1 axial chloroplast and a central pyrenoid. Reproduction is by zoospores. Apparently there is but one species reported, rather rare but widely distributed.

263b Cells not neustonic, without a floatation cap......................264

264a Chloroplast definitely star-shaped, with a central pyrenoid; cells spherical. Fig. 97......................................*Asterococcus*

264b Chloroplast not star-shaped; cells not spherical..................265

265a Cells cylindrical or subcylindric; chloroplast an axial plate. Fig. 82..*Mesotaenium*

265b Cells spheroidal to pyriform, with lateral lobes; chloroplast
    irregularly lobed. Fig. 197...*Myrmecia*

These unicells are either spherical or somewhat pyriform and usually show a thickening
of the wall at one side, giving them an unsymmetrical shape. Although the genus was
originally described from subaerial situations,
specimens in the United States have been collected from aquatic habitats.

Fig. 197. *Myrme-
cia aquatica* G. M.
Smith. (Redrawn from
G. M. Smith).

266a (262) Cells spherical...**267**
266b Cells oval or ellipsoid (sometimes nearly round)................**274**
267a Cells large (up to 300 μ or more in diameter); wall thin;
    chloroplasts numerous, irregular in shape and lumpy with
    starch grains, arranged in radiating strands from the center of
    the cell, and also parietal. Fig. 198.....................*Eremosphaera*

This is one of the largest spherical
cells (up to 300 μ, rarely 800 μ in
diameter) encountered among the unicellular algae. Although usually solitary these green globes may appear in
clusters of 4 enclosed by the old mother-cell wall. There are 5 recognized
species, one of which represents a
transfer from *Oocystis Eremosphaeria*
G. M. Smith. The cells have numerous,
disclike chloroplasts in radiating cytoplasmic strands from a central region
as well as lining the wall. They are
lumpy with attached starch grains. The

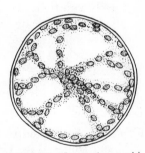

Fig. 198. *Eremosphaera viridis* De Bary.

cells occur mostly in acid habitats and are associated with desmids
(at one time were thought to be a desmid).

267b Cells not as above... 268
268a Cells enclosed in mucilage; individual cells usually with
    lamellate sheaths...**269**
268b Cells not enclosed in mucilage...**271**
269a Cells usually solitary (sometimes gregarious), enclosed ec-
    centrically in a much-lamellated sheath; cell contents in-
    definite and chloroplast not clear; pyrenoid lacking; cells
    brownish or orange-colored. Fig. 18.........................*Urococcus*
269b Plants otherwise...**270**

270a   Cells sometimes solitary but mostly many together in an irregularly globular, mucilaginous matrix which is lamellate; individual cells usually showing a lamellate sheath; cells mostly solitary within the colonial mucilage and irregularly scattered (not in pairs); cell with a cup-shaped parietal chloroplast with a pyrenoid; contractile vacuoles present; colonies mostly aquatic (sometimes on moist subaerial strata). Fig. 85..*Gloeocystis*

270b Cells globular or oval, many within an amorphous, gelatinous matrix which is homogeneous (not lamellate, but individual or paired cells showing thin lamellate sheaths; cells without contractile vacuoles; plants terrestrial and usually macroscopic. Fig. 12...*Palmella*

271a (268) Chloroplast 1 (rarely 2); cells solitary, although sometimes gregarious, but not colonial...**272**

271b Chloroplasts several to many parietal, angular plates, pyrenoids lacking. Fig. 199...*Bracteacoccus*

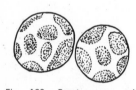

Fig. 199. *Bracteacoccus minor* (Chod.) Petrova.

This genus resembles *Planktosphaeria* in the form of its flat, angular and parietal chloroplasts, but the cells occur singly rather than in colonies. The plants are easily confused with other 1-celled, spherical algae which grow in or on soils. There are about 7 species which have been isolated and cultured. See Appendix.

272a Cells associated to form an extended stratum on trees, wood and stones. Fig. 120...
.................................*Desmococcus (Protococcus; Pleurococcus)*

272b Cells not forming such a stratum...**273**

273a Chloroplast a thin layer along the wall; pyrenoid usually lacking; free-living or in tissues of animals (sponges, etc.), reproduction by autospores (replicas of the adult cell. Fig. 153
....*Chlorella* (Including *Palmellococcus*)

273b Chloroplast a massive cup with a pyrenoid; occurring in soil or on damp subaerial substrates probably occurs in water also); reproducing by zoospores. Fig. 86...........*Chlorococcum**

*See Appendix for other unicellular green algae.

274a (266) Cells oval, ovate or irregularly globose, with thick-layered walls bearing knobs and prominent protrusions....275

274b Cells without thick walls and knoblike protrusions.........276

275a Chloroplasts numerous, parietal, coneshaped. Fig. 200...........
....*Excentrosphaera*

This is the only species reported for the genus. It is found both in the water and in subaerial habitats and is identified by its irregular shape produced by lamellated thickenings of the wall in 1 or more places. The chloroplasts are cone-shaped and are all directed inwardly from the parietal position along the wall.

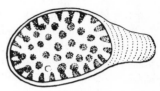

Fig. 200. *Excentrosphaera viridis*
G. T. Moore.

275b Chloroplast a massive, axial body with processes which are flattened against the wall. Fig. 201....................*Kentrosphaera*

There are 2 or 3 species of this genus (sometimes included in the genus *Chloro-chytrium*, Fig. 158). *Kentrosphaera Bristolae* G. M. Smith and *K. facciolae* Borzi have been found in the United States. The cells are similar in shape to *Chlorochytrium* but have a free-living habit, usually occurring on damp soil; *K. facciolae* Borzi has been found in Antarctica. There are several irregularly shaped chloroplasts.

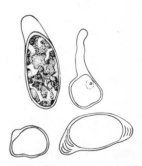

Fig. 201. *Kentrosphaera Bristolae* G. M. Smith.

276a (274) Cells with spines...277

276b Cells without spines...279

277a Spines distributed over the wall..278

277b Spines localized at the poles or at the midregion of the cell. Fig. 192..*Chodatella (Lagerheimia)*

278a Spines shorter than the diameter of the cell. Fig. 128..............
....*Bohlinia*

278b Spines as long as or usually longer than the diameter of the cell, needlelike; cells solitary or in 2's. Fig. 127............*Franceia*

279a (276) Cells with spiral, longitudinal ribs on the wall. Fig. 202
....*Scotiella*

This genus contains a number of species, most of which have been collected in the flora of red snow at high altitudes. Differences lie in the shape of the (in general) oval cells and the type of ridged decorations on the wall. Occasionally *Scotiella* species are collected in the tychoplankton at low altitudes. Some authorities have suggested placing this genus in the Volvocales because of the type of chloroplast and the evidence of a basal-distal differentiation in the cell; whereas others include it in the Chlorococcales.

F i g.   202.
Scotiella nivalis (C h o d.)
Fritsch.

279b Cells without longitudinal ribs..280

280a Cells small, less than 4.5 μ long, with a platelike chloroplast at one end. Fig. 189..........................*Diogenes (Nannochloris)*

280b Cells relatively large, without such a chloroplast arrangement..281

281a Two or more masses of dark mucilage appearing at either end or making X-bands over the cell wall or over the mother-cell wall of the previous generation; usually 2 or 4 cells in the old mother-cell, but often found solitary. Fig. 139..*Gloeotaenium*

281b Without such dark masses of mucilage about the cells......282

282a Cells enclosed in a mucilaginous sheath, cells relatively small and numerous within a gelatinous investment; cells round or oval..283

282b Cells not enclosed in a mucilaginous sheath, but usually several together enclosed in the old mother-cell wall which may be expanded and gelatinized (appearing upon first observation to be a sheath), sometimes solitary; cells oval, ellipsoid or lemon-shaped; chloroplasts 1, or 2, or in a few species many parietal plates or irregular discs; reproduction by autospores. Fig. 143...*Oocystis*

283a Cells oval, often solitary but usually gregarious, forming a mucilaginous expanse on moist, subaerial substrates. Fig. 153
....*Chlorella (Palmellococcus)*

283b Cells solitary aquatic, ellipsoid, enclosed in a very wide, gelatinous, brownish sheath which is impregnated with iron. Fig. 203..*Sphaerellocystis*

The cells appear like a non-motile *Chlamydomonas,* enclosed in a wide, ample, gelatinous sheath. The sheath bears nodules of brown iron deposits. There are 4 species; not yet reported from the United States but are to be expected.

F i g. 203. S p haerellocystis e l l i psoidea E t t l. (Redrawn from Ettl).

284a (247) Cell body actually spherical but with 4, long, narrow, brown armlike appendages radiating from it. Fig. 204.......... ....*Pachycladon*

This rare plant (1 species only known for the genus) occurs in the euplankton of lakes. The long, darkly colored appendages from a relatively small, subspherical cell body make identification certain.

Fig. 204. *Pachycladon umbrinus* G. M. Smith. (Redrawn from G. M. Smith).

284b Cells differently shaped, or not with such appendages......285

285a With several long spines forming a tuft at the angles of the cell. Fig. 205..*Polyedriopsis*

There are 2 species in this genus, both of which are euplanktonic. They are rectangular or polyhedral in shape with from 1 to 4 long spines at each angle. *Polyedriopsis quadrispina* G. M. Smith has but 1 stout spine at the angles; is quadrate in shape.

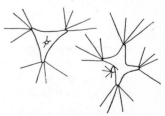

Fig. 205. *Polyedriopsis spinulosa* G. M. Smith.

285b With 1, 2 or 3 spines, or without spines at the angles of the cell..286

286a Without spines...287

286b With 1 to 3 spines at the angles...288

287a Body of the cell gradually narrowed at the angles to form hornlike, twisted processes. Fig. 206..........................*Cerasterias*

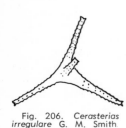

Fig. 206. *Cerasterias irregulare* G. M. Smith

There apparently is only I good species in this genus (although 3 or 4 are recognized) which is characterized by having irregularly pyramidal cells with twisted processes from the angles. Thus far the plant has been reported only from lakes in mid-America. It should be compared with *Tetraedron* (Fig. 207) to which the genus possibly belongs.

287b Body of the cell abruptly narrowed to form hornlike processes. Fig. 207..*Tetraedron*

288a (286) Cells with 1 spine at each angle.................................289

288b Cells with 2 or 3 spines at the angles. Fig. 207.......*Tetraedron*

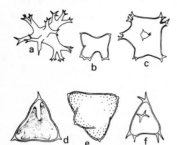

Fig. 207. (a) *Tetraedron limneticum* Borge; (b) *T. asymmetricum* Presc.; (c) *T. lobulatum* var. *crassum* Presc.; (d) *T. regulare* var. *granulatum* Presc., showing chloroplast; (e) showing granular wall; (f) *T. regulare* var. *bifurcatum* Wille.

This genus contains a large number of species which vary considerably in their shape and in the number of arms and spines. Whereas some are simple, smooth-walled, and have rounded anles ,others are trapeziform or polyhedral in shape and have lobes and lobules at the angles. They occur in both tycho- and euplankton; reproduce by autospores.

289a Spines slender and needlelike. Fig. 205................*Polyedriopsis*
289b Spines broader at the base, and stout, decidedly tapering.
Fig. 208..*Treubaria*

This free-floating plant is similar
to *Pachycladon* (Fig. 204) but the
processes are not darkly colored and
are not toothed at the tip but terminate as a stout spine.

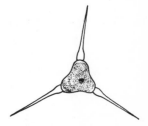

Fig. 208. *Treubaria crassis-pina* G. M. Smith.

290a (80) Plant a microscopic (structures of the plant not visible
without a microscope), *unbranched* filament, attached or free-
floating, or if macroscopic (form of the plant determinable
without a microscope) the thallus in the form of an expanded
sheet, a tube, or a *branched,* arbuscular, (treelike), gelatinous and beaded growth. (See Figs. 233a, 295b)................291

290b Plant a *branched* filament; either a coenocytic tube (without
cross walls), microscopic; cells in 1 series, sometimes in a wide
gelatinous sheath; *or* an attached prostrate filament or
cushion; *or* disclike thallus in which the branching habit
is obscure because of closely appressed branches................358

291a Cells constricted in the midregion, with 2 large chloroplasts,
1 in either part of the cell..292

291b Cells not constricted in the midregion................................300

292a Cells adjoined by the interlocking of short, straight, hornlike
or hooked processes, or by button like knobs....................293

292b Cells adjoined by their end walls, either along the entire
apical surface or by armlike extensions of the cell apex......295

293a Cells adjoined by overlapping, slender horns or by hooked
processes..294

293b Cells adjoined by buttonlike processes at the apex. Fig. 209
....*Teilingia*

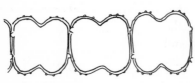

Fig. 209.   *Teilingia granulata* (Roy et Biss.) Bourr.

This genus of filamentous desmids is composed of those forms in which there are short, buttonlike apical projections on the apical wall. These adjoin similar projections of other cells to form filaments. Formerly the genus was included in *Sphaerozosma* (Fig. 210) in which there are longer, more prominent and hornlike process which interlock to form filaments. The cells have about the same shape and proportions of some *Cosmarium*.

294a Interlocking processes in the form of forked lobes which bear recurved spines. Fig. 178................*Micrasterias foliacea*

294b Interlocking processes slender, straight and hornlike. Fig. 210
....*Sphaerozosma*

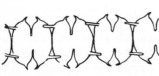

Fig. 210.   *Sphaerozosma laeve* var. *latum* (W. et W.)

Cells in this filamentous desmid have relatively long apical processes which interlock with those of adjoined cells. The processes may bear knobs at their tips. The cells are similar to *Cosmarium* in shape and proportions. Included in this genus according to one classification scheme is *Onychonema* of other authors.

295a (292) Semicells transversely elliptic or oval, the median incision of the cell relatively deep. Fig. 211.......*Spondylosium*

Fig. 211.   *Spondylosium planum* (Wolle) W. et W.

Although this genus can have cells that are triangular in end view, most species have cells that are compressed and are much like some species of *Cosmarium* (Fig. 185), arranged in a filament. One species which is rather rare is *S. pulchrum* (Bail.) Archer. It has semicells which are much extended laterally so that the cell is much wider than long. The apices of the cells in this species are furnished with a protrusion which adjoins that of adjacent cells in the filament. The walls are smooth and undecorated.

295b Cells not transversely elliptic; median incision not deep, sometimes only a slight concavity of the lateral wall.........296

296a Cells cylindrical, subcylindrical or barrel-shaped...............297

296b Cells quadrate or angular, usually with the margins conspicuously lobed. (See Fig. 215, *Desmidium Baileyi*, however.) 299

297a Cells barrel-shaped or subcylindrical, enlarged at the base of the semicells where there is a notch or sinus, the lateral margins either smooth or bearing a circle of spines on each semicell; wall with a ring of creases or folds near the apices of the cell; chloroplast axial, stellate as seen in cross section. Fig. 212................................*Bambusina (Gymnozyga)*

There are at least 5 species of this genus in the United States; one of the most frequently collected of the filamentous desmids. The species are differentiated mostly on the size and proportions of the cell. *Bambusina* occurs sometimes

Fig. 212. *Bambusina Brebissonii* Kuetz. (*Gymnozyga moniliformis* Ehr.)

in pure growths in *Sphganum* bog pools. Conjugation tubes are formed between cells of reproducing filaments. In cell division there is a characteristic infolding of the cross walls.

297b Cells other shapes, without a circle of creases near the apex of the semicell...298

298a Cells very slightly if at all inflated in the midregion; median incision very shallow; often with rings of pores in the wall near the apices; chloroplast stellate. Fig. 213........*Hyalotheca*

In this filamentous desmid the median incision is merely a slight invagination and sometimes is obscure. The cell contents are divided, however, with an axial chloroplast in each cell half. The most common species have somewhat rectangular cells and one,

Fig. 213. *Hyalotheca dissiliens* (Smith) Bréb.

Hyalotheca mucosa (Dill.) Ehr. is identified by having a wide gelatinous sheath. In *H. dissiliens* (Smith) Bréb. there are transverse rings of puncta near the poles.

298b Cells cylindrical, slightly constricted in a median enlargement; chloroplast an axial plate or ribbon. Fig. 214.................
....*Groenbladia*

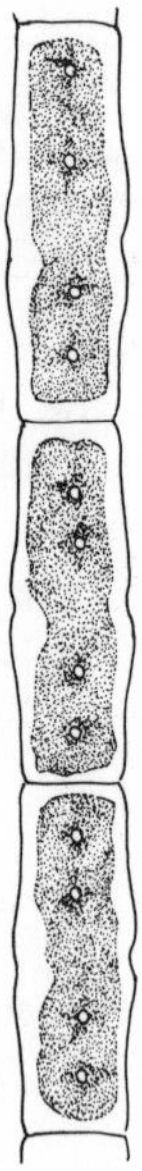

The long, cylindrical cells of this filamentous desmid are somewhat swollen in the midregion where there is a slight notch. The chloroplast (1 in each semicell) is an axial plate, with 2 pyrenoids. One species placed in this genus has a whorl of stout spines on each semicell.

Fig. 214.
*Groenbladia
neglecta*
(Racib.) Teil-
ing.

299a (296) Cells wider than long or as wide as long, without a median incision or with but a slight median notch; walls at the poles of young semicell infolded or replicated. Fig. 215
....*Desmidium*

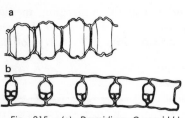

Fig. 215. (a) *Desmidium Grevilli* (Kuetz.) De Bary; (b) *D. Baileyi* (Ralfs) Nordst.

Cells of this filamentous desmid vary much in shape. Some are oval and moniliform when seen in end view, some are triangular and some are quadrangular. When seen in 'front' view (in filamentous arrangement) one must focus carefully upward and downward to detect the presence of lobes in a vertical plane. A characteristic habit of some species is to show a spiral twisting of the cell arrangement so that in any one view they do not have their lobes or processes in the same plane throughout the length of the filament. *D. Baileyi* (Ralfs) Nordstedt has 3 or 4 polar processes which adjoin those of other cells in the filament so that there are fenestrations between the individuals. In such a species the cells are triangular or quadrangular in end view.

299b Cells a little longer than wide, rectangular with a narrow median incision; 4-lobed in end view; margins of the cells parallel; poles of young cells infolded. Fig. 216........................
....*Phymatodocis*

Although rarely found, this filamentous desmid may be the dominant form in some acid habitats which are especially favorable for these plants. The cells appear somewhat quadrangular when seen in 'front' view, as they occur in the filament, but are quadrilaterally symmetrical and are 4-lobed as seen in end view.

Fig. 216. *Phymatodocis Nordstedtiana* Wolle.

300a (291) Chloroplast parietal, of various shapes, netlike, ringlike, or platelike, with pads and thin areas (Fig. 245); *or* if axial, plants in the form of a macroscopic thallus as in Fig. 219) **315**

Three types of parietal chloroplasts: a complete parietal ring; an incomplete ring; a parietal network.

Fig. 217. Three types of parietal chloroplasts; a complete parietal ring; one incomplete ring; a parietal network.

300b Chloroplast axial, an irregularly shaped plate, a broad band, or star-shaped; *or* if parietal, in the form of a ribbon as in Fig. 227); microscopic..301

Types of chloroplasts: a parietal ribbon (*Spirogyra*); axial stellate (*Zygnema*); axial band or plate (*Mougeotia*).

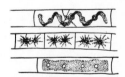

Fig. 218. Three types of chloroplasts; a parietal ribbon (*Spirogyra*); axial stellate (*Zygnema*); axial band or plate (*Mougeotia*).

301a Chloroplast 1, or 2 in a cell; stellate, with radiating processes from a central core which includes a pyrenoid................302

301b Chloroplasts other shapes...305

302a Cells quadrate, with 1 star-shaped chloroplast containing a single pyrenoid. Fig. 219.......................................*Schizogonium*

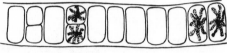

Fig. 219.   *Schizogonium murale* Kuetz.

This species and 2 others are found in the United States, growing on dripping rocks or wet soil. *Schizogonium crenulatum* (Kuetz.) Gay has short, crinkly filaments. The basically filamentous habit may become expanded so that a frondlike thallus is produced. This genus, together with *Prasiola* (Fig. 234) have sufficient structural and reproductive characteristics to warrant placing them in a separate family (Schizogoniaceae), and the order Schizogoniales. The star-shaped chloroplast is helpful in making determinations.

302b Cells mostly longer than wide, with 2 chloroplasts............303

303a Chloroplasts 2 to 6, relatively small and biscuit-shaped or star-shaped, connected in the midregion of the cell by a strand of cytoplasm enclosing the nucleus; conjugating cells becoming filled with layers of pectic substances; zygospores cushion-shaped, compressed spheroid or subquadrangular. Fig. 220...*Zygnemopsis*

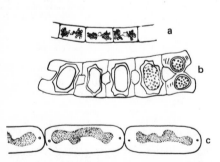

Fig. 220.   (a) *Zygnemopsis decussata* (Trans.) Trans., vegetative cell with cushionlike, axial chloroplasts; (b) conjugation to form zygospores; (c) *Z. desmidioides* (W. et W.) Trans.

The differences between this genus and *Zygnema* (Fig. 221) occur mostly within the reproductive habit details; hence determination of plants in the vegetative condition cannot be certain. In *Zygnema the* chloroplasts are definitely star-shaped, often with long rays; whereas in *Zygnemopsis* the chloroplasts are more padlike with a few, short radiating processes. The latter genus is much less common than *Zygnema;* has fewer species. In *Zygnemopsis desmidioides* (W. et W.) Trans. the cholorplast is an axial plate and not at all stellate.

303b Chloroplasts different in shape, or if star-shaped, larger than above, and always 2; conjugating cells not becoming filled with pectic substances; zygospores globose, compressed globose or oval...304

304a Chloroplasts 2, definitely star-shaped, each containing a large, central pyrenoid; aquatic. Fig. 221..................*Zygnema*

There are numerous species of *Zygnema*, differentiated on the basis of zygospore morphology (shape, size, wall markings). The paired, definitely star-shaped chloroplasts in each cell, each with a conspicuous pyrenoid, make identification possible. Frequently the

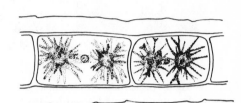

Fig. 221. *Zygnema pectinatum* (Vauch.) C. A. Agardh, vegetative cells showing stellate, axial chloroplasts.

cells are so densely packed with starch grains and cytoplasmic granules (waste material) that the shape of the chloroplast is obscured. Application of an iodine solution often facilitates observations, or if one examines several lengths of filaments under low magnification the stellate form of the chloroplasts will become apparent. A few species have a conspicuous gelatinous sheath and a very thick wall. The filaments of *Zygnema* form green clumps and floating mats, but not the large, ballooonlike or 'cloud' masses in the water as does *Spirogyra;* usually are not as densely green as in that genus.

304b Chloroplast axial as above but with radiating processes, much reduced, sometimes bridged so as to form a dumb-bell-shaped mass; terrestrial or subaerial. Fig. 222.....*Zygogonium*

These filaments are somewhat irregular because the cell walls are unevenly thickened and usually are invested by a layer of mucilaginous substance. The cells have the habit of putting out rhizoidal protrusions rather frequently. Sometimes the protrusions are branched. Occasionally the conjugation tubes, when they fail to meet another

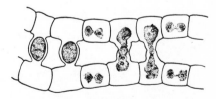

Fig. 222. *Zygogonium ericetorum* Kuetz.

tube, will continue to grow as rhizoidal processes. The plant usually is found in subaerial habitats, sometimes in the water on submersed stumps, *etc.*

305a (301) Cell sap or chloroplast purplish or violet green.........306

305b Cell sap not purplish...308

306a With 2 disclike chloroplasts. Fig. 223....................*Pleurodiscus*

Fig. 223. *Pleurodiscus purpureus* (Wolle) Lag., showing disclike chloroplasts.

There is but 1 species of this genus reported thus far from the United States. It is a plant readily identified by the unique curved, platelike chloroplast and purplish cell sap.

306b With 1 bandlike chloroplast...307

307a Cells elongate-oval to subcylindric, in short interrupted filaments; pyrenoids 1 or 2; chloroplast often purplish or violet-green. Fig. 224..*Ancylonema*

Fig. 224. *Ancylonema Norden-skioldii* Bergg.

The cylindrical cells with broadly rounded poles form short filaments, either continuous or interrupted. The 1 species is known from snow and glaciers; forms what is called 'black snow' or 'black ice.' The cell contents are often violet-green or reddish.

307b Cells long-cylindric, occurring in long filaments; chloroplast axial, bandlike, often twisted, with several pyrenoids. Fig. 225 ....*Mougeotia*

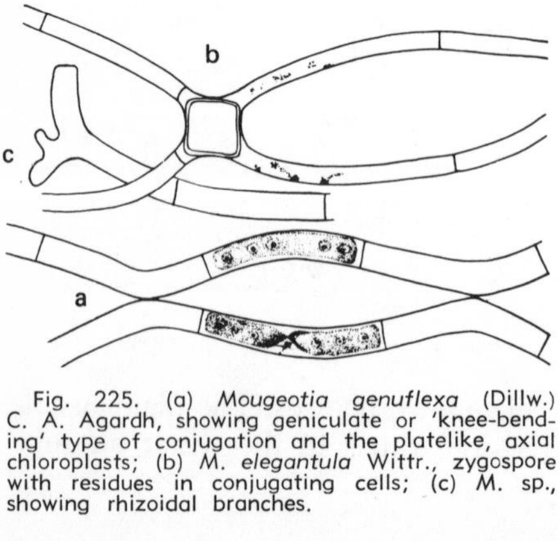

Like *Spirogyra* (Fig. 227) there are many species of *Mougeotia*, separable by zygospore shape and wall markings. Most species have a relatively wide, bandlike, axial chloroplast containing a row of pyrenoids. The chloroplast is capable of rotating within the cell so that when seen on edge it appears as a narrow, axial ribbon. The shifting of the chloroplast is thought to be a favorable response to light direction.

Fig. 225. (a) *Mougeotia genuflexa* (Dillw.) C. A. Agardh, showing geniculate or 'knee-bending' type of conjugation and the platelike, axial chloroplasts; (b) *M. elegantula* Wittr., zygospore with residues in conjugating cells; (c) *M.* sp., showing rhizoidal branches.

308a (305) Chloroplast in the form of a parietal, spiral or twisted ribbon, with many pyrenoids.....................................309
308b Chloroplasts axial bands or plates; pyrenoids none, or few 311
309a Cell wall densely and minutely granular. Fig. 174..............
....*Genicularia*
309b Cell wall smooth...310
310a Chloroplasts nearly parallel, only slightly twisted; conjugation without the formation of tubes between the gametangia. Fig. 226..*Sirogonium*

This genus is differentiated from *Spirogyra* (Fig. 227) by the arrangement of the chloroplasts which are practically straight or only slightly twisted in the cell. Further, in *Zygogonium* conjugation is accomplished by geniculations of the filament rather than by tubes. The reproducing filaments are brought into juxtaposition by a bending of the reproducing plants.

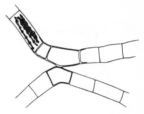

Fig. 226. *Sirogonium sticticum* (Engl. Bot.) Kuetz., showing parallel, ribbonlike chloroplasts.

310b Chloroplasts definitely spiralled; conjugation by the formation of tubes from one or both gametangia, either between two different filaments (scalariform conjugation) or between adjacent cells in the same filament (lateral conjugation). Fig. 227..*Spirogyra*

This is the most frequently encountered member of the order Zygnematales (Conjugales). There are about 300 species, differentiated by a combination of vegetative characters and reproductive details, mostly in reference to the morphology of the zygospore and its wall markings. Some species have replicate (infolded) cross walls. Identification of *Spirogyra* species is not possible without mature zygospores. These plants form green 'clouds' of filaments below water; appear as floating mats when mature and in the reproductive state at which time they are yellowish-brown. Conjugation may be either lateral or scalariform.

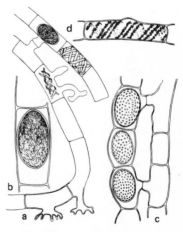

Fig. 227. (a) *Spirogyra rhizobrachiales* Jao, showing rhizoidal branches and conjugation; (b) zygospore; (c) *S. aequinoctialis* G. S. West; (d) cell showing chloroplasts and numerous pyrenoids.

311a (308) Chloroplast a folded plate or short band, without a pyrenoid; conjugation scalariform; zygospores occurring in the conjugation tube and extending into the gametangia. Fig. 228..*Mougeotiopsis*

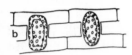

Fig. 228. *Mougeotiopsis calospora* Palla. (a) vegetative cells with plate-like chloroplasts (without pyrenoid); (b) zygospores.

This is a relatively rare genus, only 2 species of which are known for the United States. It is possible to make tentative identification because the chloroplast lacks a pyrenoid. The cells are characteristically short-cylindric. In reproduction it is similar to *Debarya* (Fig. 230) in that the entire contents of the conjugating cells (gametangia) become fused to form the zygospore.

311b Chloroplasts with 2 to several pyrenoids.............................312

312a Conjugating cells (gametangia) shortened by division of vegetative cells; (plants relatively rare). Fig. 229..................
....*Temnogametum*

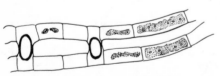

Fig. 229. *Temnogametum* sp. showing plate-like chloroplasts with pyrenoids, the gametangial cells cut off from the vegetative cells, and 2 zygospores.

At the time of reproduction vegetative cells in this genus become divided, cutting off a small portion which serves as a gametangium. There is scarcely a tube formed between conjugating cells. The resulting zygospores are formed between the conjugating filaments but extend into the two gametangia. The chloroplast is an axial band, with pyrenoids either in a linear series, or scattered.

312b Conjugating cells not shortened by division of vegetative cell
....313

313a Filaments composed of cylindrical cells with 1 or more
axial ribbons and many pyrenoids; filaments formed by
incidental adherence of cells following division; wall with
short spines or sharp granules. Fig. 175................*Gonatozygon*

313b Filaments long and composed of permanently adjoined
cells; walls smooth...314

314a Filaments of slender cells, mostly under 12 μ in diameter
(rarely as much as 30 to 42 μ); chloroplast an axial plate,
usually not filling the cell; conjugating cells becoming filled
with pectic substances; granular residues not found in the
emptied reproductive cells; plants relatively rare. Fig. 230
....*Debarya*

This genus, named for De-
Bary the famous botanist, has
filaments that resemble slender
species of *Mougeotia* (Fig.
165), and cannot be positively
identified in the vegetative condition. The cells are more delicate and the chloroplast is a
relatively small, usually twisted plate. *Debarya* is much
less frequently collected than
Mougeotia. In reproduction all

Fig. 230. *Debarya* sp., showing formation of zygospores and the lamellated
substance deposited in the conjugating
cells.

of the contents of the conjugating cells enter into the formation
of the zygospores and the space once occupied by the protoplasts becomes filled with lamellated substance which is light
refractive.

314b Filaments wider; cells long-cylindric or rarely short-cylindric;
chloroplast a broad, axial band with conspicuous pyrenoids,
usually filling the diameter of the cell but not always in
length; conjugating cells not filled with pectice substances;
granular residues present in the emptied reproductive cells;
plants common. Fig. 225..*Mougeotia*

315a (300) Plant a tuft of short, erect filaments (usually branched but sometimes appear unbranched when young); some species forming prostrate, attached discs. Fig. 231.........................
....*Coleochaete*

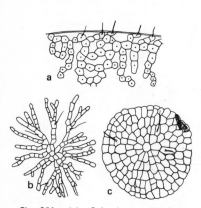

Fig. 231. (a) *Coleochaete Nitellarum* Jost; (b) *C. soluta (Bréb.)* Pringsh.; (c) *C. orbicularis* Pringsh.

There are 9 species of this genus reported from the United States. They are differentiated by the habit of growth (prostrate and dislike, or in erect tufts), and by size of cells. One species, *Coleochaete Nitellarum* Jost occurs only in the walls of *Nitella* (Fig. 3) which is nearly always found with the endophyte. *Coleochaete* appears conspicuously when *Nitella* is allowed to age in the laboratory. The sheathed setae which characterize *Coleochaete* arise from a granule (the blepharoplast) within the cell and emerge through a pore in the wall. The dislike thallus formed by some species is frequently found on the sides of glass aquaria. In nature such colonies occur on other algae or on submersed stems of cattail, or on glass and crockery in the water.

315b Thallus not in the form of a cushion, nor as a tuft of filaments...316

316a Thallus a macroscopic, expanded sheet, 1 cell in thickness (usually in salt water, but also in brackish and fresh water, especially in cold streams); attached. Fig. 232...*Monostroma*

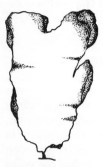

Fig. 232. *Monostroma latissimum* (Kuetz.) Wittr.

In salt water this genus includes species which form relatively large, sheetlike or foliose thalli, several centimeters long and wide, whereas in fresh water the plants are mostly 5 or 6 centimeters (up to 10 cm.) long. Marine species are sometimes carried inland and become established on stones and shells in hard water. Mostly the fresh-water species, (about 5 known for the United States) occur in cold, mountain streams.

316b Thallus not a large, flat, crinkled sheet; attached.................317

317a Thallus an intestiniform, hollow tube, with the wall 1 cell
   in thickness. Fig. 233..*Enteromorpha*

Like *Monostroma* (Fig. 232) *Enteromorpha* is
primarily a marine alga but becomes adapted rather
successfully in fresh-water habitats. The long, hollow
tubes are frequently branched, forming slender
threads or crinkled, elongate sacks. The plants are
always attached (at least when young) to submersed aquatic plants, sticks and stones, especially
in flowing water and nearly always in hard (calcareous) or saline waters. One species is common
in far western United States where it often occurs
in troublesome abundance in irrigation ditches.

Fig. 233.
*Enteromorpha
intestinalis* (L.)
Grev. (a) habit
of branched
thallus; (b)
cells showing
parietal posi-
tion of chloro-
plasts.

317b Thallus not an intestiniform tube..318

318a Plant a lobed or ruffled disc of cells, 2 to 3 or up to 10 cm.
   across; chloroplast axial and somewhat radiate; attached by a
   central, short stipe; usually on rocks in alpine and arctic
   hatitats. Fig. 234..*Prasiola*

Eight species of *Prasiola* have been reported from the United States, mostly
from alpine or subalpine habitats. In the
Arctic the plant is a conspicuous element
of the subaerial flora, growing on bones,
boards or on the ground, especially where
there has been an enrichment from nitrogenous matter. The thalli are foliose when
fully developed but may be filamentous
and ribbonlike when young. The genus
and *Schizogonium* (Fig. 219) comprise
the Schizogoniaceae, a family with star-
shaped, axial chloroplasts.

Fig. 234. *Prasiola crispa*
(Lightf.) Menegh. (a) several forms of thallus; (b)
diagram to show cells in 4's.

318b Plant otherwise; a filament or a gelatinous strand.............319

319a A filament of cells...327

319b A gelatinous strand, or tube, or a plant which includes a gelatinous tube that may or may not have cross partitions 320

320a Thallus a short, tubelike strand, sometimes forked, containing many transverse lamellations (layers); cells at the tips of the strands. Fig. 235...*Hormotila*

This curious plant is a branched colonial form by virtue of the fact that as the cells divide they secrete mucilage and construct gelatinous strands that branch and rebranch, the cells always occurring at the distal end of the

Fig. 235.   *Hormotila mucigena* Borzi.

strands. Zoospores produced in asexual reproduction are biflagellate. In *Hormotilopsis*, a somewhat similar genus, the zoospores are quadriflagellate. *Hormotila* is usually regarded as a member of the Tetrasporales near *Gloeocystis* (Fig. 85). Possibly *Urococcus* Hansg. is a synonym.

320b Thallus not as above...321

321a Cells located at the ends of undivided tubes, the cells bearing a seta with a sheathed base. Fig. 115............................
....*Chaetosphaeridium*

321b Cells without setae...322

322a Cells constricted in the midregion; occurring at the ends of parallel tubes which are united in colonies and are impregnated with lime. Fig. 236..*Oocardium*

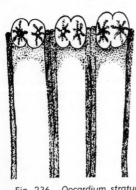

This is a very rare desmid, or at least it has been reported but few times, probably because it is easily overlooked by collectors. The *Cosmarium*like cells occur in colonies or aggregations of tubes which are formed in limestone or in calcareous concretions. Each cell is located at the end of such a calcareous tube with the long axis of the cell at right angles. Each semicell has a star-shaped chloroplast with a central pyrenoid. *Oocardium* is to be found in hard-water streams on sticks and stones with limey encrustments.

Fig. 236. ,*Oocardium stratum* Naeg.

322b Cells not constricted in the midregion; not arranged as above
....323

323a Cells in tubes which are attached to microfauna. Fig. 118
....*Colacium*

323b Cells not attached to microfauna.......................................324

324 a Cells elongate-oval...325

324b Cells round, not a brackish water habitats.........................326

325a Cells at the ends of jointed, branching tubes; protoplast with
an eye-spot; plants of brackish water, or marine. Fig. 237
....*Prasinocladus*

Although essentially marine, *Prasinocladus lubricus* Kuck. has been found in brackish water and may occur in fresh water in coastal regions. It is an attached, branching tube composed of a series of compartments, forming a tree-like thallus in which the oval protoplasts occur only at the tips of the branches. There is 1 chloroplast at the forward end of the cell which actually is the posterior pole because like some of its relatives (*Malleochloris,* Fig. 160) the cells are in an inverted position with the anterior end downward; have a red eye-spot. The genus belongs to the Chlorangiaceae in the Tetrasporales.

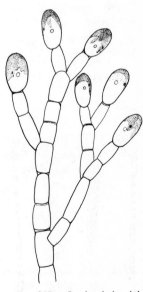

Fig. 237. *Prasinocladus lubricus* Kuckuck.

325b Cells at the ends of a series of membranous cups, telescoping one within another, formed from the remains of old mother-cell walls, the chain of cups often branching. Fig. 116 ....*Ecballocystis*

326a (324) Cells in 1 series or in several irregular series within unbranched (rarely branched) tubes of mucilage; chloroplasts 2, laminate. Fig. 238...*Palmodictyon*

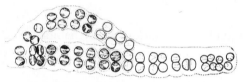

Fig. 238. *Palmodictyon viride* Kuetz.

Palmodictyon viride Kuetz. and *P. varium* (Naeg.) Lemm. are fairly common in mixtures of algae from shallow ponds or the tychoplankton of lakes, but never appear in any abundance. The former species has cells enclosed in individual sheaths, whereas the latter is without cellular sheaths. Some strands of colonial mucilage may be simple, others irregularly branched and sometimes anastomosing.

326b Cells in many series, *i.e.*, arranged in clusters of 4 throughout an elongated strand of mucilage; chloroplast 1, a parietal cup; (colonies of some species saccate or ballooonlike, Fig. 78........ ....*Tetraspora*

327a (319) Filaments of more than 1 series throughout (axes with corticating cells); either microscopic or macroscopic, branched thalli encased in mucilage...355

327b Plants otherwise; either uniseriate throughout, or uniseriate in the basal portion and multiseriate above; microscopic....328

328a Filaments uniseriate below, becoming multiseriate in the upper or older portions of the plant...329

328b Filaments uniseriate throughout...331

329a Filaments of cylindrical cells below, soon multiseriate with bricklike, angular cells; walls thick. Fig. 239.........*Schizomeris*

There are only 2 species in this genus, 1 of which is widely distributed over the world. The filaments are relatively large when fully developed and rather coarse. They occur in dark green clumps in standing water and have the macroscopic appearance of *Spirogyra* (Fig. 227) or of some large *Ulothrix* (Fig. 256). But unlike those genera, *Schizomeris* filaments separate readily and can be seen individually within a clump of collected material. There is some evidence that the plant favors water rich in nitrogenous matter and is to be looked for in shallow water of lakes near the entrance of drains, effluent of sewage treatment plants, *etc.*

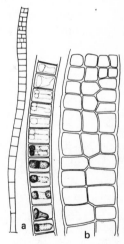

Fig. 239. *Schizomeris Leibleinii* Kuetz. (a) base of filament and uniseriate portion; (b) multiseriate upper portion of filament.

329b Filaments otherwise, upper cells not bricklike....................330

330a Filaments of cylindrical cells, uniseriate throughout most of the plant's length, finally developing globular cells in more than 1 series anteriorly (palmelloid). Fig. 240..................................
....*Pseudoschizomeris*

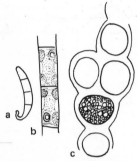

The plants are filamentous and ulotrichoid when young but become palmelloid and form multiseriate strands when older. The only species has been cultured from Texas soil.

Fig. 240. *Pseudoschizomeris caudata* Deason et Bold. (a) young plant; (b) cells showing chloroplasts; (c) palmelloid phase of old plant (in culture). (Redrawn from Deason et Bold.)

330b Filaments of cylindrical cells at first in 1 series, becoming multiseriate and forming packets of sarcinalike, angular cells above. Fig. 241...*Trichosarcina*

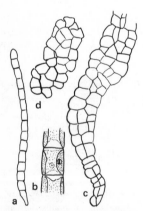

This genus was established for plants which begin as uniseriate filaments that eventually form multiseriate arrangements of cubical packets of cells. It is sometimes regarded as synonymous with *Pseudendoclonium*. *Trichosarcina* is monospecific; has been cultured from Texas soils.

Fig. 241. *Trichosarcina polymorpha* Nichols et Bold. (a) young plant with uniseriate arrangement of cells; (b) cells with chloroplasts; (c), (d) multiseriate arrangement of cells in older plants. (Redrawn from Nichols et Bold.)

331a (328) Filaments rarely solitary, mostly in tufts from a prostrate cluster of cells, the cells of the filament embedded in a
wide, firm gelatinous sheath and separated from one another;
plants gray or olive-green with several chloroplasts. (Rhodo-
phyta). Fig. 242...*Kyliniella*

In this genus of fresh-
water red algae there are
horizontal plates of cells that
give rise to erect tufts of unbranched filaments. These
are relatively short and inconspicuous at first but become several centimeters
long when mature. The cell
contents are pink at times
although the plant mass is
gray-green. The cells may
be adjoined or the proto-
plasts may be widely sep-
arated in a relatively wide
sheath. Plants are to be
sought in swiftly running
water. As far as known
K. latvica Skuja is the only
species and has been found
in eastern United States.

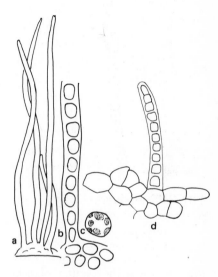

Fig. 242. *Kyliniella latvica* Skuja. (a) habit
of thallus with upright filaments from prostrate growth; (b) cell arrangement; (c) cell
in detail to show chloroplasts; (d) prostrate
portion with young erect filament.

331b Plants otherwise..332

332a Chloroplast a parietal network, usually close and dense, covering the entire wall; pyrenoids many and conspicuous......333

332b Chloroplast otherwise; pyrenoids few or lacking..................334

333a **Cells cylindrical, usually many times their diameter in length (sometimes only 3 times longer than wide); wall thick, usually lamellate. Fig. 243**..*Rhizoclonium*

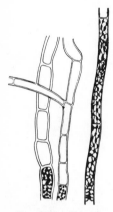

Fig. 243. *Rhizoclonium Hookeri* Kuetz., left; *R. hieroglyphicum* (C. A. Agardh) Kuetz., right.

The species belonging to this genus are all coarse, wiry and but very little (if at all) branched. The filaments are composed of relatively long, cylindrical, coenocytic cells, or if somewhat shorter cells, with lateral walls slightly convex and irregular. The walls are frequently lamellate in the larger species, especially at the cross walls. There are numerous chloroplasts, often compactly arranged and sometimes difficult of determination in respect to shape and organization. Sometimes the chloroplasts seem to form a meshwork, with the pyrenoids in the interconnections, or in the chloroplasts. The branches of the filament are usually short and mostly at right angles to the main axis, and irregular in plan. When the branches are long, as in some species, the plants intergrade with some forms of *Cladophora* (Fig. 292) in which the regular plan of branching has been reduced or lost. *Rhizoclonium* forms dense, tangled mats in standing water, or long, stringy, sometimes ropelike strands in flowing water. *R. hieroglyphicum* (Ag.) Kuetz. is the most common species, one which has rather uniformly cylindrical cells with relatively thin walls, and does not branch.

333b **Filaments of cells which are not quite cylindrical but are slightly larger at the anterior end; (practically cylindrical in some species); plants with a hold-fast and basal-distal differentiation; cells with 1 or more ringlike scars on the wall just below the cross wall (rings formed during cell division); when mature showing enlarged female cells (oogonia) and small, boxlike cells (antheridia). Fig. 244**...........................*Oedogonium*

There are over 300 species of this genus which belongs to the Oedogoniaceae, a family which includes only 2 other genera. (*Bulbochaete*, Fig. 294; *Oedocladium*, Fig. 266). Species are differentiated and are identified when in the reproductive condition by the size, shape and morphology of the sex organs and the mature oospore. Whereas some species have the male organs (antheridia) on filaments the same size as those which bear the female (oogonia), others possess dwarf male plants which grow as epiphytes on or near the oogonia. *Oedogonium* plants begin as attached filaments and may remain so throughout life, or they may become free-floating and form cottony masses near or on the surface of water, usually becoming pale yellow-green or cream-colored in age. Often these masses are so dense that if left to dry by the evaporation of habitat water they form what is known as "algal paper." Very common habitats are on overhanging grass leaves or the culms of rushes, old cattail stalks, *etc.* Bewildering to the student, several species may grow together in close proximity and some care and patience is required to differentiate.

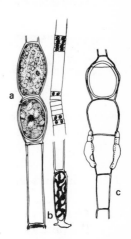

Fig. 244. (a) *Oedogonium crispum* Kuetz., portion of filament with 1 fertilized and 1 unfertilized egg; (b) basal hold-fast cell and portion of a filament containing antheridia and antherozoids; (c) Oe. *Westii* Tiff., showing dwarf male filaments epiphytic on female plant.

334a (332) Chloroplast a parietal plate, a ring, or a band which incompletely encircles the cell (but see *Ulothrix*, Fig. 256) **335**

334b Chloroplast massive and dense, difficult of determination, *or* a parietal sheet of thick and thin areas (padded appearance), *or* a branched, beaded thread (see *Microspora*, Figs. 245, 261)..**352**

Types of chloroplasts found in *Microspora*.

Fig. 245. *Microspora* chloroplasts. Right padded, parietal; left, beaded.

335a Filaments of cylindrical cells with a broad, parietal chloroplast that has a fringed margin (fingerlike extensions), with several pyrenoids. Fig. 246..*Entransia*

Fig. 246.   *Entransia dichloroplastes* Presc.

This plant is enigmatic;! having cells which are ulotrichoid in part but with Zygnemataceous pyrenoids. Conjugation has never been observed in the 2 known species. Apparently the plant is to be sought only in soft water or acid situations.

335b Filaments and chloroplasts otherwise....................................336

336a Filaments composed of long, cylindrical units; chloroplast in the form of several parietal rings in each unit. Fig. 247............ ....*Sphaeroplea*

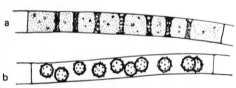

a

b

Fig. 247.   *Sphaeroplea annulina* (Roth) Ag. (a) vegetative cell with ringlike chloroplasts; (b) one cell containing fertilized eggs.

Four species of this genus have been reported from the United States, but only S. *annulina* (Roth) Ag. is at all common, and this is relatively rare. Whenever or wherever it occurs it is found in abundance. The characteristic long, cylindrical cells may be mistaken for species of *Rhizoclonium* (Fig. 243), especially when preserved material is examined. The annualr, bandlike chloroplasts aid in identification. The plants are to be expected in shallow water of marshes and bays of lakes.

336b Filaments not composed of long, multinucleate units; chloroplasts otherwise, usually 1 in each cell....................................337

337a Filaments prostrate, creeping on or in other algae; cells bearing 1 or 2 bristles, sometimes with branched hairs............338

337b Filaments not creeping on other algae; floating or if prostrate with cells in discontinuous series...339

**338a Filaments epiphytic, 'creeping' over the walls of larger, fila-
mentous algae in a 'wormlike' fashion; some cells bearing a
bulbous-based hair. Fig. 248**..................................*Aphanochaete*

There are 6 species of
this reported from the
United States, 3 of which
are very common but are
easily overlooked because
of their small size and because of their habit of
'creeping' over the fila-
ments of larger algae. The
simple setae, with swollen

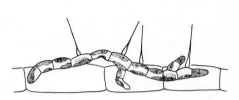

Fig. 248.   *Aphanochaete repens* A. Braun.

bases, extending from the cell wall are helpful in making identification. *A. polychaete* (Hansg.) Fritsch is characterized by having
several such setae borne on a single cell. *A. repens* A. Br. often has
the habit of a minute measuring worm.

**338b Filaments endophytic, creeping beneath the wall of other
algae, upper outer wall of some cells bearing long, tapering
bristles. Fig. 249**..*Ectochaete*
(See also *Coleochaete Nitellarum*, Fig. 231)

This is somewhat like
Aphanochaete (Fig. 248)
which is growing beneath
the wall of algae rather
than on them. The hairs
on them. The hairs on
on the wall do not have
swollen bases. Such al-
gae as *Cladophora* and
Rhizoclonium are fre-
quently endophytized by
Ectochaete.

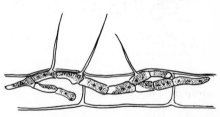

Fig.   249.   *Ectochaete endophytum*   (Moeb.)
Wille.

**339a (337) Filaments very short (up to 20 cells) often in interrupted
series**..**340**

339b Filaments longer, in continuous series of cells..................**342**

340a **Choloroplast a parietal, folded plate or merely a disc extended over but a small part of the wall; cells short-cylindric, with rounded poles. Fig. 250**..*Stichococcus*

Fig. 250.   *Stichococcus bacillaris* Naeg.

The difference between *Strichococcus* and the small filaments characteristic of *Chlorhormidium* (Fig. 258) is difficult to define. In the former genus the filaments are usually relatively short (10 to 20, or 40 cells) and have a tendency to break into short sections intermittently. Of the 11 species which occur in the United States most are found on the bark of trees, old boards, or damp soil. The species illustrated is the most common, often occurring with *Desmococcus* (Fig. 120) in subaerial habitats, the short filament twisted and contorted, or coiled in 1 plane.

340b **Chloroplast broader and cells different in shape**..................341

341a **Cells long-cylindric, or if short-cylindric with rounded poles; chloroplast ribbonlike or a broad plate covering most of the wall; filaments sometimes coiled. Fig. 251**....................*Gloeotila*

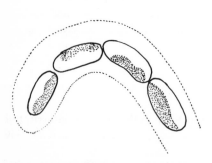

Fig. 251.   *Gloeotila contorta* Chodat, portion of coiled filament with gelatinous sheath.

These free-floating filaments have cylindrical cells adjoined in short or long series. In 1 species the cells have rounded poles and the filaments are coiled and twisted. The filaments are enclosed in a wide, gelatinous sheath. The plants appear much like a *Stichococcus* with long, slender cells. The plants have no basal-distal differentiation; and the cells lack a pyrenoid.

341b Cells transversely oval, in short, interrupted series, often 2 or 4 cells enclosed in a separate gelatinous sheath. Fig. 252......
....*Hormidiopsis*

The species illustrated is the only one reported from the United States and possibly cannot be differentiated from *Chlorhormidium* (Fig. 258) except that the filaments are frequently interrupted and are decidedly constricted at the cross walls, the cells being oblong or oval rather than cylindrical. Characteristically, the chloroplast extends only part way around the cell wall.

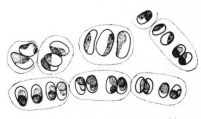

Fig. 252.   *Hormidiopsis ellipsoideum* Presc.

342a (339) Filaments composed of units which include 2 oval or subspherical protoplasts; the space between the protoplasts and the wall filled with layered (lamellose) material. Fig. 253
....*Binuclearia*

There are 3 species of this genus reported from the United States, but the one illustrated is the most frequently found. The plants occur intermingled among other filamentous algae, especially in mixtures taken from bogs.

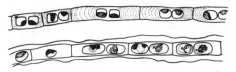

Fig. 253.   *Binuclearia tatrana* Wittr., one filament showing a gelatinous sheath.

The paired protoplasts within each cylindrical unit of the filament make identification certain.

342b Filaments of cells without paired protoplasts as above......343

343a Filaments with a gelatinous sheath...344

343b Filaments without a gelatinous sheath.................................349

344a Cells cylindric-quadrate, globose or ellipsoid; adjoined at the end walls...345

344b Cells oblong, not adjoined at the end walls Fig. 254...............
....*Geminella*

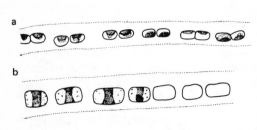

These are filamentous plants which have cylindrical or broadly oval cells encased in a wide sheath of mucilage. The cells may be adjoined, or rather evenly spaced one-half to 2 cell lengths apart. Like *Chlorhormidium* (Fig. 258) the chloroplast covers but a small portion of the wall.

Fig. 254. (a) *Geminella interrupta* (Turp.) Lag.; (b) *G. mutabilis* (Bréb.) Wille.

345a Cells quadrate, cylidrical or subelliptic, with rounded poles; wall in 1 piece...346

345b Cells globose, subglobose, or ellipsoid; wall usually of 2 overlapping pieces that meet in the midregion of the cell and which form short, lateral projections (resulting from a rim about the cell in the midregion). Fig. 255...............*Radiofilum*

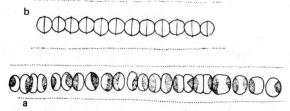

Fig. 255. (a) *Radiofilum flavescens* G. S. West; (b) *R. conjunctivum* Schmidle.

The globose or subglobose cells of these filaments help to separate *Radiofilum* from *Geminella* (Fig. 254) which also possesses a gelatinous sheath. Some species, *R. conjunctivum* Schm., *e.g.* have the walls in 2 sections which form a conspicuous overlapping in the midregion. There are 10 species reported from the United States, differentiated by shape, size and morphology of the cells.

346a Filament of cylindrical cells with a lobed, parietal chloroplast and 1 pyrenoid; (filaments becoming multiseriate, with the cells globular in age). Fig. 240...............*Pseudoschizomeris*

346b Filaments otherwise...347

347a Filaments composed of slender, cylindrical cells, truncate or
      sometimes rounded at the apices, enclosed in a wide, gelatin-
      ous sheath; chloroplast a broad plate or a twisted band.
      Fig. 251...*Gloeotila*

347b Filaments otherwise...**348**

348a Cells short-cylindric with rounded poles; chloroplast a small
      plate or a narrow band covering but only about one-third of
      the cell wall; filament enclosed in a wide, gelatinous sheath;
      (cells usually in interrupted series). Fig. 254............*Geminella*

348b Cells quadrate to long-cylindric; chloroplast a broad, parietal
      band covering most of the wall, or a median band completely
      encircling the cell; pyrenoids 1 to several; at least 1 species
      with basal-distal differentiation and a hold-fast cell; without a
      wide gelatinous sheath, but may have a close, firm sheath
      immediately external to the wall. Fig. 256....................*Ulothrix*

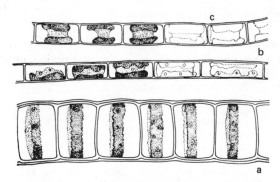

Fig. 256   (a) *Ulothrix zonata* (Weber et Mohr) Kuetz., with ringlike chloroplasts; (b) *U. cylindricum* Presc.; (c) *U. aequalis* Kuetz.

Species of this genus have short, rectangular cells, or relatively
long, cylindrical cells. There is considerable variation in cell-
diameter, some species having cells wider than long. The most
familiar species and the largest is *Ulothrix zonata* (Weber et Mohr)
Kuetz. It has a basal hold-fast and shows basal-distal differentiation.
The chloroplast, at least in mature cells forms a complete, parietal
band with one or more pyrenoids. Other species have chloroplasts
which encircle the wall two-thirds or three-fourths of a circle.
Whereas most species occur in standing water, *U. zonata* prefers
rapidly flowing streams, or wave-washed shores where it forms
bright green, streaming clumps or fringes on rocks and submersed
wood. Reproduction is by quadriflagellate zoospores, formed 4 to
8 in a cell, or by biflagellate isogametes produced 16 to 64 in a cell.

349a (343) Filaments not showing basal-distal differentiation......350
349b Filaments with a basal hold-fast..351
350a Filaments short, 2 to 6 (rarely up to 32) cells; filaments tapered at both ends. Fig. 257................................*Raphidonema*

Some species of this genus are scarcely filaments, the plants consisting of only a few cells adjoined. The cells are more fusiform at times than cylindrical and the poles are tapering so that the cross walls are oblique. Very frequently this genus is found in snow fields at high altitudes. The genus *Koliella* (Fig. 257A) has similar cells, occurring singly or in linear pairs, decidedly pointed at the apices. This genus is know to have oogamous reproduction. *Raphidonema*, according to the above interpretation includes species with filaments up to 32 cells long; reproduces only by cell division as far as known.

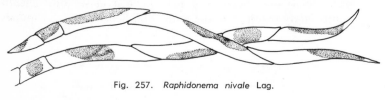

Fig. 257.   *Raphidonema nivale* Lag.

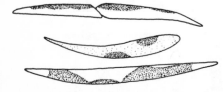

Fig. 257A. *Kobiella* sp. from snow banks in Olympic Mountains.

The species illustrated is an example of the cell arrangement that characterizes the genus and which according to some students separates it from *Raphidonema* (Fig. 257).

350b Filaments indefinitely long; cells not tapered at the filament ends. Fig. 258................................*Chlorhormidium (Hormidium)*

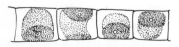

Fig. 258.   *Chlorhormidium dissectum* (Chod.) Fott.

This is a synonymous name for *Hormidium*. The genus includes several species of simple, unbranched filaments of cylindrical (or somewhat quadrangular) cells which are characterized by having chloroplasts which extend only part way around the cell and which are only about one-half the cell in length. Species are both aquatic, intermingled with other filamentous algae and subaerial, occurring on wet soil and on dripping rocks or in seeps.

351a (349) Cells elongate-cylindric, the apical cell unsymmetrically
pointed. Fig. 259...*Uronema**

Five species of
this genus have been
described, but these
are in questionable
position inasmuch as

Fig. 259.   Uronema elongatum Hodgetts.

there is justification for considering the plants as growth forms of
Ulothrix. The cells are long and cylindrical with a ulotrichoid
chloroplast. Usually the filament is only a few cells in length.
The unsymmetrically pointed apical cell is the chief identifying
character. Younger stages in the development of *Stigeoclonium*
(Fig. 270) should be kept in mind when identification of *Uro
nema* is made.

351b Cells short-cylindric, apical cell not tapering. Fig. 256.........
....*Ulothrix*

352a (334) Cells quadrate or oval to subglobose, enclosed in a wide,
stratified, gelatinous sheath. Fig. 260................*Cylindrocapsa*

Although filaments of this genus begin as
attached plants they soon become free-floating and are found intermingled with other
filamentous algae, especially in soft water
or acid lakes and bogs. The chloroplasts are
so dense and the cell contents include so
much food storage material that few structural characteristics can be determined. The
female reproductive organ (oogonium) is
globular and greatly swollen to several times
the diameter of the vegetative cells. The
oogonium contents (female gamete) are red,
especially after fertilization at which time
an oospore wall is formed. The antheridia occur as a single or double row of small, somewhat quadrangular cells (also are red). Each
antheridial cell produces 4 quadriflagellate
sperm.

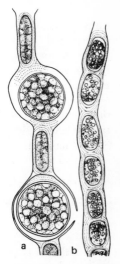

Fig.   260.   Cylindro-
capsa   geminella   var.
minor Hansg. (a) portion
of filament with oogon-
ia; (b) vegetative cells.

*Sometimes assigned to *Ulothrix*, Fig. 256.

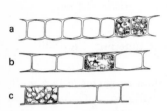

Fig. 261. (a) *Microspora Loef-grenii* (Nordst.) Lag.; (b) *M. Wil-leana* Lag.; (c) *M. floccosa* (Vauch.) Thur.

In this genus the simple, unbranched filaments have quadrangular to short-cylindric cells. The chloroplast varies greatly in appearance, being either a parietal, folded, discontinuous plate, or a meshwork of strands (Fig. 245). There are 15 or 16 species, differentiated by size and proportions of the cells and by the wall characters. The wall is in 2 sections which overlap in the midregion. The overlapping is conspicuous especially in the thick-walled species, but at least can be determined by examining the broken ends of filaments where the sections protrude. When the filaments fragment characteristic H-shaped sections may be formed. The plants produce akinetes rather frequently and often an entire filament may appear as a chain of globular spores. Because of the wall features and the nature of the chloroplast *Microspora* is usually placed in its own family and order.

356a Branches whorled (beaded effect); when mature with dense
clusters of spores (carpospores) formed around the base of the
female sex organ (carpogonium) as a result of fertilization.
(*B. Dillenii* not beaded). Fig. 262...................*Batrachospermum*

This genus belongs to the Rhodophyta and is one of the most common of the fresh-water representatives of red algae. Although it does not show a red color, the pigments do contain phycoerythrin and others peculiar to the Rhodophyta. The macroscopic thalli, highly branched and beaded are encased in a copious, soft mucilage. They form arbuscular growths on stones and sticks in flowing water; although some species occur in pools of soft or acid water, usually growing on vertical walls of *Sphagnum* bog pools. The thallus may be gray-green, blue-green or olive in color (sometimes tawny). *Batrachospermum vagum* (Roth) Ag. is perhaps the most common species in the United

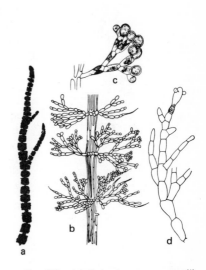

Fig. 262.   (a) *Batrachospermum monili-forme* Roth, habit of plant; (b) portion of thallus showing small antheridial cells at tips of branches; (c) *B. vagum* (Roth) Ag., antheridial branch in detail; (d) *B. Boryanum* Sirod., carpogonial branch with 2 male cells attached to trichogyne of the carpogonium (female organ).

States, occurring in large patches on stones in flowing water. Some species seem to prefer shaded areas. Microscopically *Batrachospermum* is one of the most elegant of fresh-water algae. Species are differentiated by the morphology of the carpogonium (female sex organ), by the habit of branching, and by the location of the sex organs; some species monoecious; others dioecious. The spermatia (male) cells occur as small, spherical units at the tips of the ultimately cells of branches. Characteristically, the sperm are non-motile and reach the carpogonium by drifting. When mature, and after fertilization, dense heads of carpospores form about the base of the carpogonium. These can be easily detected under low magnification, appearing as dark clumps scattered about in the whorls of branches.

356b Thallus similar to above; carpospores solitary or in small clumps, not forming dense heads, the spores produced on wandering filaments (gonimoblast filaments) which develop from the carpogonium after fertilization of the female gamete. Fig. 263..*Sirodotia*

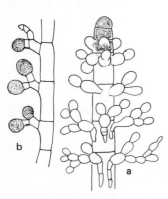

Fig. 263. *Sirodotia suecica* Kylin. (a) apex of filament with branches; (b) carpospores in detail, borne on gonimoblast filament which develops from carpogonium after fertilization of the egg.

These plants occur in the same type of habitat as *Batrachospermum* (Fig. 262) and appear much like that genus macroscopically. The chief difference is that the zygote in *Sirodotia* develops filaments (gonimoblast filaments) that grow through the thallus, cutting off clusters of spores, 2 or 3 together, here and there. In *Batrachospermum* the spores are produced in dense clumps in the immediate vicinity of the carpogonium where the egg has been fertilized.

357a (355) Filaments uniseriate below, becoming multiseriate in the upper section, with the cells bricklike in shape and arrangement; cells adjoined. Fig. 239....................*Schizomeris*

357b Filaments multiseriate throughout; cells not adjoined but arranged in irregular, linear series within a gelatinous strand to form a false filament. Fig. 238..............................*Palmodictyon*

358a (290) Plants composed of cellular units; cross walls present 359

The thallus in this genus is a disc, 1-celled thick, formed by closely appressed, branched filaments radiating from a common center. The cells are thick-walled and multinucleate. Apparently the plants grow only on the carapaces of turtles.

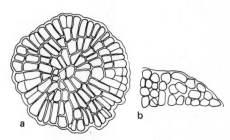

Fig. 264. *Dermatophyton radians* Peter. (a) surface view of epizoic thallus; (b) thallus in cross section (semidiagrammatic).

Fig. 264A. *Trichophilus Welcheri* Weber van Bosse, short-branched filaments on hair scales of sloth. (Redrawn from Bourrelly.)

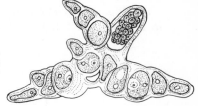

**Trichophilus Welcheri* Web. v. Bosse (Fig. 264A) is a sparsely branched, semipalmelloid species which grows among the hair scales of the sloth along with *Cyanoderma* (Fig. 19).

361a Filaments subterranean with tufts of branches appearing above the surface; apices of branches pointed but without setae. Fig. 265..*Fritschiella*

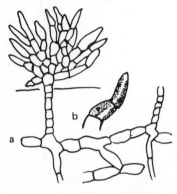

This thallus has tufts of branches arising above soil from a subterranean filament, which also gives rise to downward growing rhizoidal branches. First found in India, this genus is now knwn from southwest United States. The prostrate portion produces zoospores and gametes on diploid and haploid individuals respectively, thus exhibiting an alternation of isomorphic generations.

Fig. 265. *Fritschiella tuberosa* Iyengar. (a) portion of thallus showing horizontally growing, subterranean filaments and an erect tuft of branches; (b) tip of branch showing parietal, folded chloroplast.

361b Plants branched filaments growing on moist soil, with rhizoidal extensions; cells cylindrical, the apical cell with a cap (thimble); reproduction by sperm and non-motile egg borne in an enlarged cell (oogonium). Fig. 266..........*Oedocladium**

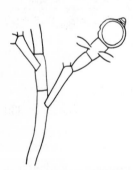

The branched, filamentous plants in this genus have been found only on damp soil (incidentally under water). There are 9 species reported from the United States, but probably there are more which have been overlooked. In nature the plants greatly resemble moss protonema. Like other members of the Oedogoniaceae, the cells are slightly larger at the anterior end. The female organ (oogonium) is distinctly enlarged, whereas the antheridium is produced in a dwarf male plant that grows as an epiphyte on or near the oogonium.

Fig. 266. *Oedocladium Hazenii* Lewis, portion of branched filament with an oogonium and 2 epiphytic male plants; growing on soil.

*In humid, subtropical regions *Oedogonium* also grows on moist soil and subaerial substrates; is unbranched.

362a (360) Plants *prostrate*, growing horizontally; mostly epiphytic or endophytic and forming discs or flat expanses; upright branches also present in some forms..363

362b Plants *erect*, not growing horizontally on a substrate, but sometimes a thallus with some horizontal growth at the base of the erect portions; free-floating or attached; or epiphytic or parasitic on higher plants; in some forms perforating wood or shells..378

363a Filaments short and incidentally formed as series of cells arising from encrusting patches of globular cells growing on trees and boards. Fig. 120..............*Desmococcus (Pleurococcus)*

363b Filaments otherwise...364

364a Thallus a freely and openly branched filament; cells usually bearing setae or spine-shaped hairs..365

364b Thallus not freely branched, but forming a disc, cushion (pseudoparenchymatous), or a flat expanse of cells..............372

365a Endophytic in the walls of other algae.................................366

365b Not endophytic in the walls of other algae..........................367

366a Thallus irregularly branched; angular cells lying within or under the walls of *Nitella;* cells bearing setae (sometimes very scarce) which are sheathed at the base. Fig. 231............
....*Coleochaete Nitellarum*

366b Cells not angular; branches short; cells never bearing setae. Fig. 267...*Entocladia*

This genus includes only 3 species in the United States but there are others in Europe and they are probably widely distributed over the world and are easily overlooked. The thalli are small and grow inconspicuously within the walls of larger algae. The filaments are short and irregularly branched; have a parietal ulotrichoid chloroplast.

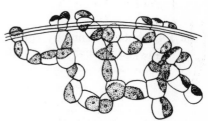

Fig. 267. *Entocladia polymorpha* (G. S. West) G. M. Smith.

Unlike somewhat similar plants the cells do not bear setae.

367a (365) Some cell walls bearing setae with a sheathed base; terminal cells of branches not tapering to form setae. Fig. 231
....*Coleochaete*

367b Cells with setae not sheathed at the base, or if without setae, ends of branches tapering to hairs or spinelike extensions; sometimes endophytic..368

368a Setae and terminal hairs multicellular.................................369

368b Setae one-celled...371

369a Multicellular setae in the form of especially slender branches arising from lateral walls of some cells. Fig. 268......................
....Pseudochaete

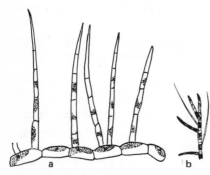

The species illustrated is rarely found. It grows partly prostrate, partly erect on submersed plants and other substrates. The branched filaments taper at both ends. Some of the branches form long, narrow and finely tapering hairs. Some students of the algae regard *Pseudochaete* as a growth form of *Stigeoclonium* (Fig. 270).

Fig. 268. (a) *Pseudochaete crassisetum* G. S. West; (b) *P. gracilis* W. et W.

369b Plants with multicellular hairs resulting from the apical tapering of branches..370

370a Filaments horizontally spreading in and on duckweed thalli; with erect branches that taper to fine points. Fig. 269............
....Endoclonium

The branched filaments 'creep' among the cells of *Lemna*, especially *L. minor*. There are both prostrate and erect portions of the thallus. As a genus *Endoclonium* is not well understood. Some regard it as a growth form or a juvenile stage of some species of *Stigeoclonium*.

Fig. 269. *Endoclonium polymorphum* Franke, habit on and in tissues of *Lemna*.

370b Filaments growing as erect, branched tufts or plumes; branching alternate or opposite, the branches thornlike and short, or long and tapering to fine points. Fig. 270..........*Stigeoclonium*

There are several species of this genus, differentiated by size, by plan of branching, and the general morphology of the thallus as a whole. Some species form long, graceful tufts; others are bunched growths with part of the thallus prostrate. It must be compared with *Cloniophora* (Fig. 287).

Fig. 270. *Stigeoclonium flagelliferum* Kuetz. (a) portion of thallus showing tapering branches; (b) cell showing laminate chloroplast and pyrenoid.

371a (368) Growing in the mucilage of other algae. Fig. 271...........
....*Chaetonema*

Apparently there are only 2 species described for this genus. It is rather rarely seen because its habitat is the gelatinous matrix of highly branched algae such as *Chaetophora* (Fig. 295) and *Batrachospermum* (Fig. 262) where it is well-camouflaged.

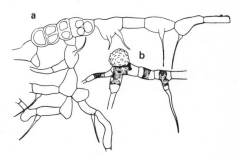

Fig. 271. *Chaetonema irregulare* Nowak. (a) branches containing antheridial cells; (b) portion of filament with an oogonium.

371b Growing in a 'creeping' fashion on the walls of larger algae. Fig. 248..*Aphanochaete*

372a (364) Cells bearing setae with sheathed bases. Fig. 231...........
....*Coleochaete*

372b Cells without setae, or if setae present without a sheathed base..373

373a Plants endophytic or epiphytic..374

373b Not epiphytic or endophytic in walls of other algae...........375

374a Filaments 'creeping' beneath the walls of other algae. Fig. 267
....*Entocladia (Endoderma)*

374b Filaments growing on and among the cells of *Lemna* thalli. Fig. 269..*Endoclonium*

375a (373) Some cells with setae on the walls. Fig. 272..*Chaetopeltis*

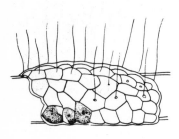

Fig. 272. *Chaetopeltis orbicularis* Berth.

This plant forms relatively small, circular discs composed of indistinctly radiate 'filaments' which grow closely side by side. It should be compared with *Coleochaete.* It is rather oddly placed in the Tetrasporales because the cells bear pseudocilia which are very long and erect. These have a different morphology than the hairs or setae produced by other somewhat similar prostrate plants. *Chaetopeltis orbicularis* Berth. is to be found as an epiphyte on larger filamentous algae and on the stems of aquatic plants.

375b Setae lacking..376

376a Thallus a thin expanse, 1 cell in thickness; a circular disc, or with somewhat irregular margins. Fig. 273............*Protoderma*

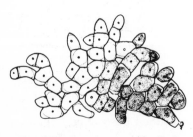

Fig. 273. *Protoderma viride* Kuetz.

This prostrate plant forms a cushionlike thallus 1 cell in thickness at the margin and one which shows very irregular branching of short filaments. It is to be found growing on the stems of submersed aquatic plants; cells have a single, parietal chloroplast.

376b Thallus cushionlike, several cells in thickness in the midregion **377**

377a Cells with several chloroplasts; thallus enclosed in a muci-lage; disc several cells thick in the midregion, 1 cell in thick-ness at the margin. Fig. 274..................................*Pseudoulvella*

The prostrate, disclike thalli of this plant are relatively large; often are visible to the unaided eye, growing on cattail stems, rushes, and *Chara.* The entire thallus is enclosed by a gelatinous sheath which is evident at the margin. The sheath often bears gelatinous bristles which are deciduous and frequently the hair-bearing character does not show. The thallus is 1-celled thick at the margin, several cells thick in the midregion. Reproduction is by quadriflagellate zoospores; sexual reproduction seems never to have been reported. The one species is known from western and midwest United States.

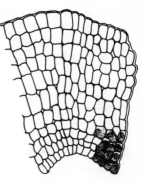

Fig. 274. *Pseudoulvella americana* (Snow) Wille.

377b Cells with but 1 chloroplast; thallus not enclosed in a sheath. Fig. 275..*Ulvella*

There is some confusion between this genus and *Dermatophyton,* one species of which has been referred to *Ulvella* (but apparently incorrectly). Both of these disclike thalli may occur on turtle carapaces, but *Ulvella,* also grows on aquatic plants and on stones; seems to have thinner

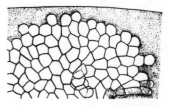

Fig. 275. *Ulvella involvens* (Savi) Schm., diagram of attached colony showing arrangement of cells.

walls and biflagellate zoospores. The cells are uninucleate. There are both marine and fresh-water species of *Ulvella,* the one illustrated having been found on turtles.

378a (362) Plant a sparsely branched filament growing erect from the walls of other algae; cells bearing 1 to 3 setae with inflated bases. Fig. 276..*Thamniochaete*

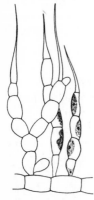

This genus has both prostrate filaments and erect branches; occurs as an epiphyte on filamentous algae. The cells are either subcylindric, barrel-shaped or nearly globular. The terminal cells of the branches especially, but others as well, bear long, colorless setae. Thus far one species has been reported from California in the United States.

Fig. 276. Thamniochaete Huberi Gay, filaments growing erect from algal host.

378b Plants not as above..**379**

379a Filaments irregularly branched, composed of moniliform cells, mostly erect but sprawling and prostrate in part, on tree trunks and leaves of higher plants. Fig. 277.............*Physolinum*

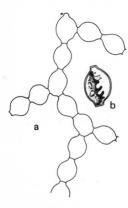

This plant consists of lemon-shaped cells adjoined to form branched chains without any definite central axis and apparently without basal-distal differentiation. The thallus is mostly prostrate as an epiphyte on higher plants (especially leaves in humid situations). The genus is sometimes included in *Trentepohlia* (Fig. 7). The cells divide by producing a 'bud' which enlarges and constricts, after which a cross wall is formed separating the new cell from the old. There is 1 parietal chloroplast, often with projections, or the chloroplast may become divided into 2 or 3 dislike bodies, but always without pyrenoids. Like *Trentepohlia* the cells are yellow or orange with carotenoid type of haematochrome.

Fig. 277. *Physolinum monilia* (de Wild.) Printz. (a) prostrate and erect filaments of moniliform cells; (b) cell with chloroplast.

The branched filaments of this genus are enclosed in a soft, mucilaginous tubelike sheath, the sheaths sometimes anastomosing. The subquadrate to subglobose cells are in chains and are not always in contact with one another. At times there is vertical as well as transverse division of the cells.

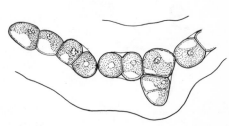

Fig. 278. *Hazenia mirabilis* Bold. (Redrawn from Bold.)

The chloroplast is ulotrichoid. As far as known there is no basaldistal differentiation, but the apical cell is definitely conical. Only one species is known, from soil in Tennessee.

386b Filament irregularly twisted, composed of irregularly shaped, vermiform or subcylindrical cells, enclosed in an oval or globular sheath; branching indefinite. Fig. 279.........................
...Helicodictyon (Heterodictyon)

Fig. 279. *Helicodictyon planc-tonicum* Whitford. (R e d r a w n from Bourrelly.)

This genus like *Hazenia* (Fig. 278) has a filament enclosed in a wide, gelatinous sheath. The cells are short, bacilliform or irregularly lobed and often are arranged in a twisted, rather indefinite branched filament. There is a ulotrichoid chloroplast with a pyrenoid. The name is synonymous with *Heterodictyon* Whitford.

387a (385) Chloroplast an axial plate or band with conspihuous pyrenoids, wall relatively thin. Fig. 225.....................*Mougeotia*

387b Chloroplast a parietal network of thickenings and thin strands, with many pyrenoids in the meshwork; walls thick, sometimes lamellate. Fig. 243..*Rhizoclonium*

388a (383) Growing in wood, shells or within limestone. Fig. 280
...*Gomontia*

Fig. 280. *Gomontia Holdenii* Collins, habit of the thallus showing erect branches.

These plants must be sought within old wood, shells or in limy concretions, or on the surface in part. The thallus occurs as a cushionlike, irregularly tangled mass of short filaments from which some elements grow downward to form rhizoidal, penetrating threads. Reproductive structures (sporangia) are borne on the upper parts of the thallus at the ends of short, erect branches. Akinetes are also produced. In germination these often form aplanospores. Cell walls, especially in the prostrate portion, are thick-walled and lamellate; there is a dense, laminate chloroplast with several pyrenoids. Most species are marine.

388b Not growing *in* wood nor in shells, but may occur *on* wood and old shells; sometimes on tree trunks.................................389

389a Plants containing reddish carotenoid haematochrome........390

389b Plants without such carotenoids...391

390a Plants erect filaments, forming orange-colored, cottony growths on tree trunks, wood and rocks in moist situations. Fig. 7...*Trentepohlia*

390b Plants consisting of horizontal filaments growing prostrate, epiphytic on leaves of higher plants. Fig. 4...........*Phycopeltis*

391a Thallus encrusted with lime...392

391b Thallus not encrusted with lime...393

392a Thallus in the form of a cushion, giving rise to compactly arranged, upright branches; cells broadest near the tip of the filaments; growing on wood or shells (sometimes on other plants in the water). Fig. 281......................................*Gongrosira*

Like *Gongrosira* (Fig. 280) these plants grow on shells and submersed wood, or on aquatic plants, but form entirely external thalli rather than penetrating the substrate. Plants are sometimes lime-encrusted. The erect branched portion of the thallus is more extensively developed than in *Gomontia* (some filaments are very long). The chloroplast is parietal and more definite in outline than in the latter genus and less of a dense meshwork. Some authors include the genus *Ctenocladus* (Fig. 284) in *Gongrosira*.

Fig. 281. *Gongrosira Debaryana* Rab., horizontal and erect branches with terminal sporangia.

392b Thallus composed of loosely branched filaments, the branches arising unilaterally. Fig. 282.................................Chlorotylium

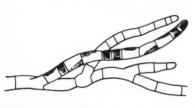

Fig. 282. *Chlorotylium cataractum* Kuetz., portion of plant showing characteristic habit of branch development.

The attached, lime-encrusted thalli of this branched, filamentous plant are usually found in flowing water. The filaments present a distinctive appearance when seen microscopically because pairs of short, green cells with a parietal chloroplast (often with a reddish tinge) alternate with a more elongate and sometimes nearly colorless cell. Of the 5 known species 2 occur in the United States.

393a (391) Thallus a tuft of dichotomously branched, radiating, yellow-green filaments. Fig. 283.................................Leptosira

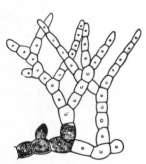

Fig. 283. *Leptosira Mediciana* Borzi, portion of plant showing horizontal and erect branching systems.

Filaments occur in yellowish (light green) tufts and are usually attached to substrates. The irregularly branched filaments of beadlike or barrel-shaped cells arising from a prostrate portion of the thallus help in making identification. The chloroplast is a dense, parietal plate (usually). Of the 3 known species 1 only is known for the United States, rather rare but widely distributed.

393b Thallus not a dense tuft of yellow-green filaments.............394

394a Bearing enlarged, thick-walled akinetes (vegetative spores), interspersed among the cylindrical cells of the filament, or with such spores at the ends of branches.............395

394b Without akinetes, or if rarely present, scattered, not arranged as above.................................396

395a Akinetes globular, in chainlike series. Fig. 284......*Ctenocladus*

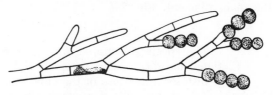

Fig. 284.   *Ctenocladus circinnatus* Borzi, showing a terminal series of akinetes.

This is a branched filamentous plant with cylindrical cells which seems to prefer hard-water or alkaline situations. They grow epiphytically on angiospermous plants (stems and exposed roots), sometimes forming extensive growths throughout an entire lake. The branches terminate in chains of globular akinetes. *Ctenocladus* is sometimes included under *Gongrosira* (Fig. 281).

395b Akinetes barrel-shaped or oval, solitary. Fig. 285....*Pithophora*

There are 8 species of this irregularly branched, filamentous genus in the United States, differentiated by dimension of the filament and by the size and shape of the much-swollen akinetes that are formed intermittently throughout the plant. The cells are coenocytic and have the cladophoraceous type of chloroplast. When occurring in laboratory aquaria, usually having been brought in on material obtained from biological supply houses, the filaments often fail to develop the characteristic akinetes, the cells becoming exceedingly long and losing some of the appearance by which they are usually identified. Branches arise mostly at right angles to a main axis; frequently an akinete will bear a branch.

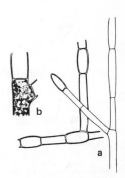

Fig. 285. (a) *Pithophora Mooreana* Collins; (b) *P. Oedogonia* (Mont.) Wittr. showing a sample of the chloroplast.

396a Growing on submersed wood and stones, with a prostrate, cushionlike mass of branches from which vertical branches arise. Fig. 281..*Gongrosira*

396b (394) Thallus formed differently..397

397a Plants growing on shells of turtles (rarely on submersed brick or rough stones); branches arising only from the extreme base of the main filament. Fig. 286................................*Basicladia*

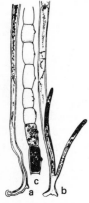

The species illustrated and 3 others (differentiated mostly by size) comprise the genus which is distinctive because of the very long, cylindrical cells and the habit of producing branches only at the extreme base. The genus is invariably found on the backs of snapping (and a few other) turtles. Occasionally plants will be found on bricks in water or other especially rough surfaces. The upper cells become zoosporangia and develop lateral pores in the midregion for the release of zoospores.

Fig. 286. *Basicladia Chelonum* (Collins) Hoffman et T i l d e n. (a) cells at the base of filament; (b) branching habit; (c) series of sporangia formed in the upper portion of the filament.

402a Filaments with arbuscular branching; branches thornlike and short and also long and slightly tapering on the same axis, the cells of the branches smaller than those of the main axis. Fig. 287...*Cloniophora*

These erect, branched filaments have a profuse growth of downward-directed rhizoidal branches and fascicled, arbuscular branches above. The cells of the main axis are larger than those of the branches, but not the same great variation in diameter found in *Draparnaldia* (Fig. 297). Unlike *Stigeoclonium* (Fig. 270) which it resembles, the branches do not end in tapering chaete. The cells contain a chaetophoraceous chloroplast. Three species are recognized, mostly from tropical and subtropical streams.

Fig. 287. *Cloniophora spicata* (Schm.) Islam, upper portion of branching thallus.

402b Filaments irregularly branching, partly prostrate and partly erect, with all cells approximately the same size; chloroplast a parietal plate; plants showing a tendency to form a palmelloid stage. Fig. 288............................*Pseudendoclonium* (Possibly synonymous with *Trichosarcina*, Fig. 241.)

The filaments in this genus grow horizontally on moist substrates but have irregular, short, erect branches. The filaments frequently have dissociated cells which form individual cells which develop palmelloid packets and show the characteristics described for the genus *Trichosarcina* (Fig. 241). Sometimes the erect branches occur as tufts. Plants are known to produce zoospores but sexual reproduction has not been observed. Of the 2 known species, 1 is marine.

Fig. 288. *Pseudendoclonium submarinum* Wille, prostrate and erect branches.

403a (401) **Thallus arbuscular, minute, sometimes densely tufted, attached (but easily broken from the substrate and floating freely). Fig. 289**..*Microthamnion*

This genus is frequently overlooked because of the small size of the branched, epiphytic growths. Although beginning as attached thalli they frequently float freely and are found in the tychoplankton intermingled with other filamentous algae. A characteristic which helps in identification is that the septation of the branch occurs some distance above the level of origin. The branches may taper somewhat but do not terminate in hairs. The taxonomic position of the genus is under question.

Fig. 289.
M i crotham-
nion strictis-
simum Rab.

403b **Thallus gelatinous, free-floating or entangled among other algae, with radiating series of irregularly dissociated cells; branching scarce and incidental. Fig. 290**...........*Heterococcus*

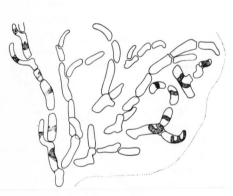

The thallus of this genus consists of irregularly radiating series of (often) dissociated cells. Branches form from near the apex of a cell, the new cell soon becoming dissociated. The apical cells are tapered or thornlike and curved in the species illustrated. The chloroplast is a parietal, chaetophoraceous, plate covering part of the cell wall. Although lightly green in color, the genus belongs to the Xanthophyceae (Tribonematales).

Fig. 290. *Heterococcus arcticus* Presc., habit of branching and radiate arrangement of short 'pseudofilaments' within a gelatinous matrix.

404a (400) **Branching open and spreading; apices not tapering to form setae**...**405**

404b Branching close and entangled, resulting in a spongy thallus. Fig. 291..*Aegagropila*

This genus is more irregularly branched than *Cladophora* (Fig. 292); is sometimes included in that genus. It has a profuse development of downward-directed, rhizoidal branches. The upper filaments are densely entangled and the cells are more irregular in shape than in *Cladophora*. The species illustrated is well-named for it is found growing on the bottom of lakes at depths up to 200 feet, especially in clear water. The chloroplast is cladophoraceous and the cells are coenocytic.

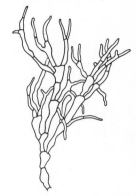

Fig. 291. *Aegagropila profunda* (Brand) Nordst.

405a Branching forming fascicles, both short and long branches from the same axis; walls thick in lower part of the filament but not lamellate; chloroplast a parietal band with 1 or a few pyrenoids. Fig. 287..*Cloniophora*

405b Branching not tufted, arising singly (or in pairs), arbuscular, the branching becoming irregular in old plants or in water-washed thalli); cell walls thick and usually lamellate; chloroplast a parietal network with numerous pyrenoids; coenocytic. Fig. 292..*Cladophora*

There are numerous species of this genus in both fresh and salt water. Many of the names, however, have been shown to be given to growth form or habitat variations of the same species. They are differentiated by size, habit of branching and over-all thallus form. The cell walls are often thick and lamellate. Chloroplasts are disc-like thickenings interconnected to form a meshwork and there are many pyrenoids. Although the general habit is arbuscular, plants which winter over or which become wave-washed often develop irregular habits of branching and in many instances intergrade with branched species of *Rhizoclonium* (Fig. 243). Perhaps the most characteristic habit of fresh-water *Cladophora* is flowing water, especially on dams and waterfalls.

Fig. 292. *Cladophora* sp. (a) cell showing parietal, netlike chloroplast (which often appears broken into small plates); (b) habit of branching.

406a (398) Vegetative cells very long and cylindrical, somewhat regularly interrupted by swollen, thick-walled spores (akinetes). Fig. 285..*Pithophora*

406b Akinetes lacking; cells all cylindrical or nearly so................**407**

407a Branches scarce and short, or wanting altogether; if branches present, without repeated branching. Fig. 243...........................
....*Rhizoclonium*

407b Branches many-celled, bearing secondary branches which arise irregularly so that the arbuscular habit is almost lost. Wave-washed and winter forms. Fig. 292........................*Cladophora*

408a (382) Setae without cross walls at the base, formed by lateral extensions of cells just below the anterior cross partition of the cell. Fig. 293..*Fridaea*

The species illustrated is very rare (the only one known for the genus) but occurs in abundance in particular habitats. It is readily identified by the long, cylindrical cells which bear threadlike extensions that are given off laterally just below the anterior cross walls. The filaments occur in compact tufts and usually are yellowish-green. The chloroplast is parietal and laminate, but often so dense that the exact organization is difficult of determination. Zoosporangia are elongate and saclike, produced laterally on the filaments.

F i g. 293.
Fridaea tor-
r e n t i c o l a
Schmidle.

408b Setae formed otherwise..**409**

409a Setae bulblike at the base. Fig. 294......................*Bulbochaete*

Like its close relative *Oedogonium* (Fig. 244) this genus contains numerous species which are likewise differentiated by dimensions and characteristics of the sex organs and the oospore. They cannot be identified to species in the vegetative condition. The branched filaments are attached (at least when young) and are readily recognized by the bulbous-based, unicellular setae that develop at the anterior end of the cell (but lateral). The plants can be sought on overhanging grass, or on the culms of rushes, submersed plants, *etc.* Most species have dwarf male plants that grow epiphytically on the female sex organ (oogonium).

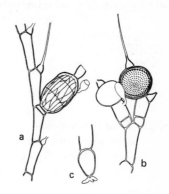

Fig. 294. (a) *Bulbochaete insignis* Pringsh., showing oogonium with oospore and an attached dwarf male plant; (b) *B. congener* Hirn; (c) hold-fast cell.

409b Setae shaped otherwise...**410**
410a Setae sheathed at the base. Fig. 231......................*Coleochaete*
410b Setae not sheathed at the base...**411**
411a Thallus not embedded in mucilage, or if so, enclosed in a very soft, watery mucilage without definite shape...........**412**
411b Thallus enclosed in a firm mucilaginous matrix of definite shape, globular or somewhat elongate and irregularly arbuscular (sometimes strands are 4 to 14 cm. long). Fig. 295
....*Chaetophora*

Microscopically, species of this genus are delicately and gracefully branched filaments that occur in macroscopic tufts or as gelatinous balls. One, *Chaetophora incrassata* (Huds.) Hazen, is composed of cables of elongate cells which give off laterally dense tufts of dichotomous branches. The resulting growth produces a somewhat arbuscular, gelatinous strand which may be as much as 14 cm. long. Other species form spherical or irregularly globose balls, 1 or 2 mm. in diameter on submersed leaves and wood (especially in cold water), or on cattail stems. Within the globular colonies

Fig. 295. (a) *Chaetophora elegans* (Roth) C. A. Agardh, habit of thallus; (b) *C. incrassata* (Huds.) Hazen, habit of thallus; (c) portion of thallus showing longitudinal filaments with out-turned branches.

the filaments are radiate and dichotomously branched. Colonies are often gregarious and may form extensive patches. The firmness of the mucilage in which the plants are encased macroscopically differentiates *Chaetophora* from *Draparnaldia* which has very soft, amorphous mucilage, and from *Stigeoclonium* (which exhibits no mucilage).

412a Thallus composed of slender, repeatedly branched filaments; cells all about the same size but tapering to fine points or setae at the apices of the branches. Fig. 270.......*Stigeoclonium*

412b Thallus consisting of main filaments of large cells from which arise tufts of branches composed of much smaller cells........413

413a Main axis consisting of cells of 2 sizes, cylindrical or barrel-shaped, and short rectangular, the tufts of branches arising opposite only from the short cells. Fig. 296...*Draparnaldiopsis*

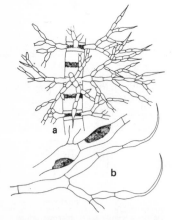

This genus is similar to *Draparnaldia* (Fig. 297) but the main axis cells are of 2 sizes, the longer cells alternating with short ones which bear the lateral branches. The branchings are somewhat dichotomous and rather rigid in appearance. Two species are known for the United States, both western in distribution.

Fig. 296. *Draparnaldiopsis sali-shensis* Presc. (a) portion of main axis with branch tufts; (b) sample of branch showing shapes of cells.

413b Main axis composed of cylindrical or barrel-shaped cells all the same length; branches arising opposite, alternate or in whorls. Fig. 297..*Draparnaldia*

The genus is strikingly character- ized by having a filament of large cells forming an axis from which tufted plumes of branches of smaller cell size arise. Different species vary in size and shape of the branching tufts. The thallus is enclosed in am- orphous, soft and watery mucilage; occur mostly in cold, flowing water and trickles from springs. Macro- scopically the plants appear as pale yellow-green gelatinous strands that easily slip through the fingers when gathered.

Fig. 297. *Draparnaldia glomera- ta* (Vauch.) Ag., showing tufts of lateral branches, with barrel-shaped axial cells containing bandlike chloroplasts.

414a (358) Parasitic in higher plants such as *Arisaema* (Indian Turnip). Fig. 156...*Phyllosiphon*

414b Not parasitic...**415**

415a Filaments repeatedly, dichotomously branched, regularly con- stricted at the base of the forkings. Fig. 298.............................
....*Dichotomosiphon*

The species illustrated is the only one in the genus. It occurs in dense, tangled tufts and mats usually on the bottom of lakes, al- though occasionally on damp soil and seeps about springs. There are downward-growing, rhizoidal branches and upward-directed vegetative and sex organ-bearing branches. The oogonia when ma- ture are so large that they can be discerned with the naked eye. They are yellowish and globular. Curved, antheridial organs are borne immediately below the

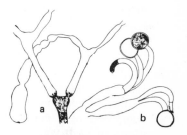

Fig. 298. *Dichotomosiphon tuber- osus* (Braun) Ernst. (a) habit of branch- ing showing constrictions; (b) tip of reproductive branching showing glob- ular oogonia and hooklike antheridia.

oogonia. The plants seem to reproduce sexually only when growing in relatively shallow water (up to 4 feet) suggesting a light factor relationship. Plants dredged from 60 feet or more never seem to have reproductive organs. The filaments are siphonous, coenocytic tubes. The chloroplasts are numerous, parietal discs or ovals, and starch is produced as a food reserve. Now placed in its own family, *Dichotomosiphon* was at one time associated with *Vaucheria* (Xan- thophyceae, Fig. 290).

**415b Filaments not dichotomously branched; without constrictions.
Fig. 299**...*Vaucheria*

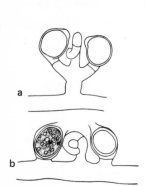

Fig. 299. (a) *Vaucheria geminata* (Vauch.) De Cand., sex organs on a short pedicel; (b) *V. sessilis* (Vauch.) De Cand.

This genus usually forms dark green, velvety mats on damp soil, on rocks in flowing water, or occasionally wooly strands streaming from stones. Plants may break away from the substrate and form floating, often 'dirty' mats at the surface. The siphonous filaments are large enough to be seen individually with the unaided eye. Several species are common in fresh water, but there are also many marine species. They are differentiated by shape and position of the sex organs, and by size of the filaments. The mats harbor a veritable zoological garden of small animals. Long considered as a member of the Chlorophyta, this genus is actually a member of the Xanthophyceae in spite of its dense green color. The food reserve is oil rather than starch and the multiflagellate zoospores have pairs of flagella unequal in length.

416a (6) Chloroplasts violet, gray-green, bluish (rarely reddish); macroscopic plants may appear tawny or brownish; mostly *macroscopic* Rhodophyta (a few microscopic)......................**417**

416b Chloroplasts some other color than above; yellow-green, golden-yellow, or brownish with xanthophylls and carotenes predominating; rarely bluish or bluish-green; *microscopic*....428

417a Thallus macroscopic, spinelike or spurlike (2 to 5 cm. high), with nodelike swellings; relatively stiff and cartilaginous; thallus simple and mostly unbranched (but microscopically composed of a complex of filaments which are branched); plants of swift water and waterfalls. Fig. 300...........*Lemanea*

Fig. 300. *Lemanea annulata* Kuetz., habit of plant.

This genus is a member of the Rhodophyta, but like other freshwater red algae it is some other color, being gray- or olive-green or tawny. The thalli are cartilaginous and stand erect from an attached base—but are bent flat in swiftly flowing water over dams and rapids. The slender, spinelike growths (up to 20 cm. in length), devoid of practically any macroscopic branching, make the plant readily identified. The 'spurs' have intermittent swellings or nodes. The thallus is composed of a complex of branched filaments with apical growth. Carpogonia are internal (in the nodal regions) and the spermatia are borne externally in clusters near pores which appear in the nodes. At least 13 species have been reported from the United States; are widely distributed in rapidly flowing water.

417b Thallus otherwise, not spurlike...418

418a Plant a protoplasmic meshwork over and in *Sphagnum;* parasitic; with brownish-green chloroplasts (sometimes showing as blue-green). Fig. 154..*Chlamydomyxa*

418b Plant otherwise; not a protoplasmic network.....................419

419a A motile, reniform cell with 2 laterally attached flagella; chloroplast brownish, sometimes bluish, parietal, a lobed plate covering most of the cell wall. Fig. 301......*Protochrysis*

This reniform cell is much like *Heteromastix (Nephroselmis)* (Fig. 53) in shape but has no eye-spot or gullet. It is included here because of the brownish or bluish chloroplast. Although the classification is not certain these genera comprise the Nephroselmidaceae in the Cryptophyta. Both genera are similarly pigmented. Apparently only 1 species each are reported from the United States.

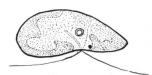

Fig. 301. *Protochrysis phaeophycearum* P a s c h e r. (Redrawn from Pascher.)

419b Plant otherwise...420

420a Plants *microscopic,* a uniseriate, branched filament, or an unbranched filament, uniseriate below, becoming multiseriate in the upper portion... 426

420b Plants *macroscopic,* several to 20 cm. or more long, with whorls of branches; multiseriate with corticating cells; or a multiaxial thallus...421

421a Thallus embedded in soft mucilage, consisting of an axial filament with corticating cells and with whorls of branches at regular intervals (in *Batrachospermum Dillenii,* however, the branch whorls are not evident)...422

421b Thallus otherwise..423

422a Mature plants bearing dense clusters of carpospores which develop around the base of the carpogonium (female organ) after fertilization of the egg. Fig. 262..........*Batrachospermum*

422b Mature plants with carpospores borne mostly singly (not showing as dense heads throughout the thallus) along filaments which have developed from the fertilized egg and which wander through the thallus. Fig. 262..................*Sirodotia*

423a (421) Thallus consisting of multiaxial filaments (strands of filaments) with numerous, feathery branchings; without definite nodes and internodes, and without whorls of branches. Fig. 302..*Thorea*

This is a feathery thallus macroscopically; microscopically composed of a multiaxial cable of filaments with short, compactly arranged, out-turned branches. They may be as much as 50 cm. in length. The genus is of infrequent occurrence but abundant in habitats where it does appear. Sexual reproduction has not been observed as yet. Four species have been reported from the United States; widely distributed.

Fig. 302. *Thorea ramossisima* Bory, habit of plant showing numerous fine branches.

423b Thallus otherwise...424

424a Thallus cartilaginous and irregularly dichotomus in branching; composed of a complex of central filaments from which a thick cortex of superficial cells develops (examine slightly crushed tips of branches to determine the structural plan of the thallus). Fig. 303...*Tuomeya*

This rather rigid and cartilaginous member of the Rhodophyta is identified by the complex, dichotomous or antler-like habit of thallus branching. The thallus is composed of multiaxial series of filaments and corticating cells. There are 2 species reported from the United States but only in the eastern half.

Fig. 303. *Tuomeya fluviatilis* Harvey. (a) habit of thallus; (b) apical portion of branch.

424b Thallus composed otherwise; not cartilaginous....................425

425a Thallus rather regularly branched, arbuscular, composed of a monaxial filament which is enclosed and surrounded by a cortex of compactly arranged and appressed, polygonal cells which form and develop just behind the apex (examine tips of branches); plants of fresh, often hard water. Fig. 304..........
....*Compsopogon*

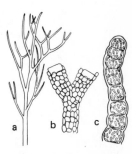

This is a member of the Rhodophyta which occurs more often in hard or brackish water, attached to stems of woody plants, weeds and stones. *Compsopogon coeruleus* (Balb.) Mont. is the most common species; has been found in irrigation ditches in the far western United States. Although essentially filamentous, the thallus becomes macroscopic in proportion and appears as a rather delicately branched, tufted or bushy growth, blue-green to gray- or violet-green in color. The main axial filament becomes encased in a cortication of small, angular cells. Sexual reproduction is unknown. It is primarily a tropical and subtropical genus.

Fig. 304. *Compsopogon coeruleus* (Balbis) Mont. (a) habit of thallus; (b) portion of axis showing corticating cells; (c) apical portion of uncorticated branch showing chloroplasts.

425b Thallus regularly dichotomously branched; multiaxial (several associated filaments), and corticated; thallus partly prostrate and somewhat dorsiventrally differentiated, with the concave side down, the branches tending to curl at the tips; somewhat tufted, dark gray to blackish green in color; plants of brackish situations (or marine). Fig. 305.................................*Bostrychia*

This genus is mostly marine, growing on mangrove but at least 1 species occurs in brackish water and in estuaries. *Bostrychia scorpioides* (Gmel.) Mont. is found on the walls of locks in the Panama Canal and on *Typha* in the adjacent lakes. The thallus is dichotomously branched, somewhat flattened with a tendency to have enrolled margins; the branches curled at the tips.

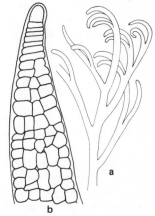

Fig. 305. *Bostrychia scorpioides* (Gmel.) Mont. (a) habit of branching; (b) apex of branch showing development of cortex.

426a (420) Filaments violet or brownish-green, unbranched (except for rhizoidal proliferation at the base)....................................427

426b Plants branched, violet or gray-green, usually growing in tufts; branches not tapering at the apex; cells with 1 disclike or ribbonlike chloroplast. Fig. 306..
......................................*Rhodochorton (Audouinella, Acrochaetium)*

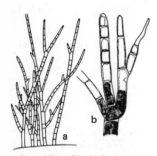

Fig. 306. *Rhodochorton* sp. (a) habit of thallus; (b) branches in detail.

This member of the Rhodophyta has been known previously as *Audouinella.* The erect, branched (and usually tufted) filaments are violet- or gray-green, at least when occurring in macroscopic clumps. The main axial cells of the filament have disclike or short ribbonlike chloroplasts. In size and form and habit of growth these plants may be mistaken for juvenile stages of *Batrachospermum* and if that genus is present in the same habitat, it may be assumed that what appear at first observation to be *Rhodochorton* is the so-called "Chantransia" stage of *Batrachospermum*. The chloroplast of the juvenile stage of *Batrachospermum* ("Chantransia" filaments) is platelike and extends the full length and width of the cell (at least in young, alive specimens).

427a Filaments relatively stout, mucilaginous or cartilaginous, with a gelatinous sheath enclosing cells separated from one another; chloroplast stellate, microscopically reddish, growing solitary or gergarious. Fig. 307..*Bangia*

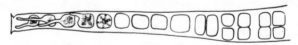

Fig. 307. *Bangia atropurpurea* (Roth) Ag., habit of filament showing downward projecting proliferations of basal cells.

This is a simple, unbranched member of the Rhodophyta, either greenish or light purplish in color. Filaments occur in tufts, sometimes dense, attached to submersed rocks and sticks. Although most species of *Bangia* occur in marine habitats, *B. atropurpurea* (Roth) Ag. is found inland. Possibly the plant known as *B. fuscopurpurea* (Dillw.) Lyngb. from marine and estuarian habitats is the same.

The filaments are uniseriate below but become multiseriate above, the protoplasts separate from one another in a firm gelatinous sheath. The lowermost cells send down rhizoidal elongations as holdfast structures. The chloroplast is stellate. Thus far, *B. atropurpurea* is known in the United States only from the Great Lakes, and possibly from Pennsylvania.

427b Filaments gray-green in colonial mass (sometimes brownish), but cells pinkish microscopically; tufted, the filaments arising from a prostrate patch of cells; chloroplasts several parietal plates. Fig. 242...*Kyliniella*

428a (416) Chloroplasts yellow, yellow-brown, or dark golden-brown; plants motile or non-motile.......................................**496**

428b Chloroplasts not yellow-brown nor golden-brown...............**429**

429a Chloroplasts yellow, pale yellow-greeen with xanthophyll predominating (rarely blue or blue-green); iodine test for starch negative; cell contents often with leucosin showing a metallic lustre. (See *Botrydium*, Fig. 320 and *Vaucheria*, Fig. 299, members of the Chrysophyta but green, chlorophyll predominating the carotenoids and yellow pigments.) Mostly Xanthophyceae in the Phylum Chrysophyta.........................**442**

This group of the algae is difficult of separation on the basis of the chloroplast color alone inasmuch as the shades of green, and the relative abundance of the carotenoid pigments cannot be clearly distinguished from the green color of the Chlorophyta. In addition to the iodine test for starch (which ordinarily is confirmative when negative in determining that an alga is *not* a member of the Chlorophyta, heating plants in concentrated sulphuric acid (when the specimens lend themselves to such a treatment) provides a helpful differentiation. The yellow-green algae (Heterokontae or Xanthophyceae) become blue-green in acid, whereas Chlorophyta remain unchanged in color.

429b Chloroplasts not yellow-green...**430**

430a Cells with blue or bluish protoplasts.................................**431**

430b Cells with chloroplasts or protoplasts not blue...................**436**

431a Organisms biflagellate...**432**

431b Organisms not flagellated..**433**

432a Cells ellipsoid or oval, or slipper-shaped, usually bilobed anteriorly with the flagella somewhat lateral; chloroplasts 3, blue or bluish, parietal plates. Fig. 308....................*Chroomonas*

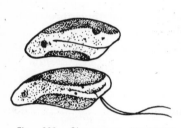

These minute, slipper-shaped organisms have 2 parietal, blue or bluish-brown chloroplasts and 2 flagella that are attached just below the cell apex. They move rapidly and determinations cannot be made unless some medium is introduced to the mount to retard action. Use 5% glycerin. *Chroomonas* should be compared with *Cryptomonas* (Fig. 16) which has yellowish-green chloroplasts or at times red chloroplasts. The latter genus has a gullet whereas *Chroomonas* does not.

Fig. 308. *Chroomonas Nordstedtii* Hansg., dorsal and ventral surfaces.

432b Cells reniform, with laterally attached flagella and 2 blue or bluish-green chloroplasts. Fig. 301...........................*Protochrysis*

433a (431) Organism an anastomosing, protoplasmic mucilage, creeping by pseudopodia over *Sphagnum*, with blue-green chloroplasts. Fig. 154...*Chlamydomyxa*

433b Organisms otherwise..434

434a One to 4 spherical or oval cells in a mucilaginous sheath which bears a gelatinous bristle; protoplast a blue, parietal cup. Fig. 309..*Gloeochaete*

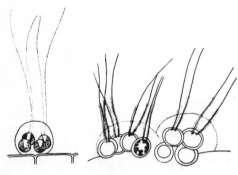

This is an anomalous organism, the morphology and physiology of which are interpreted as that of symbiotism involving a colorless member of the Tetrasporaceae (Chlorophyta) and a blue-green (Cyanophyta) endophyte. The protoplast is a parietal cup similar to the chloroplast of many of the green algae. The long,

Fig. 309. *Gloeochaete Wittrockiana* Lag.

slender, gelatinous hairs make this genus readily identified. Cells occur in clumps (rarely solitary), attached to filamentous algae.

434b Plants not as above; sheaths present or absent although cells may be enclosed in old mother-cell walls.............................**435**

435a A linear series of globular or oblong cells within a mucilaginous matrix, chloroplasts star-shaped. Fig. 310......*Asterocystis*

The bright blue-green, star-shaped chloroplasts of this genus help in making identification. The cells are oval or oblong, arranged in (mostly) uniseriate, false filaments, being enclosed by a mucilaginous sheath. The gelatinous strands may branch. It occurs attached as an epiphyte, usually on members of the Cladophoraceae, but may appear in mixtures of free-floating algal ty-

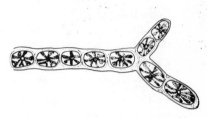

Fig. 310. *Asterocystis smaragdina* (Reinsch) Forti.

choplankton. The genus is regarded as a 'lower' member of the Rhodophyta, based on the pigmentation and the nature of the food reserve.

435b Two to 4 or 8 globose or oval cells contained within an enlarged mother-cell wall; chloroplastlike bodies vermiform (few and long, or many and short). Fig. 311............*Glaucocystis*

There are about 5 species of this genus which, like *Gloeochaete* (Fig. 309) involve an endophytic blue-green alga and a colorless member of the Chlorophyta, an oocystaceous host. The protoplasts are bright blue-green and occur in different shapes and arrangements within either globular or oval cells, according to species. The plants are free-floating, soli-

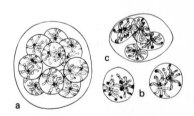

Fig. 311. (a), (b) *Glaucocystis duplex* Presc.; (c) *G. Nostochinearum* Itz.

tary or in families enclosed by the old mother-cell wall. They seem to prefer soft-water or acid habitats.

436a (430) Cells in compact, irregularly shaped colonies, appearing brown or orange-colored because of dark mucilage. Fig. 93 ....*Botryococcus*

436b Cells not in opaque or orange-colored mucilage as above; contents red, violet-red or green with a red tinge................**437**

437a Living in snow and alpine regions (red snow). Fig. 17...........
....*Chlamydomonas*

437b Not living in snow..**438**

438a A colony of oval or globose cells enclosed in a layered sheath. Fig. 85...*Gloeocystis*

438b Cells not enclosed in a layered sheath.................................439

439a Cells irregular in shape; living as an endophyte in higher plants. Fig. 157...*Rhodochytrium*

439b Cells not endophytic...440

440a Cells spherical, solitary or gregarious, in thin, mucilaginous strands; terrestrial, forming dark red or purplish patches on damp soil (common in greenhouses). Fig. 9............*Porphyridium*

440b Cells round, ellipsoid, or fusiform, not arranged as above; not terrestrial (or rarely so)... 441

441a Cells fusiform; orange-red carotenoid coloring the green cell with 1 flagellum. Fig. 13...*Euglena*

441b Cells round or ellipsoid; protoplast with a wide wall which appears as a gelatinous sheath; flagella 2, but usually not showing when cells are encysted at which time they exhibit a red color. Fig. 41...*Haematococcus*

442a (429)..Plants filamentous...443

442b Plants not filamentous...451

443a Filaments false; cells not adjoined in continous series..........444

443b Plant a true filament; cells in continuous series...................446

444a Thallus an attached, dichotomously branched stalk with transverse striations; cells pyriform, thick-walled, solitary or in pairs at the end of the stalk branches. Fig. 312.......................
....*Malleodendron*

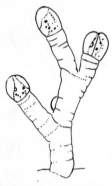

Fig. 312. *Malleodendron gloeopus* Pascher. (Redrawn from Pascher.)

The branched, gelatinous stalks are relatively thick, being about the same diameter as the cells they bear. The stalks have transverse lamellations. *Malleodendron* grows epiphytically on filamentous algae. The cells divide vertically and the daughter cells add to the gelatinous stalk from their lower side. The genus is known from both the United States and Europe but is relatively rare.

444b Thallus otherwise..**445**

445a Thallus a series of branched, gelatinous tubes arranged in a chain with 1 or 2 globular cells in the apex of each joint of the branching, tubelike strands. Fig. 313....................*Mischococcus*

The globose, yellow-green cells of this species occur at the ends of repeatedly branched, gelatinous stalks, attached to filamentous algae. Only 1 species seems to be known and this is widely distributed in the United States.

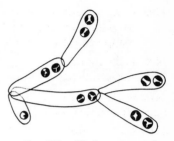

Fig. 313. *Mischococcus confervicola* Naeg.

445b Thallus consisting of a floating, gelatinous mass in which short, interrupted series of cells radiate as short, branched, interrupted filaments. Fig. 290...........................*Heterococcus**

446a (443) Filaments prostrate, laterally adjoined to form a plate or an attached disc. Fig. 314...............................*Phaeodermatium*

This plant forms a disclike, encrusting growth, several cells thick in the center; 1-celled thick and showing radiating filaments at the margin. It has been suggested that it is a stage in the life cycle of *Hydrurus*, which grows in the same habitat—cold mountain streams.

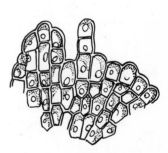

Fig. 314. *Phaeodermatium rivulare* Hansg. (Redrawn from Pascher.)

446b Plants otherwise...**447**

---

*Heterococcus is regarded by some to be synonymous with *Monocilia* (Fig. 315).

447a Filaments branched, erect. Fig. 315.................. ....*Monocilia*

This and 1 other species, *M. flavescens* Gerneck are the only ones reported from the United States, although if included with the genus *Heterococcus* as recommended by some authors there are many species. *Monocilia* occurs as an irregularly branched filament in soil. A member of the Chrysophyta, the disclike chloroplasts are yellow-green or bright yellow and the food reserve is oil; starch test negative.

Fig. 315. *Monocilia viridis* Gerneck.

447b Filaments not branched..448

448a Filaments short, of from 2 to 8 barrel-shaped cells; chloroplasts brownish. Fig. 316...*Stichochrysis*

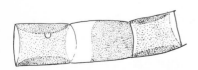

This odd genus has very short filaments of cylindrical or barrel-shaped cells. There are usually 2 laminate chloroplasts along the lateral walls. Cell division is the only known method of reproduction. The only species known has been reported from the United States.

Fig. 316. *Stichochrysis immobilis* Pringsh. (Redrawn from Pringsheim.)

448b Filaments otherwise...449

449a Cells long-cylindric; wall of cells in 2 pieces which overlap at the midregion, the 2 sections usually evident when empty

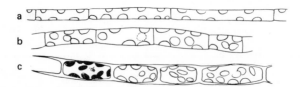

Fig. 317. (a) *Tribonema bombycina* var. *tenue* Hazen; (b) *T. bombycinum* (Ag.) Derbes et Solier; (c) *T. utriculosum* (Kuetz.) Hazen.

cells are viewed; filaments showing H-shaped pieces upon
fragmentation; cells with parallel or slightly convex lateral
margins; chloroplasts 2 to many parietal discs. Fig. 317..........
....*Tribonema*

There are many species of this simple, unbranched filamentous
member of the Xanthophyceae (Heterokontae), differentiated by
size and proportions of the cells and by the shape and number of
the pale, yellow-green chloroplasts. Like *Microspora* (Fig. 261)
in the Chlorophyta, the cell walls are composed of 2 sections which
adjoin and overlap in the midregion. Hence when the filaments
fragment, the cells disjoin at the midsection rather than at the
cross walls, resulting in the characteristic H-shaped sections. By
careful focusing the overlapping of the wall sections can be seen
in the unfragmented portions of the filament, especially in those
few species which have a thick wall. The cells are rectangular or
cylindrical although some species have somewhat convex lateral
walls. The chloroplasts are parietal discs or folded plates. In
northern latitudes *Tribonema* is one of the very first of the algae
to appear in ditches and swamps after ice thaw.

449b Cells otherwise...**450**

450a Cells quadrate, the sides decidedly parallel; the wall in 2
sections but overlapping not at all evident except at the
broken ends of filaments; occasionally and intermittently with
brownish collars about the cells where the 2 sections over-
lap. Fig. 318...*Bumilleria*

Fig. 318.   *Bumilleria sicula* Borzi.

There are 2 species of the 3 that are known for this genus in
the United States. *Bumilleria exilis* Klebs is common and much
the smaller (6 μ in diameter). The unbranched filaments are
similar to *Tribonema* (Fig. 317) but the cells are more nearly
rectangular in optical section, with decidedly parallel lateral walls.
Sometimes external overlapping H-shaped sections of thicker wall
layers, brownish in color, occur intermittently along the filament.

450b Cells oval with truncate apices, the filaments distinctly constricted at the cross walls; cell walls in 1 section only; chloroplasts 1 or 2 parietal, folded plates. Fig. 319.................
....*Heterothrix**

Fig. 319. *Heterothrix ulothricoides* Pascher. (Redrawn from Bourrelly).

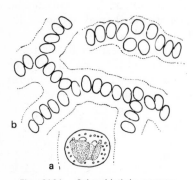

Fig. 319A. *Sphaeridothrix compressa* Pascher et Vlk. (a) single cell showing chloroplast; (b) portion of thallus. (Redrawn from Pascher).

In this genus the filaments are composed of cylindrical or sub-cylindric cells which may have broadly rounded poles. The filaments are usually relatively short and some species have a tendency for the cells to dissociate. Occasionally there is also a tendency to produce branches in the dissociation as in *Heterothrix stichococcoides* Pascher. There is no basal-distal differentiation. The wall, unlike *Tribonema* is in 1 section. Chloroplasts are 1 or 2 parietal, folded plates; reproduction by zoospores. Of the 13 described species only 1 has been reported from the United States (Massachusetts).

451a (442) Plant a small (1-2 mm. diam.) green vesicle, balloon-shaped; terrestrial. Fig. 320...*Botrydium*

---

*See *Sphaeridiothrix*. Fig. 319A in which oval, unadjoined cells are uniseriately arranged as a filament within a gelatinous sheath, sometimes forming anastomosing branches and becoming multiseriate, resembling some expressions of a filamentous relative of *Heterothrix, Heterococcus*, Fig. 290.

These tiny, green, balloonlike algae appear on damp soil in greenhouses or on mud where water has receded. *Botrydium* is siphonaceous and coenocytic; has underground, rhizoidal extensions. Here the cell contents may concentrate followed by rounding up of segments to form a special kind of spore known as a hypnospore. Chloroplasts are numerous, green discs. Oil rather than starch is produced as a food reserve and zoospores have 2 flagella of different length, characteristic of the Xanthophyceae. Besides the species illustrated there is another which is less frequently found, *B. Wallrothii* Kuetz. in which the vesicle has a thick, wrinkled and lamellate wall.

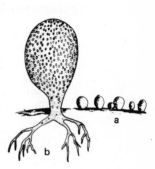

Fig. 320. *Botrydium granulatum* (L.) Grev. (a) habit of thalli on soil; (b) vesicle enlarged (semidiagrammatic) to show subterranean rhizoidal extensions.

This curious genus has a colorless, vaselike lorica that lies on its side on aquatic substrates (especially leaves of aquatic plants). The protoplast within has a yellowish chloroplast and a rhizopodial thread extending toward or through the lorica aperture. There are 3 species known, differentiated by the shape of the lorica.

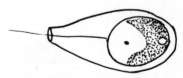

Fig. 321. *Kybotion eremita* Pascher.

456a Cell membrane in 2 sections, the upper lifting off at maturity to allow escape of aplanospores (small globular spores); cells oval or short-cylindric. Fig. 322..........................*Chlorothecium*

This cylindrical plant with parietal, yellow-green chloroplasts is attached by a short stalk and a disc to submersed plants, including larger algae. It is rather rare in the United States; only 1 of the 12 species being reported. It is easily overlooked because it occurs in dense mixtures of algae from bogs.

Fig. 322.
Chlorothecium
Pirottae Borzi.

456b Cell membrane not in 2 sections..457

457a Cells globose or subglobose; cytoplasm reticulate. Fig. 323
....*Perone*

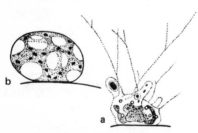

There is a freely moving, amoeboid stage and an attached or epiphytic encysted stage in the life history of this organism. In the resting stage the cell is to be found in *Sphagnum* or other moss leaves, and in this state shows a highly reticulated, faintly pigmented protoplast. The chloroplasts are several small discs. In the amoeboid phase the cell throws out long, fine, threadlike and branched pseudopodia. Heterokont zoospore are formed in reproduction. The species illustrated is the only one reported thus far.

Fig. 323. *Perone dimorpha* Pascher.
(a) rhizopodial stage; (b) vegetative cell, or sedentary stage.

457b Cells shaped otherwise; cytoplasm not highly reticulated nor alveolar. Fig. 324..*Characiopsis*

There are several fairly common species of this genus which occur as epiphytes on filamentous algae. They vary in shape and in length of the attaching stalk. Unlike the genus *Characium* (Fig. 147), some species of which are very similar in shape, oil is formed rather than starch as a food reserve, and the chloroplasts are pale yellow-green. The starch-iodide test must be used to differentiate the 2 genera.

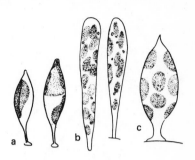

Fig. 324. (a) *Characiopsis acuta* (Braun) Borzi; (b) *C. cylindrica* (Lambert) Lemm.; (c) *C. spinifer* Printz.

458a (454) Cells with a vaselike, pitcher-shaped lorica (envelope) with a neck and a terminal opening. Fig. 325...........................
...*Stipitococcus*

There are 5 or 6 species of this genus of rather uncommon occurrence, although in particular habitats the various species are relatively abundant on filamentous algae. *Stipitococcus urceolatus* West et West is perhaps more frequently seen than others and is readily identified by the pitcher-shaped lorica. There is a pale, yellow-green platelike chloroplast and a rhizopodial thread (which often is obscure).

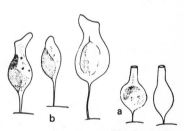

Fig. 325. (a) *Stipitococcus vasiformis* Tiff.; (b) *S. urceolatus* W. et W.

458b Cells without a lorica..459

459a Cells cylindrical, straight or curved, sometimes with a spine at one or both ends. Fig. 326..................................*Ophiocytium*

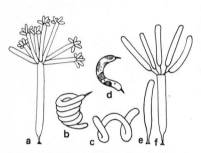

Fig. 326. (a) *Ophiocytium arbuscula* Rab.; (b) *O. cochleare* A. Braun; (c) *O. parvulum* (Perty) Braun; (d) *O. capitatum* Wolle. (e) *O. desertum* fa. *minor* Presc.; (f) *O. gracilipes* (Braun) Rab.

The factors which determine the distribution of this genus are unknown, but there is good evidence that highly refined chemical qualities of water are critical. Several species always occur in the same habitat, along with other genera of the Xanthophyceae. Species are differentiated by presence or absence of polar spines and whether free-floating or stalked and epiphytic. They usually occur intermingled with miscellaneous algae in bogs or swamps which are acid. Most species are solitary but *Ophiocytium arbuscula* Rab. is colonial because of the habit of zoospores to germinate at the apex of the parent cell.

459b Cells shaped differently..**460**

460a Cells club-shaped or somewhat pyriform; walls in 2 sections, the upper lifting away to permit escape of spores. Fig. 322 ....*Chlorothecium*

460b Cells spherical, angular (in 'front' view), fusiform or oval; wall in 1 piece..**461**

461a Stipe slender, threadlike, longer than the cell body. Fig. 327 ....*Peroniella*

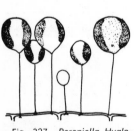

Fig. 327. *Peroniella Hyalothecae* Gobi.

Species of this genus occur solitarily or in gregarious clusters on other algae, or are attached in the mucilage of colonial forms. The one illustrated seems to occur no other place but on the filaments of the desmid *Hyalotheca*. Like other members of the Chrysophyta, the chloroplasts are not grass-green but a pale, apple-green, and there are usually refractive globules of oil or some other food reserve than starch. The chloroplasts are parietal plates.

461b Stipe stout, shorter than the cell body in length (or rarely equalling it)...**462**

462a Cells transversely fusiform, attached from the side by a short stalk. Fig. 328..*Dioxys*

The attached cells in this genus vary in shape but mostly are triangular and somewhat flattened. At least 1 species has 3 horns. The attaching stipe is relatively slender but short. The yellowish chloroplasts (2 to 4) are disclike plates folded around the wall. Two of the 6 known species occur in the United States, but are very rare.

Fig. 328.   *Dioxys inermis* Thompson. (Redrawn in part from Thompson).

462b Cells elongate-fusiform or tubular, attached by a broad stipe at the posterior end. Fig. 324...................................*Characiopsis*

463a (453) Cells with 2 flagella of unequal length*........................**464**

463b Cells without flagella...**465**

464a Cells metabolic, changing shape in swimming, sometimes with pseudopodia; chloroplast yellowish-green. Fig. 329....................
....*Chloramoeba*

The shapeless, almost colorless members of this genus have 1 very short and 1 very long flagellum that is directed forward. There are several faintly pigmented chloroplasts. The cells are metabolic; readily changing shape in motion; often found on aquatic plants. It is to be expected in the United States but so far has not been reported in literature.

Fig. 329.   *Chloramoeba* sp., showing two cell shapes and the heterokont flagella.

---

*See *Phaeaster* (Fig. 350). This organism exists for the most part as a globular, palmelloid colony, but it also has a solitary, uniflagellate swimming stage, regarded by some as being a zoospore produced from the cells of the colony.

464b Cells firm, oval or pyriform, usually not metabolic. Fig. 330
....*Ochromonas (Chlorochromonas)*

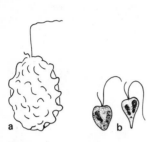

Fig. 330. (a) *Ochromonas verrucosa* Skuja. (Redrawn from Popovsky); (b) *O. (Chlorochromonas) minuta* (Lewis).

The cells in this genus are broadly or narrowly pyriform, but may be metabolic and change shape in motion. The flagellation is heterokont. There are 2 parietal chloroplasts, contractile vacuoles and a red eye-spot has been reported to occur. Non-motile, pear-shaped cells with yellowish chloroplasts which occur in the microscope field should be examined carefully for flagella or traces of them. Frequently the cells come to rest and attach themselves to a substrate at the posterior end. Eight species have been reported from the United States of the 15 that are known, differentiated by the presence or absence of a pyrenoid, the color of the chloroplasts and the morphology of cysts that are formed as resting stages. Some species have passed under the genus *Chlorochromonas.*

465a (463) Cell wall smooth...**466**
465b Cell wall sculptured or decorated, sometimes spiny..........**476**
466a Cells spherical, subglobose, or broadly ovate to subpyriform
....**467**
466b Cells rectangular, cylindrical or crescent-shaped...............**471**
467a Cells contained in a gelatinous envelope. Fig. 331..................
....*Chlorobotrys*

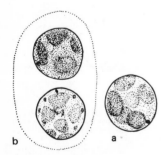

Fig. 331. *Chlorobotrys regularis* (West) Bohlin; (a) single cell; (b) two cells enclosed in common mucilage.

The identifying character of the species illustrated is the paired arrangement of the spherical cells enclosed in a mucilaginous sheath. There are several parietal chloroplasts and invariably a red spot which is an oil globule. Even though preserved, when some identifying characteristics are lost, the cells retain the dark-colored spot. *Chlorobotrys* is both eu- and tychoplanktonic. Six species have been reported from the United States, differentiated by cell shape, number of cells in the colony and number of chloroplasts.

467b Cells not enclosed in a gelatinous envelope..............................468

468a Cell wall in 2 sections, separating and persisting as membranous sections near the liberated autospores. Fig. 332......
....*Diachros*

The species illustrated is the only one reported from the United States. It is somewhat like *Schizochlamys* (Fig. 92) in the Chlorophyta in that the mother-cell wall fragments are retained after new cells (autospores) are released and the pieces persist as hemispherical, transparent cups near the daughter cells. There are 1 or 2 parietal chloroplasts.

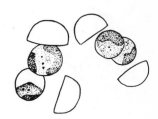

Fig. 332. *Diachros simplex* Pascher.

468b Cell wall in 1 piece; mother-cell not forming persisting sections but disintegrating to liberate spores..............................469

469a Cells spherical..470

469b Cells broadly ovoid or pyriform. Fig. 333..................*Leuvenia*

Although essentially unicellular, this genus may occur as a film at the water surface. Young cells are spherical and have 1 or 2 chloroplasts, whereas older cells become pyriform or ovate and have numerous yellow-green chloroplasts. Only 1 species is known for the genus and in the United States is reported from only 2 localities.

Fig. 333. *Leuvenia natans* Gardner. (Redrawn from G. M. Smith).

470a Cells solitary (rarely clumped), with 1 or 2 parietal, golden-yellow chloroplasts, attached or free-floating. Fig. 334...........
....*Chrysosphaera (Epichrysis)*

The cells are solitary or clumped; have 2 bright yellowish chloroplasts. They may be free-floating but often form aggregations of indefinite numbers on stems of aquatic plants, appearing as epiphytes. Reproduction is by autospores or by uniflagellate zoospores.

Fig. 334. *Chrysosphaera paludosa* (Korsch.) Bourr. (a) cluster of cells in mucilage on a filamentous alga; (b) single cell.

470b Cells solitary or in clusters, with a parietal reticulation of yellow-green chloroplasts; organisms attached but usually free-floating, often forming "blooms." Fig. 335......Botrydiopsis

Fig. 335. Botrydiopsis arhiza Borzi.

In the same habitats where *Ophiocytium* (Fig. 326) occurs one may find *Botrydiopsis*, spherical unicells or sometimes in clumps and colonial. Small cells, when young may contain a single, parietal chloroplast, but in age there are many yellowish-green bodies. *B. eriensis* Snow is larger than the species illustrated and is euplanktonic whereas the latter is tychoplanktonic.

471a (466) Cells rectangular, with a spine at each corner. Fig. 336 ....Pseudotetraedron

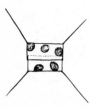

Fig. 336. Pseudotetraedron neglectum Pascher.

The rectangular cells in this genus have a slender spine at each corner. The chrysophyte relationship is illustrated by the fact that the wall is in 2 sections, a feature that can be seen only when the cells are turned on their 'side.' In end view the cells are narrowly elliptic. There are several yellow-green chloroplasts; oil occurs as a food reserve. There is but 1 species reported for the genus and this is very rare.

471b Cells cylindrical or crescent-shaped.......................................472

472a Cells elongate-cylindric, coiled or S-shaped, equally rounded at both poles. Fig. 326...Ophiocytium

472b Cells oblong, sides convex, short-cylindric or fusiform, sometimes not equally rounded at both poles; curved but not coiled nor twisted...473

473a Cells short-cylindric, 1½-2 times as long as broad; poles symmetrically rounded. Fig. 337.......Ellipsoidon (Monallantus)

This genus occurs in the same habitats as *Ophiocytium* (Fig. 326) and *Bumilleriopsis* (Fig. 338). There are 2 thin, folded, parietal platelike chloroplasts. Two species have been reported from the United States (1 under the name of *Monallantus* which is regarded as being synonymous).

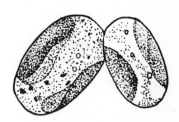

Fig. 337. *Ellipsoidon brevicylindrus* (Pascher) Bourr.

473b Cells fusiform or cylindric only in part; poles sometimes un-symmetrical...474

474a Cells fusiform or sickle-shaped.................................475

474b Cells irregularly cylindrical; poles unsymmetrical. Fig. 338 ....*Bumilleriopsis*

Cells in this genus have yellow-green chloroplasts and occur singly or several together in incidental clusters (not colonial). The irregularly curved cylinders (rarely somewhat fusiform) with the two poles different in shape help to identify *Bumilleriopsis*.

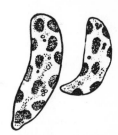

Fig. 338. *Bumilleriopsis brevis* Pascher.

475a Cells broadly fusiform, abruptly narrowed at the poles. Fig. 339...*Pleurogaster*

The chief difference between this genus and *Bumilleriopsis* (Fig. 338) is the definitely fusiform shape, and the two poles of the cells similar in shape. There are 2 laminate chloroplasts and usually several refractive globules. Two of the 4 known species occur in the United States.

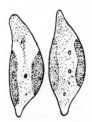

Fig. 339. *Pleurogaster lunaris* Pascher.

475b **Cells narrowly fusiform, spindle-shaped or sickle-shaped. Fig. 340**..*Chlorocloster*

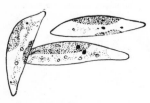

In this genus the cells are narrowly spindle-shaped and usually are distinctly curved or even sickle-shaped (according to species). They are found intermingled sparingly among other algae in the tychoplankton. The chloroplasts are similar to those of *Pleurogaster* (Fig. 339). Only 1 of a dozen species is reported from the United States.

Fig. 340. *Chlorocloster pyreniger* Pascher.

476a **(465) Cells elongate-cylindric, with a spine at one or both poles**..477

476b **Cells short-cylindric, spherical or angular**.............................478

477a **Cells nearly straight or only slightly bent. Fig. 341**................. ....*Centritractus*

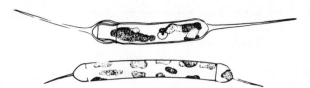

Fig. 341. *Centritractus belanophorus* Lemm.

Species in this genus are either short or relatively long cylinders with a long spine at either pole. The cells are either straight or slightly curved. Some species resemble *Ophiocytium* (Fig. 326) but are not S-shaped nor coiled. The wall is in 2 sections which either overlap in the midregion, or there may be a 'cap' formed near either end of the cylinder. There are usually 2 laminate chloroplasts but these may fragment and appear as several. There is 1 nucleus whereas *Ophiocytium* is multinucleate; has several parietal chloroplasts. Apparently reproduction in *Centritractus* is still unknown except that zoospores have been reported with some question.

477b **Cells coiled, S-shaped, or hooked at one end. Fig. 326**........... ....*Ophiocytium*

478a **(476) Cells spherical**..479

478b **Cells some other shape**...480

479a Cell wall serrate at the margins, the surface of the cell showing broad depressions (sometimes faintly seen). Fig. 342 ....*Arachnochloris*

Cells in this genus are spherical; the wall regularly scrobiculate so that the margin appears to be spiny. The projections are the tops of ridges formed by the depressions in the wall. There are 2 tonguelike or bandlike parietal chloroplasts. Two of the 9 known species occur in the United States. Plants occur rarely, intermingled in tychoplanktonic algae especially in soft-water or acid habitats which favor the development of many other genera of the Xanthophyceae.

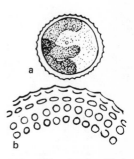

Fig. 342. *Arachnochloris minor* Pascher. (a) cell showing chloroplasts; (b) sample of wall showing circular thin areas.

479b Cell wall bearing curved or straight spines. Fig. 343............ ....*Meringosphaera (Acanthochloris)*

Although this is a marine genus, 1 species which seems to belong here has been reported from the United States. The cells are spherical, have spiny walls and many parietal chloroplasts. In many respects it is similar to *Acanthochloris* and P. Bourrelly has appropriately suggested that *M. spinosa* Presc. should be assigned to that genus. *Acanthochloris* with spherical cells and a single, handlike chloroplast has not been reported from the United States otherwise.

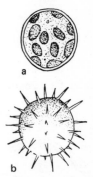

Fig. 343. *Meringosphaera spinosa* Presc. (a) optical section of cell showing chloroplasts; (b) exterior of cell showing spines on wall.

480a (478) Cells broadly fusiform or subtriangular, narrowed abruptly at one or both poles to form spinelike projections. Fig. 339...*Pleurogaster*

480b Cells other shapes..481

481a Cells circular with lobes in one view, narrow and crescent-shaped when seen from the side; membrane ornamented with scrobiculations. Fig. 344..................................*Chlorogibba**

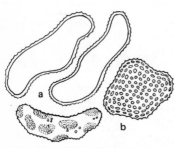

The cells in this genus are flattened; circular in one view, compressed and curved or hemispherical as seen from the 'side.' The wall is scrobiculate. There are about 6 species, differentiated by cell shape, occurring in both Europe and the United States. Like other related genera they are to be sought in the tychoplankton of shallow ponds and swamps.

Fig. 344. *Chlorogibba ostreata* Pascher. (a) cell shapes in side view; (b) cell in 'front' view showing wall scrobiculations.

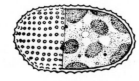

Fig. 344A. *Chlorallantus oblongus* Pascher, representing portion of wall removed to show chloroplasts.

481b Cells shaped otherwise...482

482a Cells oval or biconvex. Fig. 345...........................*Trachychloron*

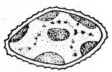

Cells in this genus, like *Chlorallantus* (Fig. 344A) have depressions in the wall. They are broadly elliptic, oval or fusiform in shape and contain a gracefully curved chloroplast, or several parietal plates. Two of the 9 known species occur in the United States.

Fig. 345. *Trachychloron biconnicum* Pascher.

482b Cells triangular, pyramidal or tetragonal...............................483

---

*An oval to subcylindric cell also with a scrobiculate wall is *Chlorallantus* (Fig. 344A). This cell separates into 2 equal parts transversely when autospores are released.

483a Cells pyramidal or tetragonal. Fig. 346..
....*Tetraedriella (Tetragoniella)*

The cells of this genus are beautifully sculptured by regularly arranged rows of depressions. According to position the cells show different shapes, triangular, tetragonal or cushion-shaped. There are numerous disclike chloroplasts. This genus is apparently synonymous with *Tetragoniella;* only 1 species occurring in United States bogs.

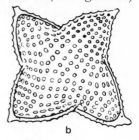

Fig. 346. *Tetraedriella gigas* (Pascher) Bourr. (a) optical section showing chloroplasts and reticular nature of the protoplast; (b) exterior of cell showing scrobiculate wall.

483b Cells flattened, appearing triangular in 'front' view, fusiform in side view. Fig. 347..*Goniochloris*

Cells in this genus are variously shaped according to their position in view. They are usually elliptic when seen from the 'side.' In this view the overlapping of the 2 wall pieces is discernible. The wall is sculptured with rectilinear rows of circular pits. There are 3 or 4 curved, parietal platelike chloroplasts. There are about 12 known species but apparently only 1 has been reported from the United States.

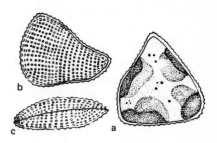

Fig. 347. *Goniochloris sculpta* Geitler. (a) optical section showing chloroplasts; (b) exterior showing regularly arranged depressions in the wall; (c) lateral view showing junction of the 2 wall sections (sometimes discerned with difficulty).

484a (452) Cells attached by a stipe..**485**

484b Cells without a stipe..**486**

485a Cells globular on a long slender stalk; plants ordinarily solitary but often so densely clumped as to appear colonial; epiphytic on filamentous algae, especially desmids. Fig. 327
....*Peroniella*

485b Cells cylindrical on a short stipe; colonies formed by zoospores germinating on the rim of mother-cells, repeatedly to form arbuscular chains. Fig. 326...................................*Ophiocytium*

486a (484) With a mucilaginous sheath..487

486b Without a sheath...492

487a Cells oval, many in a gelatinous matrix................................488

487b Cells shaped and arranged otherwise..................................489

488a Cells in 2's and 4's in a single layer at the periphery of a saclike or globular, gelatinous matrix, with the long axes practically parallel. Fig. 348...*Chlorosaccus*

Fig. 348. *Chlorosaccus fluidus* Luther. (a) diagram of colony shape; (b) cell arrangement; (c) single cell.

This rare alga occurs as macroscopic, gelatinous balls or mounds, with oval cells more or less oriented at the periphery with the longitudinal axis at right angles to the surface. The colonies occur on aquatic plants or on stems of *Chara*. Not infrequently the colonies are found adrift. The cells have from 2 to 6 parietal, yellow-green chloroplasts. There is but 1 known species.

488b Cells irregularly arranged in a globular mucilage, each cell or pair of cells surrounded by a sheath; cells containing 2 contractile vacuoles. Fig. 349...........*Heterogloea (Gloeochloris)*

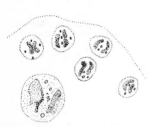

Fig. 349. *Heterogloea endochloris* Pascher. (Redrawn from Pascher).

The oval cells, (usually colonial) occur in the tychoplankton. There are several yellowish chloroplasts and 2 contractile vacuoles, characteristic of the Heterocapsales in the Xanthophyceae. Reproduction is by cell division or biflagellated zoospores. *Heterogloea endochloris* Pascher has appeared in collections of algae from midwest and western United States but apparently has not been reported in published accounts.

489a (487) Cells solitary or in pairs at the ends of branched, gelatinous tubes. Fig. 313...*Mischococcus*

489b Cells arranged otherwise...490

490a Cells spherical, 2 within a globular envelope. Fig. 331..........
....*Chlorobotrys*

490b Cells spherical, many within a gelatinous matrix...............**491**

491a Cells compactly arranged to form a hollow, palmelloid colony;
chloroplast parietal and radiate (star-shaped), turned outwardly against the free wall of the cell, each showing a central
granule of leucosin. Fig. 350.....................................*Phaeaster**

In this genus the cells are grouped or
definitely colonial, enclosed by a gelatinous sheath. *Phaeaster Pascheri* Scherf. is
one of the species which has a stellate
chloroplast bearing a central pyrenoid
and a granule of leucosin. The cells are
so arranged that the chloroplast is dis-
played outwardly. Reproduction is by uniflagellate zoospores bearing a chloroplast
similar in shape to that of the vegetative
cell. Another species does not have a
pyrenoid.

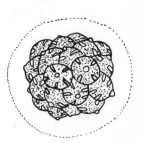

Fig. 350. *Phaeaster Pas-
cheri* Scherf., cells in colonial arrangement. (Redrawn
from Korschikoff).

491b Cells dispersed within a spherical, gelatinous sheath, chloroplasts 2 or 3 parietal plates. Fig. 351.............. ....*Gloeobotrys*

The chief difference between this genus and *Chlorobotrys* (Fig. 331) is the
presence of a definite mucilaginous sheath
about the cells so that regular colonies
are formed. The species illustrated was
assigned to *Chlorobotrys* at one time;
described from open-water plankton. Six
species have been reported from the
United States, differentiated by size of
the cells, the colonies and the chloroplasts.

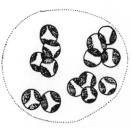

Fig. 351. *Gloeobotrys lim-
eticus* (G. M. Smith) Pascher.

492a (486) Cells forming a loose cushion or a stratum of a few cells
adherent to other filamentous algae.......................................**493**

492b Cells arranged otherwise...**494**

---

*See note on p. 205.

493a Cells hemispherical, in 2's and 4's, forming an expanse on the substrate, the cells in tetrads and relatively compact; wall smooth, chloroplasts several, without pyrenoids. Fig. 352 ....*Chlorellidium (Chlorellidiopsis)*

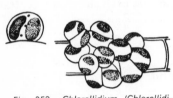

Fig. 352. *Chlorellidium (Chlorellidiopsis) separabilis* (Pascher) Bourr.

This genus is apparently synonymous with *Chlorellidiopsis*. The cells (spherical or spheroidal) are usually closely grouped in clusters and adherent to filamentous algae, but may occur singly. Plants have been collected also from subaerial habitats. There are 2 parietal chloroplasts and at least 1 dark red oil spot in mature cells. Reproduction is by autospores and by zoospores.

493b Cells oval or nearly spherical, in groups of 2 or 4; colony sessile on a substrate; chloroplasts 2 parietal plates. Fig. 353 ....*Lutherella*

Fig. 353. *Lutherella obovoidea* Pascher.

The globular or pyriform cells may be solitary but belong to a family in which the members are gregarious or adjoined to form epiphytic layers. *Lutherella* with its 2 parietal chloroplasts occurs in 2's and 4's on the walls of other algae. The cells are sessile and there seems to be no attaching disc. The habit of having the top half of the cell lift away as a cap for the escape of the zoospore is suggestive of *Chlorothecium* (Fig. 322). The zoospore is unequally biflagellate. In this country the plants seem to occur more frequently in bog waters than in lakes, and where there is a miscellany of other Chrysophyta.

494a (492) Wall in 2 sections which separate (transversely) to liberate spores and which persist nearby; cells may be incidentally colonial because of gregarious habit. Fig. 332...... ....*Diachros*

494b Wall in 1 piece, breaking down irregularly to liberate spores 495

495a Cells curved, sausage-shaped, arranged in 4's, adherent to other quartets by remains of old mother-cell walls in a radiate fashion, mucilage investment not evident. Fig. 354 ....*Dichotomococcus*

This genus is questionably placed in a family in which the cells are colonial and clumped and in which reproduction is by autospores or zoospores. The genus reproduces when the elongate-ovoid or wedge-shaped cells produce 2 autospores. Upon liberation these remain adjoined to other pairs of autospores by the gelatinous material from the mother-cell wall and in a somewhat radiate fashion. There is 1 parietal chloroplast lacking a pyrenoid. The entire colony of several generations is enclosed by a mucilaginous sheath. Both of the 2 known species have been reported from the United States.

Fig. 354. Dichotomococcus elongatus Fott. (R e d r a w n from Thompson).

495b Cells spherical, clustered to form a colony; no mother-cell wall remains evident. Fig. 335 ....*Botrydiopsis*

496a (428) Plant a branched, feathery, but gelatinous thallus, the protoplasts crowded in linear series within tough, tubular envelopes; plants of cold streams. Fig. 355 ....*Hydrurus*

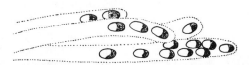

Fig. 355. *Hydrurus foetidus* (Vill.) Trev., cells in mucilage tubes at extremity of the gelatinous colony.

Usually in high mountain or very cold streams this organism forms brown, stringy, gelatinous masses attached to stones or wood. The bushy, brown tufts contain oval cells arranged in linear series within tubelike strands. The strands branch and a well-developed thallus is 'feathery.' Sometimes a small stream actually will be choked with dense growths of *Hydrurus*. The disagreeable odor is responsible for the specific name. The cells may metamorphose into curiously shaped, pyramidal zoospores that have 1 flagellum.

496b Plant not a feathery, gelatinous thallus...............................**497**

497a Cells amoeboid, interconnected by filiform pseudopodia; chloroplast faint, yellowish. Fig. 356...............*Chrysarachnion*

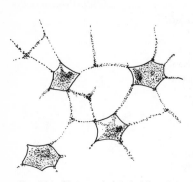

Fig. 356. *Chrysarachnion insidians* Pascher. (Diagrammed from Bourrelly).

The cells in this rhizopodlike genus are interconnected by fine, protoplasmic strands so as to form a network. The chloroplast is a pale, golden-yellow and there is a contractile vacuole. The genus belongs to a family in which the rhizopodal form is the prominent phase; flagellation, if present, being only temporary. The organism is to be expected in collections from the surface of ponds and bog waters.

497b Plants arranged otherwise...498

498a Thallus encrusting and adherent, forming a pseudoparenchymatous growth from which compactly arranged, erect branches arise; chloroplasts several brown discs. Fig. 357 ....*Heribaudiella**

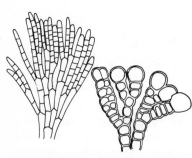

Fig. 357. *Heribaudiella fluviatilis* (Aresch.) Sved. Portion of prostrate thallus; and erect branches with sporangia. (Redrawn from Gomont).

This is one of the few freshwater members of the Phaeophyta. The genus, presently assigned to the Lithodermataceae, characteristically forms an encrusting, prostrate expanse of branches in a pseudoparenchymatous mass. From the prostrate portion, closely arranged upright branches develop. Plants live on rocks in swiftly flowing streams. The disclike chloroplasts are brownish. Apparently 1 species has been reported from the United States and only from Connecticut.

498b Thallus otherwise...499

---

*Possibly includes *Lithoderma* Aresch. and *Lithodora* Klebahn.

499a Plants sparsely branched, erect filaments arising from a few-celled, basal cluster of cells; 2 parietal chloroplasts, ochre-green or brownish. Fig. 358.................................*Phaeothamnion*

This member of the Chrysophyceae is one of 2 genera in which there is a branched filamentous thallus. The branches scarcely taper at the apices. The plants are relatively small and grow on the walls of larger filamentous algae. Each cell has 1 or 2 parietal, ochre-green to brownish chloroplasts. Reproduction is by from 4 to 8 heterokont zoospores produced in any cell.

Fig. 358. *Phaeothamnion confervicola* Lag.

499b Plants otherwise...**500**

500a A colony of vase-shaped cones (loricas), 1 or 2 cones arising from within the mouth of another and forming forked series; protoplasts with 2 flagella, but the organisms often absent from the loricas. Fig. 359......................*Dinobryon*

There are several species of this genus, all of which are characterized by having the motile protoplasts enclosed within a colorless envelope. The loricas are usually contained 1 or 2 within another so that branching chains result. Some species seem to occur solitarily. The genus is one which inhabits mostly hard water lakes, occurring in the euplankton and sometimes so abundant as to form a 'bloom.' They produce disagreeable odors and tastes in domestic water supplies.

Fig. 359. *Dinobryon sertularia* Ehr.

500b Cells arranged otherwise...**501**
501a A colonial cluster (sometimes solitary) of spherical cells, most-ly epiphytic on filamentous algae, with 2 parietal, yellow-green chloroplasts. Fig. 334................................*Chrysosphaera*
501b Cells shaped or arranged otherwise......................................**502**
502a A unicell, consisting of a yellowish protoplast contained with-in a vaselike envelope; two heterokont flagella (organism often absent from lorica). Fig. 359............................*Dinobryon*
502b Cells shaped otherwise, or located differently; solitary or colonial...**503**

503a Cells solitary, colonial or filamentous; wall siliceous and etched with grooves or rows of puncta which form definite patterns; wall in 2 sections, 1 part (epivalve) forming a lid over a smaller (hypovalve); oil drops usually conspicuous as shiny globules; especially solitary cells (if elongate or 'cigar'-shaped) showing a gliding, jerky movement. Diatoms..........651

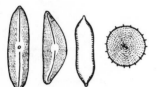

Fig. 360. (Samples of diatom cells illustrating markings on siliceous walls.

Fig. 360. Samples of Diatom frustules, illustrating markings on siliceous walls.

503b Cells without siliceous walls thus decorated; wall not in 2 sections; oil droplets lacking or inconspicuous; not showing gliding movements; if motile, equipped with flagella or moving by pseudopodia (amoeboid fashion)...............................504

504a Unicellular...505

504b Multicellular or colonial...542

505a Non-motile, without flagella.......................................506

505b With Flagella, but sometimes sedentary rather than swimming
....522

506a Cells depressed-globose, attached and sessile; 2 (usually) parietal chloroplasts; often aggregate but frequently found solitary. Fig. 334..............................*Chrysosphaera (Epichrysis)*

506b Cells shaped or situated otherwise......................................507

507a Cells tetrahedral or polyhedral; free-floating; with 1 brownish, lobed chloroplast, parietal over most of the wall. Fig. 361
....*Tetragonidium*

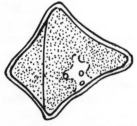

This is a member of the Cryptophyceae which is not motile in the vegetative state. The cells are tetragonal and have yellow-brown parietal chloroplasts that fold around most of the wall.

Fig. 361. *Tetragonidium verrucatum* Pascher (Redrawn from Thompson).

507b Cells shaped otherwise, with different chloroplasts..............508

508a Cells globular or transversely oval, with a raised collar about
      an apical opening, the sides of the cell extended into re-
      flexed, long, spinelike processes; chloroplast 1 or 2, parietal.
      Fig. 362...*Diceras*

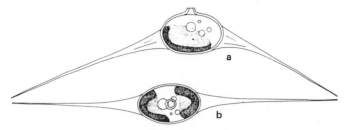

Fig. 362. *Diceras phaseolus* Fott. (a) 'front' view; (b) top view. (Redrawn from Fott).

These golden-brown, free-floating cells are enclosed by a close-
fitting lorica which bears on either side a long, sharply pointed
spine. The body of the cell is transversely oval. The protoplast has
2 fine strands extending through an apical collar. The species
illustrated has been found only in Maryland in the United
States.

508b Cells shaped otherwise...509

509a Cells globular, with a raised collar about an apical pore, the
      wall with several, slender radiating spines, some of which
      are forked at the tip; (probably the cyst of some other alga).
      Fig. 363...*Chrysastrella*

The species illustrated is one of 2 reported from the United States, occurring
either in open-water plankton or intermingled with other algae near shore. The
test or envelope bears a few long, needlelike setae which are often forked at the
tips. The round or oval test with a short
collar should be compared with *Trachelomonas* (Fig. 27).

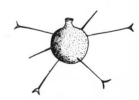

Fig. 363. *Chrysastrella paradoxa* Chod.

509b Cells shaped otherwise...510

510a Cells attached, sedentary on other algae or on aquatic plants
     511

510b Cells free-floating...517

511a Cells with variously shaped loricas, vaselike, with a long or short neck, or hemispherical without a neck, but with an apical pore, the protoplast globular, often showing a fine, threadlike protoplasmic extension through the pore. Fig. 364
....*Lagynion*

a

b

Fig. 364. (a) *Lagynion reductum* Presc.; (b) *L. triangularis* var. *pyramidatum* Presc.

Organisms in this genus are relatively small and are easily overlooked because they occur as epiphytes on filamentous algae. The shape of the lorica varies from globular to pyramidal and vase-shaped, with or without a neck. In some species the neck is bent or deflexed. Within the lorica is a globular protoplast with a faintly pigmented, yellowish chloroplast. The lorica is flattened against the substrate and is colorless. There are 7 species at least reported from the United States. As far as known division of the protoplast is the only method of reproduction.

511b Cells otherwise...512

512a Cells with a globular lorica, colorless or yellowish, with a broadly open, apical pore, extended posteriorly into 2 prongs which straddle the host algal cell; protoplast globular with a pseudopodial thread which often shows forkings at the tip; chloroplasts golden- brown. Fig. 365................*Chrysopyxis*

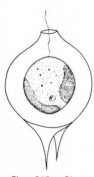

Fig. 365. *Chrysopyxis bipes* Stein.

This curious genus seems to be confined to swamps and *Sphagnum* bogs. There is a globular, colorless lorica which has two posterior, hornlike projections that straddle the host cell of some other alga. In the anterior end is a broad opening through which a fine pseudopodium extends. There is a broad, bandlike chloroplast that folds about the wall. In reproduction 2 motile cells are formed. These escape and swim about for a time, then become quiescent and construct a lorica. The protoplast fills only a small part of the envelope. Three species have been reported from the United States.

512b Cells shaped otherwise..**513**

513a Cells with a vaselike lorica, narrowed to a neck above where there is an apical pore, and narrowed to a basal attaching portion (sessile). Fig. 366...*Derepyxis*

The chief difference between this genus and *Lagynion* (Fig. 364) is the presence of a supporting membrane through the lorica at the base of the protoplast. The lorica is sessile on filamentous algae. Five species are known from the United States, differentiated mostly on the shape of the lorica.

Fig. 366. *Derepyxis dispar* Senn.

513b Cells otherwise..**514**

514a Cells inversely triangular or tetrahedral in top view, the angles tipped with 1 or 2 spines, abruptly narrowed below to an attachment. Fig. 367...*Tetradinium*

The chloroplasts of this sessile member of the dinoflagellates are typically golden-brown. The 3 or 4 corners of the cell are tipped with 2 short, sometimes curved spines. The pyramidal cells have a short stipe attaching them to filamentous algae. This genus should be compared with *Raciborskia* (Fig. 369). The species illustrated and 1 other are the only ones known from the United States.

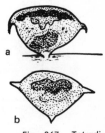

Fig. 367. *Tetradinium simplex* Presc.; (a) side view; (b) vertical view.

514b Cells other shapes, or if inversely triangular then elliptic in vertical view..**515**

515a Cells pyriform or oval, epizoic; with rhizoidal attaching organs at the narrowed posterior. Fig. 368..............................*Oodinium*

The brown, globular or ovate cells have basal rhizoidal extensions which attach the parasite to fish and to other aquatic animals. In reproduction the cells form 2 dinoflagellate-type zoospores. Starch is present in the protoplast. Only 1 species is known for the genus apparently.

Fig. 368. *Oodinium l i m n eticum* Jacobs. (Redrawn from Jacobs).

515b Cells differently shaped, without rhizoidal holdfasts..........516

516a Cells inversely triangular or transversely elliptic in 'front' view, elliptic in top view, the angles spine-tipped; narrowed posteriorly to a short, attaching stipe. Fig. 369.......*Raciborskia*

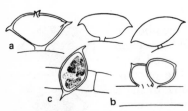

These are elliptical cells, sessile on a short stalk and attached to filamentous algae or aquatic mosses. There is a single spine at each pole of the cell as well as a pair of spines (at times) on the dorsal wall. One species only has been reported from the United States. This genus should be compared with *Tetradinium* (Fig.367).

Fig. 369. *Raciborskia bicornis* Wolosz. (a) side view, showing stipe; (b), (c) end and top views.

516b Cells globular with a long, narrow stipe that has an attaching disc at the base, and an inflation immediately below the cell body; protoplast with many brownish chloroplasts and a red spot; often showing a dinoflagellate type of a partial transverse furrow. Fig. 370.....................................*Stylodinium*

These globular cells have a relatively long, slender stipe and an attaching disc. They occur as epiphytes on filamentous algae. The membrane is relatively thick and encloses a protoplast in which there are numerous disclike chloroplasts and a red oil globule. Frequently the protoplast shows a partial transverse furrow characteristic of the dinoflagellates. In reproduction the cell forms 2 dinoflagellate zoospores which escape by a rupture of the wall. Two species are known for the United States, rare but widely distributed.

Fig. 370. Stylo-dinium globosum Klebs.

517a (510) **Cells oval or elliptic, the wall impregnated and covered with variously shaped siliceous scales (appearing like chain armor) which bear long bristles; with an apical opening (usually obscured by wall scales); actually with a single flagellum and motile, but the flagellum often obscure and the cell quiescent. Fig. 371**..*Mallomonas*

These species occur in open water plankton of mostly hardwater lakes, frequently in abundance. They are differentiated from one another by the shape and arrangement of the scales in the membrane and by the morphology and arrangement of the bristles. Electron microscopy has demonstrated some highly refined

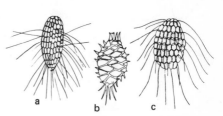

Fig. 371   (a) *Mallomonas caudata* Iwanoff; (b) *M. pseudocoronata* Presc. (c) *M. acaroides* Perty.

characteristic features of the scales and bristles which are useful in taxonomy. Some species occur regularly in lakes in which there is a high degree of pollution. Although motile, the single flagellum is hardly distinguishable unless the cells are recently collected and viewed under favorable optical conditions. The scales and spines are siliceous. Twenty-four species have been reported from the United States.

519a Pseudopodia long and needlelike, sometimes cells in a chain by interlocking of pseudopodia. Fig. 372..............*Rhizochrysis*

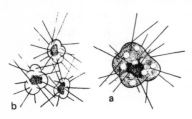

Fig. 372. *Rhizochrysis limnetica* G. M. Smith. (a) single cell; (b) cells in temporary colonial arrangement.

This amoeboid member of the Chrysophyta has long, slender, needlelike. The cells are ordinarily solitary but may occur in loose, temporarily united groups. Two species only are known from the United States.

519b Pseudopodia relatively short, spurlike, a single flagellum sometimes present after metamorphosis of the cell; solitary but sometimes appearing in chains through interjoining of pseudopodia. Fig. 373...*Chrysamoeba*

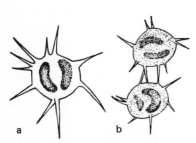

Fig. 373. *Chrysamoeba radians* Klebs. (a) single cell; (b) temporarily adjoined cells to form a 'colony.'

This rhizopodial form occurs more frequently than *Rhizochrysis* (Fig. 372). Like that genus *Chrysamoeba* has pseudopodia but they are short and thornlike rather than needlelike. The cells ordinarily occur in an amoeboid condition but may develop a single flagellum as a locomotory organ. There are two pale yellow chloroplasts. The species illustrated is widely distributed in the United States.

520a (518) Cells variously curved and crescent-shaped with pointed, sometimes reflexed or twisted horns; many brownish chloroplasts and sometimes a red spot. Fig. 374..............*Cystodinium*

Fig. 374. *Cystodinium cornifax* (Schiller) Klebs.

These are free-floating, lunate, cystlike members of the Dinoflagellata. Species are differentiated on the basis of various shapes and the direction and morphology of the polar horns. Several species of *Tetraedron* (Fig. 207) have been described incorrectly from members of the genus *Cystodinium*. The protoplast is distinctly the dinoflagellate type and usually there is a red oil droplet. Five species have been reported from the United States.

520b Cells otherwise...**521**

521a Cells globular with numerous, disclike chloroplasts in stellate clusters; often showing a single, dinoflagellate protoplast with the external cell wall serving as a cyst membrane. Fig. 375...*Hypnodinium*

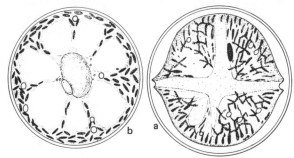

Fig. 375. *Hypnodinium sphaericum* Klebs. (a) cyst with dinoflagellate type of daughter cell; (b) cyst. (Redrawn from Thompson).

The brown, ellipsoid chloroplasts are arranged in numerous rosettes within these globular cells. Species are free-floating and have no flagella but the protoplast shows a typical transverse furrow and a red oil globule. The single species is rare and has been found only in Maryland in this country.

521b Cells oval or globular, solitary or in a few-celled cluster within a lamellate sheath; cells often showing a conspicuous transverse furrow; golden-brown chloroplasts somewhat radiately arranged but not in clusters. Fig. 376.....................*Gloeodinium*

Although these plants exist in a palmelloid, nonmotile condition they clearly show their dinoflagellate affinity by the transverse furrow and the radiately arranged, golden-brown chloroplasts. The cells are enclosed in a lamellate, gelatinous sheath, from 2 to 8 in a clump. Two species have been reported from the United States.

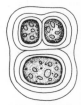

Fig. 376. Gloeodinium sp., cyst.

The cells in this genus have a cone-shaped lorica of various forms,
one which shows projections along the margins representing the
cones of previous generations. It is sometimes treated as synonymous with *Hyalobryon* (Fig. 378). The cells are sessile and epiphytic, solitary or colonial. The protoplast within the lorica has 2
parietal chloroplasts and sometimes a stigma or eyespot. Nearly
25 species have been reported from the United States (including
species referable to *Hyalobryon*).

Fig. 377. Epipy-
xis T a b e llariae
(Lemm.)   G.   M.
Smith,   protoplast
in a lorica epi-
phytic   on   fila-
mentous algae.

Fig. 377A.

---

*One-celled forms of *Dinobryon* have been referred to this genus. According
to some studies *Epipyxis* is synonymous with *Hyalobryon*.

524b Lorica cone-shaped, with marginal bristlelike projections caused by transverse "growth rings." Fig. 378......*Hyalobryon*

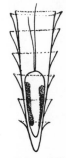

In this genus the cells are solitary and the cone-shaped envelopes have margins which appear as if bristled. These markings represent the remains of envelopes of previous generations of cells. Whereas *Dinobryon* (Fig. 359) is freely swimming, this genus is solitary or colonial as an epiphyte on filamentous algae. At least 3 species have been reported from the United States.

F i g. 378. *H y a lobryon m u c i c o l a* (Lemm.) Pascher.

525a (522) Cells with a broadly oval, colorless lorica, truncate at the apex with a median pore; protoplast elliptic, with a single flagellum extending from the narrowly pointed apex; 2 brown chloroplasts and an eye-spot. Fig. 379..*Chrysococcus*

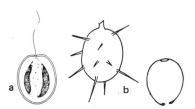

Fig. 379.   (a) *Chrysococcus rufescens* Klebs; (b) other forms.

The globular loricas of this genus have a small, often inconspicuous pore at the anterior end through which a single flagellum extends. The protoplast does not nearly fill the cavity of the lorica. There are 2 golden-brown chloroplasts. There are at least 17 species reported from the United States, many of them in the Ohio valley only.

525b Cells without a lorica..526

526a Cells oval or elliptic, with the wall impregnated or covered by overlapping siliceous scales which bear long bristles; flagellum 1, often inconspicuous. Fig. 371............*Mallomonas*

526b Cells without siliceous scales in the wall...........................527

527a Cells oval in 'front' view, flattened and narrow when seen
     from the side, lobed or 2-lipped at the apex; 2 flagella not
     the same length. Fig. 26...*Cryptochrysis*

527b Cells differently shaped...528

528a Cells broadly circular in 'front' view, flattened and narrow
     when seen from the side; without a true wall; flagella 3,
     slightly subapical in attachment; with 2 golden-yellow, lateral
     chloroplasts. Fig. 380................................ ......*Chrysochromulina*

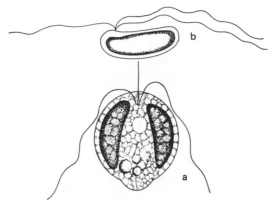

Fig. 380. *Chrysochromulina parya* Lackey. (a) 'front' view; (b) end view.
(Redrawn from Lackey).

   The cells in this genus are without a wall; have 3 somewhat laterally attached flagella arising near the anterior end. The cells are
broadly rounded in 'front' view, but narrow and somewhat reniform
when seen from the side. One species only has been reported, from
midwest United States.

528b Cells differently shaped with a cell wall; flagella 2...........529

529a Cells oval in 'front' view, with an apical depression; 2 flagella
     arising apically; cell flattened when seen from the side and
     showing the 2-valved form of the wall; transverse furrow
     lacking; 2 brownish chloroplasts. Fig. 381.................*Exuviella*

This is an unusual member of
the Dinoflagellata in that there is
no transverse furrow, and the flagella are apical rather than lateral.
Although almost entirely marine,
at least 1 species has been found
in brackish water. When seen
from the side the two valves that
compose the cellulose wall can
be detected.

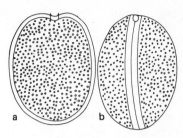

Fig. 381. *Exuviella compressa* Os-
tenf. (a) 'front' view; (b) side view.

529b Cells otherwise..530
530a Cells pyriform, with a median depression apically; wall not
      bivalved; 2 apical flagella arising from a gullet; 2 yellowish
      chloroplasts (sometimes yellow-green). Fig. 16............................
      ....*Cryptomonas*
530b Cells otherwise..531
531a Cells bean-shaped, with 2 flagella that are laterally attached;
      1 or 2 lobed, parietal, brownish chloroplasts and an eye-spot.
      Fig. 301...*Protochrysis*
531b Cells shaped otherwise...532
532a Cells oval or distinctly pyriform, with 2 flagella of nearly
      equal length, arising from the broad anterior end; 1 folded,
      broad, platelike chloroplast, brownish or olive-green (some-
      times red). Fig. 15..*Rhodomonas*
532b Cells otherwise..533
533a Cells pyriform with 2 distinctly unequal flagella from the
      broad anterior end; 2 small, yellowish chloroplasts; without
      a gullet. Fig. 330.....................*Ochromonas (Chlorochromonas)*
533b Cells otherwise..534
534a Cells with a long, anterior horn and 2 or 3 posterior horns.
      Fig. 382...*Ceratium*

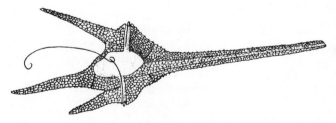

Fig. 382. *Ceratium hirundinella* (O. F. M.) Duj.

This genus possesses such a distinctive shape that it can be
unmistakably identified. It occurs either in the eu- or tychoplank-

ton but especially in the former situation, sometimes producing a 'bloom.' Water of small lakes may be gray-chocolate in color from the profuse number of individuals. There is a prominent transverse furrow that divides the cell into an epicone and a hypocone. When seen from the ventral surface the longitudinal, rather broad sulcus is discernible. Here the 2 flagella are attached, one of which trails, the other (a band type) is wound about the cell and vibrates in the transverse furrow. There are numerous, brown chloroplasts and a large red eye-spot(?). The plates which compose the wall are marked with close reticulations. *Ceratium* is the most common of all the fresh-water dinoflagellates. Seven species have been reported from fresh and brackish water of the United States.

534b Cells without prominent horns as above............................535

535a Cells without a true wall, but with a membrane which may be either delicate or thick and firm; smooth, without plates 536

535b Cells with a true wall, with a pattern of definitely arranged plates usually evident (in some the boundary lines of the plates are seen with difficulty; reduce or modify illumination); a transverse furrow encircling the cell completely or incompletely and a longitudinal (ventral) sulcus............................539

536a Cells oval; the transverse furrow spirally descending. Fig. 383 ....*Gyrodinium*

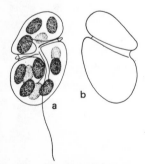

The chloroplasts of this genus are relatively large. Identification can be made by the descending, spiral transverse furrow which produces a hypocone much larger than the epicone. Species occur in marine or brackish water.

Fig. 383. *Gyrodinium pusillum* (Schilling) Kofoid et Swezy. (a) ventral view, showing relatively large chloroplasts; (b) dorsal view.

536b Cells top-shaped or fusiform; transverse furrow mostly at
     right angles to the long axis, or occurring as a 'V' near the
     apex..537

537a Transverse furrow dividing the cell approximately into 2 equal
     parts (epicone and hypocone. Fig. 384...............*Gymnodinium*

Species of this genus are numerous and are of wide occurrence
in both fresh and salt water. They
are mostly intermingled with
other algae in fresh water, whereas in the sea they produce veritable 'blooms,' the most common
cause of the infamous 'red tide.'
There is no true cell wall (hence
the genus name). The transverse
furrow extends around the cell in
a slightly downward direction.
Over 20 species have been reported from fresh-water habitats
in the United States.

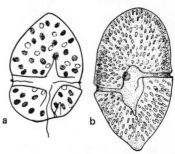

Fig. 384. (a) *Gymnodinium palustre*
Schilling; (b) G. *fuscum* (Ehr.) Stein.

537b Transverse furrow dividing the cell into a hypocone and
     epicone unequal in size...538

538a Cells mostly top-shaped, the epicone definitely larger than
     the hypocone. Fig. 385...*Massartia*

These dinoflagellate cells, without a cell wall, are broadly oval
but truncate at the poles. The transverse furrow divides the cell into an
epicone distinctly larger than the
hypocone. The brown chloroplasts
are somewhat radiate in arrangement. Compare with *Gymnodinium*
(Fig. 384).

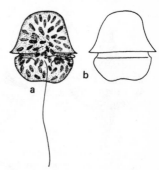

Fig. 385. *Massartia Musei* (Dan.)
Schiller. (a) ventral view; (b) dorsal view.

538b Cells subquadrate, the epicone smaller than the hypocone and appearing as an apical lobe of the cell. Fig. 386........................
....*Amphidinium*

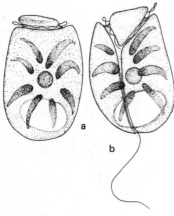

This genus is mostly marine in distribution but may be found in brackish water, or in fresh water near the sea. The chloroplasts are large and radiately arranged. The cell is unusual in that the transverse furrow is located near the apex so that the epicone is but a small lobe.

Fig. 386. *Amphidinium Klebsii* Kof.;
(a) dorsal; (b) ventral view.

539a (535) Wall thick; plates easily discerned, with a suture (usually) between the plates; transverse furrow completely encircling the cell..**540**

539b Wall thin; plates seen with difficulty (especially in filled and living cells); transverse furrow completely encircling the cells or not..**541**

540a Wall with 2 antapical plates (the plates at the posterior pole, to be seen in posterior end view); cell slightly flattened dorsiventrally in most species; posterior pole sometimes extended into a horn or into short projections. Fig. 387..............
....*Peridinium*

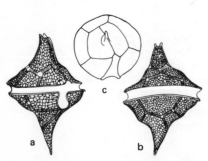

This genus is represented by more species in fresh water than any of the other dinoflagellates. They are differentiated by shape and size of the cell, and by the number, shape and arrangement of the wall plates. The 2 posterior or antapical plates can be determined by patiently rolling the cell so that

Fig. 387. *Peridinium wisconsinense* Eddy.
(a) ventral view showing longitudinal sulcus;
(b) dorsal view; (c) posterior view showing
2 antapical plates.

it can be seen from the end.
Often the apical view shows
a terminal pore. Most species
are some variety of top-
shape; others oval or globular; many are slightly flattened when seen from the
'side.' Some species have
dorsal flanges or hornlike
processes. In most species
the plates show a distinct

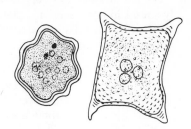

Fig. 387A. Dinoflagellate cysts.

reticulation. Over 40 species have been reported from fresh water
in the United States. Cysts (Fig. 387A) often occur.

540b Wall with 1 antapical plate; cell not flattened dorsiventrally,
round in cross section. Fig. 388..................................*Gonyaulax*

These almost spherical cells are differentiated
from *Peridinium* (Fig. 387) by the single apical
plate, and by the slightly spiral direction of
the transverse furrow. Some authorities regard
the species illustrated as belonging to *Peridinium. Gonyaulax* is more prevalent in marine
waters; is sometimes the cause of some 'red
tides' and is related to fish poisoning.

Fig. 388. *Gonyau-
lax palustre* Lemm.

541a (539) Cells strongly flattened dorsiventrally; plates not evident; transverse furrow not encircling the cell completely,
usually located in the posterior part of the cell. Fig. 389......
....*Hemidinium*

Cells in this genus are oval or elliptic
when seen from the broad side but are
much flattened in lateral view. The transverse furrow extends only part way around
the cell. Species are differentiated by
shape and size of the cell and by the
pattern of the plates in the wall which
are usually very delicate and difficult
of determination. The 2 species reported
from the United States are rare; are to
be found in the typchoplankton, especially in shallow ponds and swamps.

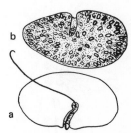

Fig. 389. *Hemidinium na-
sutum* Stein. (a) ventral
view; (b) dorsal view.

541b Cells not at all or but very little flattened dorsiventrally (near-ly round in cross section); plates evident in the wall (especial-ly clear when cells are empty); transverse furrow completely encircling the cell. Fig. 390......................................*Glenodinium*

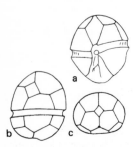

Fig. 390. *Glenodinium Kulczynski* (Wolosz.) Schil-ler. (a) ventral view showing longitudinal furrow; (b) dorsal view; (c) apical view.

The several species of this genus reported from the United States are differentiated by cell size and shape. Mostly they are broadly oval to nearly round. The plate pattern is much more easily discerned than in *Hemidinium* (Fig. 389) but even so careful observation is needed to see the plates especially when the cells are alive or filled. The cells must be rotated to be seen in various positions in making determinations. As in other genera, such as with *Peridinium* (Fig. 387), *e.g.*, it is desirable to examine empty cells to see the wall characters.

542a (504) Colony a disc of horizontally arranged cells usually showing as radiating filaments. Fig. 314................................
....*Phaeodermatium*
542b Colonies otherwise...543
543a Colony motile; cells flagellated.................................544
543b Colony non-motile, or if moving, by rhizoidal processes (pseudopodia)..550
544a Colony globose or subglobose (oval); cells ovoid or pyriform, compactly arranged or forming a hollow sphere.................545
544b Colony not globular; cells shaped otherwise.......................549
545a Cells bearing 2 long, rigid, rodlike processes at their anterior ends. Fig. 391.......................................*Chrysosphaerella*

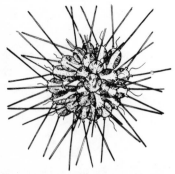

This distinctive genus is readily identified by the curious long rods borne in pairs on each cell. The rods (siliceous) have a collar at their bases, with a single flagellum between. The chloroplasts are brownish-yellow. Although widely distributed the single species is rare in occurrence.

Fig. 391. *Chrysosphaerella longispina* Lauterb.

Although rare, *Uroglena volvox* Ehr., the only species, is widely distributed in the United States and throughout the world. It is to be expected in the euplankton of lakes. The elliptic cells, with the posterior portion abruptly narrowed, are arranged at the periphery of a mucilaginous sheath. The cells are attached at the ends of fine, radiating and branched threads which can be seen after the application of a stain. The chloroplast is a parietal, folded plate, golden-yellow in color, but usually faint. The cell bears 2 flagella of unequal length. Identification is aided by the distinctive oblong shape of the colony. Conrad and other authors advocate the inclusion of *Uroglena* with *Uroglenopsis* (Fig. 395).

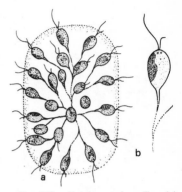

Fig. 392. *Uroglena volvox* Ehr. (a) colony; (b) single cell.

Syncrypta is a motile colony of radiately arranged, pyriform cells enclosed in a gelatinous envelope in which there are numerous, small granular bodies. The chloroplasts and the cell-shape are similar to *Synura* (Fig. 394) but the cell membrane is smooth, without siliceous spicules. The 2 flagella are of unequal length. The species illustrated is the only one known.

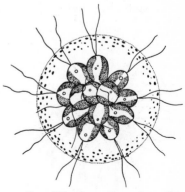

Fig. 393. *Syncrypta volvox* Ehr., showing pebbled granulations in the colonial mucilage.

547b Cells shaped or arranged otherwise..548

548a Cells elongate-ellipsoid or elongate-pyriform, rather compactly arranged to form a globular colony which is not enclosed in a gelatinous sheath; cell wall with minute siliceous scales in the anterior end; flagella 2, of equal length but dissimilar structurally; chloroplasts golden-brown. Fig. 394..........
..*Synura*

Fig. 394. *Synura uvella* Ehr. (a) colony; (b) single cell showing siliceous spicules in anterior region of cell wall.

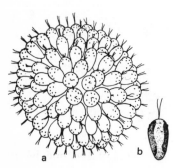

This genus is very common in hard-water lakes and may be so abundant as to produce disagreeable odors and tastes in water supply reservoirs. The chloroplasts are 2, parietal, golden-brown plates and often are so dense as to mask the small siliceous spicules in the anterior wall. The spicules can be determined by proper focusing on quiescent colonies. The species illustrated and another, *S. Adamsii* G. M. Smith are common and widely distributed in the United States, although the latter is less frequently encountered.

548b Cells ovoid or egg-shaped, separated and evenly spaced within a colonial envelope; without scales in the wall; flagella 2, of unequal length; chloroplast pale yellow. Fig. 395..........
..*Uroglenopsis*

Fig. 395. *Uroglenopsis americana* (Calkins) Lemm.

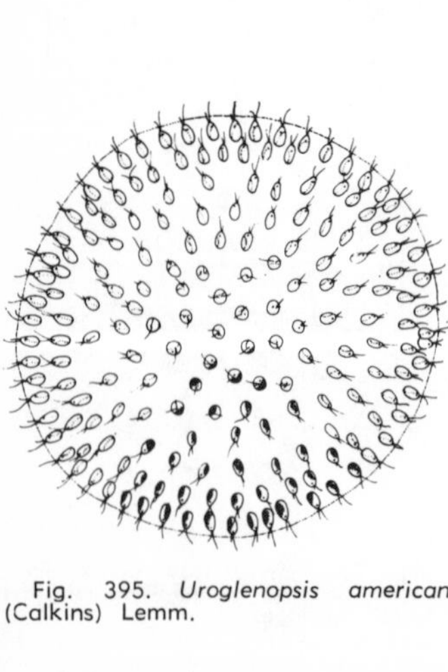

This genus frequents water that is contaminated with nitrogenous wastes. The colonies are large and contain several hundreds of cells; are sometimes mistaken for *Volvox* (Fig. 67), but are readily differentiated by the yellowish-brown color of the platelike (not cup-shaped) chloroplasts. The cells have 2 flagella of unequal length. It is interesting that this organism is sometimes the dominant member of the plankton in arctic lakes. There is some justification for including this genus with *Uroglena* (Fig. 392).

549a (544) Cells elongate-ovoid or pyriform, compactly arranged side by side in a radiate fashion in 1 plane to form a plate with a small central opening; motile by 2 flagella. Fig. 396 ....*Cyclonexis*

The flat, disclike colony of compactly arranged and radiate, pyriform cells is very distinctive. The flagella are relatively coarse and can be seen readily when the colony is quiescent. There are 2 elongate, lightly pigmented chloroplasts. Of the 3 species known 1 is reported from the United States.

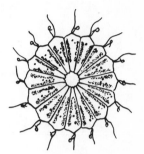

Fig. 396. Cyclonexis annularis S t o k e s. (Redrawn from Stokes.)

549b Cells not as above; contained in a vase-shaped envelope; or 2 such envelopes arising from the mouth of the one below to form a branched series. Fig. 359..........................*Dinobryon*

550a (543) Individuals furnished with pseudopodia (colony sometimes loosely formed and only temporary)..............................551

550b Individuals not furnished with organs of locomotion; colony non-motile..555

551a Cells enclosed in a brown, shell-like lorica in which there are pores through which fine pseudopodia extend to meet pseudopodia of similar cells, thus forming a meshwork over *Sphagnum;* chloroplast pale, brownish or nearly colorless. Fig. 397 ....*Heliapsis*

Although this genus belongs to the rhizopodial Chrysophyta, the protoplasts are enclosed in a thick-walled, globular lorica. In the walls of this there are pores through which pseudopodial, protoplasmic strands extend, joining those of others to form a meshwork. There is a brownish chloroplast and a contractile vacuole. The single species of the genus has been reported from the United States.

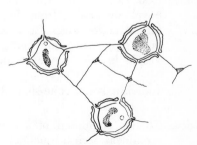

Fig. 397. Heliapsis mutabilis Pascher. (Diagrammatic).

551b Cells otherwise 552

552a Cells amoeboid with fine, firm pseudopodia, the pseudopodia adjoining those of others to form a chain in 1 series. Fig. 398 .... *Chrysidiastrum*

Fig. 398. *Chrysidiastrum catenatum* Lauterb. (Redrawn from G. M. Smith.)

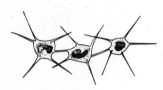

Although this pseudopodial organism may occur singly it is seen frequently adjoined in loose colonies by the interconnecting pseudopodia. There is 1 platelike or disc-shaped chloroplast, usually faintly pigmented. Plants are to be expected intermingled with other algae in swamps and bogs. The species illustrated is the only one reported from the United States.

552b Cells otherwise 553

553a Colony definite formed of amoeboid cells with knotted protoplasmic strands adjoining so as to form a network; chloroplast pale and small. Fig. 356 .... *Chrysarachnion*

553b Colony incidental and transitory, formed by union of other types of pseudopodia 554

554a Pseudopodia numerous, radiating needles; colony-formation mostly temporary and incidental. Fig. 372 .... *Rhizochrysis*

554b Pseudopodia short, protoplasmic extensions join individuals to form temporary colonies. Fig. 373 .... *Chrysamoeba*

555a (550) Colony consisting of vase-shaped envelopes, 1 or 2 such envelopes arising from the mouth of the one below to form forked series (organisms actually motile by 2 flagella, but often appearing quiescent, with the flagella completely invisible in microscope mounts). Fig. 359 .... *Dinobryon*

555b Individuals not cone-shaped; colony formed otherwise 556

556a Thallus composed of a compact layer of epiphytic cells in rectilinear series; mucilaginous sheath wanting. Fig. 399 .... *Phaeoplaca*

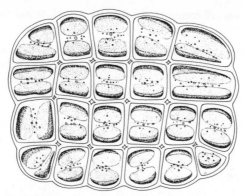

Fig. 399. *Phaeoplaca thallosa* Chod. (Redrawn from Thompson.)

This genus has angular cells with relatively thick walls, compactly arranged to form subquadrangular thalli; the cells in 1 layer. The cells contain yellow-brown chloroplasts. Of the 2 known species 1 has been reported from the United States.

556b Thallus composed of cells arranged otherwise; mucilaginous sheath present..**557**

557a Thallus a sparsely branched, gelatinous cylinder or a mucilaginous network, with cells arranged in 1 to several irregular, linear series. Fig. 400..................*Tetrasporopsis (Phaeosphaera)*

The golden-brown cells of this genus occur in gelatinous masses of irregular shape and of macroscopic size. The thallus may be a stringy mass of mucilage, occurring in skeins or meshworks. Unlike *Tetraspora* (Fig. 78) with which it should be compared, the cells are not arranged in groups of 4 but occur in irregular arrangement or in series throughout the gelatinous strands; neither are there pseudocilia. The plant is widely distributed in the United States, having been found in North Carolina and in arctic Alaska. The name is synonymous with *Phaeosphaera*.

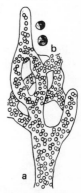

Fig. 400. *Tetrasporopsis perforata* (Whitf.) Bourrelly. (a) small portion of perforate, gelatinous colony; (b) cells showing chloroplasts.

557b Thallus not a branched, gelatinous strand or network.........558

**558a Cells as many as 150 within an epiphytic, gelatinous invest-
ment from which a tuft of fine to stout, branched hairs ex-
tends. Fig. 401...*Naegeliella***

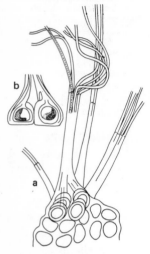

This rare genus occurs as an epiphyte
on aquatic plants. The cells are arranged in 1 or 2 layers within a mucilaginous matrix. From the surface of
the colony 1 or 2 tufts of fine gelatinous
hairs arise. One species only has been
reported from the United States.

Fig. 401. (a) *Naegeliella bri-
tannica* Godward; (b) *M. flagel-
lifera* Correns. (Redrawn from
Correns.)

**558b Cells arranged otherwise; colony not bearing a tuft of hairs
....559**

**559a Cells in a cluster of 2-4-8-16 within an irregularly globose
colonial investment. Fig. 402...................................*Chrysocapsa***

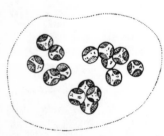

The colonies are globular or nearly so; the mucilage clear and transparent, the cells with brown chloroplasts. The species illustrated and
one other have been reported from
the tychoplankton of ponds and
swamps in the United States. But
Chrysocapsa paludosa (West et
West) Pascher is sometimes found
in the euplankton; has oval rather
than round cells.

Fig. 402. *Chrysocapsa plancto-
nica* (W. et W.) Pascher. (Redrawn
from G. M. Smith.)

559b Cells 16-32-64 within a wide, flat, colonial matrix, the mucilage impregnated with granular substances which appear as shiny bodies. Fig. 403..*Chrysostephanosphaera*

The colony of this genus is flat and disclike. The oval cells, arranged in a circle, are enclosed by a wide gelatinous matrix which contains dark granules. The interior of the colony is clear and homogeneous. There are 2 laminate, yellowish-brown chloroplasts. The species illustrated is the only 1 of 3 known for the genus that occurs in the United States.

Fig. 403. *Chrysostephanosphaera globulifera* Scherff.

560a (4) Plants filamentous or pseudofilamentous, threadlike (the thread of cells called a trichome; trichome and sheath, if present together called a filament)..561

560b Plants not definitely filamentous; cells globular, rod-shaped, or angular from mutual compression; solitary, in floating colonies, or forming cushionlike masses of isodiametric cells in which a suggestion of filamentous arrangement may be apparent...615

561a Trichomes coiled or spiralled in a regular fashion...............562

561b Trichomes otherwise, straight or irregularly twisted, not forming a regular spiral (occasionally, however, *Oscillatoria*, (Fig. 416) may become twisted about itself in a regular spiral fashion)..565

562a Trichomes unicellular (without cross walls). Fig. 404...............
....*Spirulina*

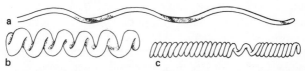

Fig. 404. (a) *Spirulina laxissima* G. S. West; (b) *S. princeps* (W. et W.) G. S. West; (c) *S. subsalsa* Oersted.

Although essentially unicellular, this genus is threadlike and is included with the filamentous Oscillatoriaceae of the Cyanophyta. Some species are solitary but they are often found in masses either by themselves or intermingled with *Oscillatoria* (Fig. 416). Species are differentiated by size and shape and by the type of coiling of the cell. The plants are very active as seen microscopically. The movement in this and other blue-green algae is accomplished by the extrusion of mucilage and by the flow of mucilage along the trichome.

562b Trichomes multicellular; *i.e.*, with cross walls......................563

563a Trichomes composed of beadlike or barrel-shaped cells, with heterocysts present (cells located here and there in the trichome which are larger and sometimes different in shape from the vegetative cells). Fig. 405............................*Anabaena*

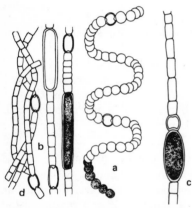

Fig. 405. (a) *Anabaena spiroides* var. *crassa* Lemm.; (b) *A. subcylindrica* Borge; (c) *A.* sp., showing oval akinetes; (d) *A. subcylindrica* Borge, showing heterocysts.

There are many species of this genus, some solitary and some forming aggregated masses of indefinite shape. When colonial they are surrounded by a conspicuous mucilage and sometimes are mistaken for *Nostoc* (Fig. 443). The colonial mass is indefinite in shape and the mucilage soft, however, rather than firm and skinlike as in *Nostoc*. Whereas some forms are truly planktonic, others occur intermingled with algae in shallow water, or epiphytic, or on moist soil. The planktonic species may form a bloom in lakes of northern latitudes during summer months, but seldom cause disagreeable conditions in lakes and reservoirs because these plants remain suspended throughout the water and do not form surface scums where disintegration occurs as with other blue-green genera. Some species of *Anabaena*, however, are responsible for the death of cattle and other animals that drink water where the plants are abundant because of the toxin they liberate.

563b Cells not beadlike but rectangular or cylindrical, usually wider than long and sometimes disc-like; heterocysts absent 564

564a Trichome with a close sheath. Fig. 406........................*Lyngbya*

Most species are straight and rigid, or sometimes curved and entangled, whereas *Lyngbya contorta* Lemm. is regularly spiralled. Trichomes are mostly rounded or conical at the apex; seldom constricted at the joints. Some species are entangled among other algae and occasionally epiphytic, but many are planktonic. The definite, rather firm sheath extending

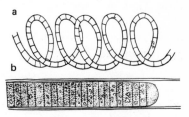

Fig. 406. (a) *Lyngbya contorta* Lemm.; (b) *L. Birgei* G. M. Smith.

beyond the apex of the trichome is characteristic and helps to separate this genus from *Oscillatoria** (Fig. 416) and from *Phormidium* (Fig. 421), the latter having a very thin and sticky sheath. Recently *Phormidium*, and *Lyngbya* have been reduced to synonymy with *Oscillatoria*.

564b Trichomes without a sheath, regularly spiral. Fig. 407..........
....*Arthrospira*

The plants in this genus are multticellular but at times the cross partitions are difficult to discern and short sections of a trichome be mistaken for *Spirulina* (Fig. 404). Species are differentiated mostly by size and form of coiling of the trichomes. The plants show a spiral motion although not so actively as *Spirulina*. *Arthrospira* occurs intermingled with *Spirulina;* is common in the *purées* of miscellaneous algae in the tychoplankton.

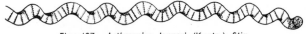

Fig. 407. *Arthrospira Jenneri* (Kuetz.) Stiz.

565a (561) Trichomes with cells all alike in shape and size (although the trichome may taper slightly at one or both ends, or the apical cell may be slightly swollen (capitate); hereocysts lacking..**566**

565b Trichomes with differentiated cells (heterocysts present); heterocysts appearing empty, or with polar plugs of mucilage; other cells enlarged, with thick walls, serving as akinetes (gonidia or spores)..**588**

566a Trichomes tapering at one or both ends..............................**567**

---

*Recently F. Drouet has combined *Lyngbya* with *Oscillatoria*.

566b Trichomes not tapering, the same diameter throughout (or narrowed slightly in the extreme apical portion).................570

567a Trichome tapering from base to apex, without branches, or if with false branches these are not U-shaped...........................568

567b Trichomes tapering at both ends, with U-shaped false branches. Fig. 408...*Hammatoidea*

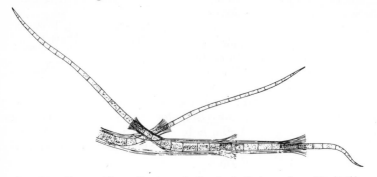

Fig. 408. *Hammatoidea yellowstonensis* Copeland. (Redrawn from Copeland.)

This genus has false branches which form U-shaped loops lateral to the main axis. Like other members of the Rivulariaceae the branches taper toward the apices—but there are no heterocysts. The plants usually occur in the mucilaginous sheaths of other algae. Two species have been reported from the United States, one from the hot springs of Yellowstone National Park.

568a Trichomes aggregated, tapering from a base which is incorporated in a prostrate cushion of cells. Fig. 409....................
....*Amphithrix*

These are tapering filaments, arranged in somewhat parallel fashion so as to form clusters (but without conspicuous mucilage) attached to substrates. There is a weakly-developed, prostrate

Fig. 409. *Amphithrix janthina* (Mont.) Born. et Flah. (Redrawn from Bornet et Flahault.)

expansion of the thallus from which the upright trichomes arise. The lack of heterocysts makes this a somewhat anomalous member of the Rivulariaceae which characteristically have a heterocyst at the base of the filament. Two species have been reported from the United States and not widely distributed.

568b Without a prostrate cushion of cells at the base of the trichome...569

569a Trichomes gregarious parallel in a colonial mass. Fig. 409
....*Amphithrix*

569b Trichomes solitary or loosely clustered, without parallel arrangement (some species possessing heterocysts). Fig. 410
....*Calothrix*

The tapering filaments of this genus are solitary or loosely clustered, 2, 3 or 4 together, although in rare instances after profuse growth they may be gregarious and form an extensive expanse. There is a basal heterocyst (sometimes lacking) and in most species there is an akinete adjacent to the terminal heterocyst. Species are differentiated on the basis of size, presence or absence of akinetes, the degree of tapering and details of the sheath which usually extends far beyond the apex of the trichome. In some species the trichomes are short and the tapering very abrupt. At least 41 species have been reported from the United States.

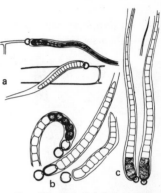

Fig. 410. (a) *Calothrix epiphytica* W. et W.; (b) C. *atricha* Frémy; (c) C. *Braunii* Born. et Flah.

570a (566) Filaments branched (search several specimens).........**571**

570b Filaments unbranched...**574**

571a Branches false (a branch formed by a proliferation of a broken trichome which pushes to one side of the main axis; not branching by the lateral division of a cell in the main axis); branching often sparse. Fig. 411...................*Plectonema*

The false habit of branching places this genus in the Scytonemataceae, but unlike other members of the family there are no heterocysts. The species illustrated is a common one, occurring in brownish-green or black cottony masses at or near the surface of the water; is a relatively

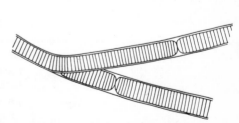

Fig. 411. *Plectonema Wollei* Farlow.

large species, being up to 50μ in diameter. Many of the smaller species form clumps, or are intermingled with other algae. Several specimens should be examined throughout the length of a filament in making determinations because branching may be sparse. There is a dozen or more species reported from the United States, all rather widely distributed.

571b Branching true; the branches formed by lateral division of cells in the main axis of the trichome....................................**572**

572a Filaments with prostrate and erect portions; dichotomous; sheaths transversely lamellate. Fig. 412.................*Colteronema*

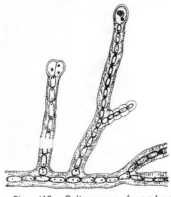

This plant is similar to *Albrightia* (Fig. 414) but the branching is dichotomous. The branches arise vertically from a more or less prostrate axial filament. The rather soft gelatinous sheath has transverse lamellations. There are no heterocysts. The single species is known only from Yellowstone National Park.

Fig. 412. *Colteronema funebre* Copeland. (Redrawn from Copeland.)

572b Filaments without a prostrate and an erect portion; sheath not transversely lamellate..**573**

573a Filaments with disjunct cells which are transversely oval, arranged in a homogeneous, gelatinous sheath which may branch or show anastomosings. Fig. 413....................................
....*Heterohormogonium*

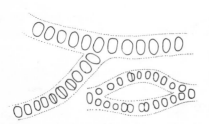

This genus has a wide, gelatinous sheath in which oval cells are arranged in a filamentous form but not in contact. The filament may be variously branched and may anastomose. The genus is known only from hot springs.

Fig. 413. *Heterohormogonium schizo-dichotomum* Copeland. (Diagrammed from Copeland).

573b Cells elongate-oval or sausage-shaped, arranged in continuous series within a gelatinous sheath. Fig. 414.................*Albrightia*

The branched filaments of this plant resemble strings of sausages enclosed in a relatively firm, colorless sheath. There are no heterocysts and reproduction occurs only by cell division as far as is known, this occurring in the apical region of the trichome. *Albrightia* is known only from the hot springs of Yellowstone National Park.

Fig. 414. *Albrightia tortuosa* Copeland. (Redrawn from Copeland).

574a (570) Trichomes without a sheath...575

574b Trichomes with a sheath...577

575a Trichome short, 3 to 10 (20) cells long. Fig. 415..............*Borzia*

This rare plant occurs as very short, hormogonialike trichomes of as many as 8 cells. The terminal cells are hemispherical. *Borzia* has been reported from several stations across the United States.

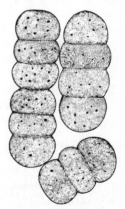

Fig. 415. *Borzia trilocularis* Cohn. (Redrawn from Daily.)

575b Trichomes longer, composed of many cells...........................576

576a Trichomes solitary or intermingled, not lying in parallel bundles, sometimes tapered slightly toward the anterior end, or with the apical cell swollen (capitate). Fig. 416..................
....*Oscillatoria*

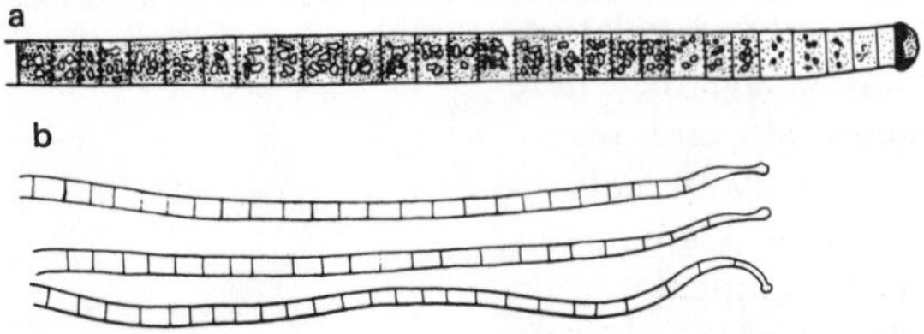

Fig. 416.　(a) *Oscillatoria rubescens* DeCand.;　(b) *O. splendida* Grev.

The chief characteristic of this genus is their active oscillating movement (at least under proper conditions) and another is their lack of a definite sheath (as in *Lyngbya*, Fig. 406). One interpretation of the taxonomy of the genus disregards the sheath characteristic and unites *Lyngbya* and *Oscillatoria*. A mass of *Oscillatoria* left in a shallow dish in the laboratory will creep up the sides or spread itself over the bottom. There are numerous species differentiated on the basis of size, cell proportions and the morphology of the apical region. Some species taper slightly toward the anterior end (there being a basal-distal differentiation), and the apical cell may be swollen or capitate (sometimes with a calyptra). *Oscillatoria* occurs both in water and on moist subaerial substrates such as soil or dripping rocks. A few species, such as *O. rubescens* are planktonic and at certain times of the year this species may cause the water to become blood-red. This color is related to the fact that the cells have pseudovacuoles that refract the light rather than to pigment coloration.

576b Trichomes not tapered at the ends, lying in parallel bundles; apical cell never capitate; planktonic. Fig. 417...........................
....*Trichodesmium*

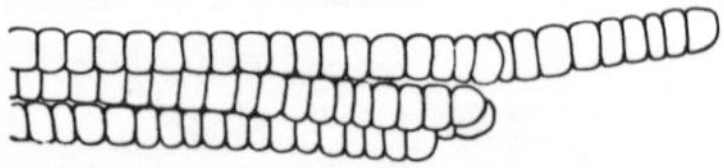

This is a genus of uncertain position because it has an *Anahaena*like filament but is without heterocysts. The trichomes are arranged parallel in bundles that occur as free-floating, dark green flakes. *Trichodesmium erythraceum* Ehr.,

Fig. 417.　*Trichodesmium lacustre* Klebahn.

a marine species, because of the refractibility of its pseudovacuoles, gives the characteristic color to the Red Sea.

The purple color of the lamellated sheath in this genus (especially *Porphyrosiphon No-tarisii* (Menegh.) Kuetz. accounts for the brightly colored patches on damp soil in subtropical United States. Denuded soil in the South fre-

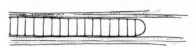

Fig. 418. *Porphyrosiphon Notarisii* (Menegh.) Kuetz.

quently shows extensive purple-red mats when colonized by this species. Occasionally the plants become involved with fungal threads to approximate a lichen.

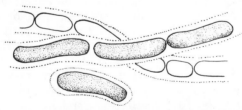

Fig. 419. *Romeria elegans* var. *nivicola* Kol, from Olympic Mountain snowfields.

This genus consists of sausage-shaped cells arranged in short trichomes, usually within a thin sheath. There are neither heterocysts nor akinetes formed as far as is known. In the United States the plant has been found only in snow fields.

582a **Plant mass having erect tufts. Fig. 420**.........................*Symploca*

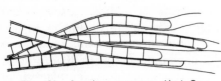

Filaments of the species illustrated occur in erect tufts in moist subaerial situations. Species which have thin, sticky sheaths should be compared with *Phormidium* (Fig. 421) with which they may be confused if

Fig. 420. *Symploca muscorum* (Ag.) Gom.

seen individually and not in colonial mass. At least 15 species have been reported from the United States.

582b **Plant mass without erect tufts. Fig. 421**................*Phormidium*

583a **(581) Filaments lying parallel in free-floating bundles. Fig. 417**
....*Trichodesmium*

583b **Filaments not in parallel bundles**..584

584a **Filaments composed of rectangular or cylindrical cells in continuous series within a close sheath, irregularly intermingled with one another. Fig. 421**........................*Phormidium*

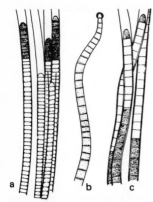

Fig. 421. (a) *Phormidium ambiguum* Gom.; (b) *P. favosum* (Bory) Gom.; (c) *P. inundatum* Kuetz.

The sheaths of filaments in this genus are very thin and sticky and the plants often adhere together forming a compact mat, or a skein over submersed surfaces or dripping rocks. The plant masses are blue or black-green and feel slimy or slippery to the touch. There are numerous species differentiated by size, sheath characteristics, and by the morphology of the apical cell. Plants should be compared with *Lyngbya* (Fig. 406). Some of the many species which occur in the United States are found in hot springs.

584b **Filaments composed of a wide gelatinous sheath (or tube) in which transversely oval cells are arranged in disjunct fashion. Fig. 413**...*Heterohormogonium*

Fig. 421A. *Phormidium* sp., isolated filament.

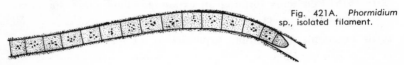

585a (577) Sheaths soft and sticky, without an even or smooth outer boundary...**586**

585b Sheaths firm and definite. Not softly mucilaginous...........**587**

586a Sheath containing 2 or 3 trichomes. Fig. 422........*Hydrocoleum*

In this genus there are only 3 (sometimes 4) trichomes within a wide, lamellate, gelatinous sheath. The filaments may be solitary or spread in a thin layer on damp soil. *Hydrocoleum oligotrichum* A. Braun is lime-encrusted where-

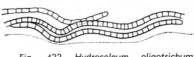

Fig. 422. *Hydrocoleum oligotrichum* A. Braun.

as *H. homeotrichum* Kuetz. is not. About 15 species have been reported from the United States, differentiated on the basis of size and characteristics of the sheath; habit of growth.

586b Sheaths containing many trichomes. Fig. 423.........*Microcoleus*

Unlike *Hydrocoleum* (Fig. 422) there are many intertwined trichomes within a rather definite sheath. Usually the trichomes show an active slithering motion over one another, may emerge from the sheath and then retract. The thallus is often of macroscopic size as it grows on damp soil. Some species, however, are more often found on sub-

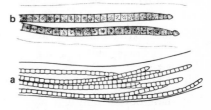

Fig. 423. (a) *Microcoleus vaginatus* (vauch.) Gom.; (b) *M. lacustris* (Rab.) Farlow.

mersed objects. Species are differentiated by size and by the morphology of the apical region of the trichome. There are 14 species reported from the United States.

587a (585) Sheaths wide, containing 2 or 3 loosely arranged trichomes (often relatively short). Fig. 424....................*Dasygloea*

The sheaths of this plant are rather firm and definite in outline; contain but 1 to 3 trichomes. See *Dasygloea amorpha* Berk. The sheaths are usually forked at the ends (as they are also in *Schizothrix*, Fig. 425), with which *Dasygloea* should be compared.

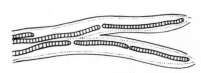

Fig. 424. *Dasygloea amorpha* Berk.

Only 1 species has been reported from the United States but is widely distributed.

587b Sheaths close, usually containing several, crowded trichomes. Fig. 425..*Schizothrix*

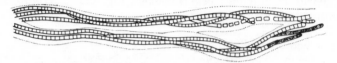

Fig. 425. *Schizothrix tinctoria* Gom.

In this genus there are but few trichomes within a definite and rather firm sheath. The plant masses are of macroscopic size and often form extended films and wefts over submersed vegetation. Several of the species quickly disintegrate when stored in a covered container for a short time without a preservative. Under this situation the plants liberate a copious amount of the pigment phycocyanin. In an aqueous solution the pigment shows a distinct fluorescence. There are at least a dozen species reported from the United States, differentiated by size, by cell proportions and by the characteristics of the sheath which often is forked.

588a (565) Trichomes definitely tapering at one or both ends......589

588b Trichomes not tapering, or rarely tapering slightly near the apex...595

589a Trichomes tapering at both ends, short, 20 cells or less long; heterocysts wanting; akinetes present. Fig. 426....................... ....*Raphidiopsis*

Fig. 426. *Raphidiopsis curvata* Fritsch et Rich.

The short trichomes taper at one or both ends. The plants are solitary, curved and twisted, or sigmoid and sickle-shaped. There are no heterocysts but akinetes occur. Thus far 1 species has been reported from a few localities in the United States (Ohio and Florida), although another species (possibly *R. mediterranea* Skuja) has been found in Minnesota.

589b Trichomes tapering from base to apex, basal-distal differentiation; with a heterocyst and often with an akinete at the base...590

590a Filaments enclosed within abundant mucilage; forming a globular or hemispherical body; attached or free-floating...... 591

Trichomes in this genus are tapering from a basal heterocyst as in *Gloeotrichia* (Fig. 428), but there is more than 1 trichome within a sheath and the gelatinous colony is very irregular in shape as it occurs on stones (sometimes in very deep water). The sheaths are wide, lamellate, and are flaring at the outer end. The spe-

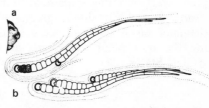

Fig. 427. *Sacconema rupestre* Borzi. (a) habit of colony; (b) filaments from colony.

cies illustrated seems to be the only one reported from the United States, and possibly the only one known for the genus.

In this genus the tapering trichomes are encased in mucilage which is usually relatively soft in the planktonic species, but firm and relatively hard in the attached forms. The trichomes are radiately arranged in the mucilage, but are not so closely compacted as in *Rivularia* (Fig. 429). *Gloeotrichia* has filaments with large, cylindrical akinetes adjoined to the basal heterocyst. When immature, species may be mistaken for *Rivularia* which never produces akinetes. Doubtless many of the records of *Rivularia* are *Gloeotrichia* in which the akinetes have not yet developed. One of the more common species is *G. echinulata* (J. E. Smith) P. Richter which occurs in abundance in the plankton of hard-water lakes. The colonies are globular and appear as 'tapioca' grains, making the

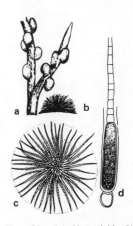

Fig. 428. (a) *Gloeotrichia Pisum* (Ag.) Thur., habit on *Ceratophyllum;* (b) diagram of filament arrangement; (c) *G. echinulata* (J. E. Smith) Richter, diagram of filaments in colony; (d) diagram of base of a single filament showing heterocyst and spore.

water buff-colored. When abundant along bathing beaches this plant causes a severe skin irritation among some persons which has been mistaken for 'swimmer's itch.' *G. natans* (Hedw.) Rab. is also fairly common. It begins development as an attached thallus but later appears at the surface in brown, gelatinous and amorphous masses, either expanded and flat or somewhat globular. *G. Pisum* Lag. forms hard, green or black balls, 1 or 2 mm. in diameter on submersed vegetation, sometimes completely covering the host plant. Nine species have been reported from the United States.

592b Spores absent; trichomes embedded in hard mucilage to form globular thalli which may coalesce, thus producing a continuous, lumpy stratum; trichomes radiate, or more often densely compacted and nearly parallel. Fig. 429......................
....*Rivularia*

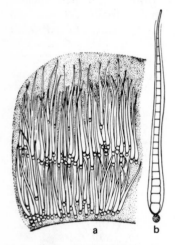

This genus may be differentiated from *Gloeotrichia* (Fig. 428) by its lack of akinetes at the base of the trichome, by the compact (almost parallel arrangement of the trichomes) and by the extreme firmness of the colonial mucilage. All species are attached, mostly to logs and stones in the water, sometimes forming extensive, pebbled patches. Some large colonies show a 'zonation' resulting from successive generations of false branches. Twenty-four species have been reported from the United States but many of the names seem to be confused with *Gloeotrichia*.

Fig. 429. *Rivularia* sp. (a) diagram of portion of attached colony to show arrangement of filaments; (b) one filament showing basal heterocysts.

593a (590) Filaments freely branched, the branches usually lying several within the sheath of the main filament for some distance, then diverging. Fig. 430..............................*Dichothrix*

In this genus the tapering trichomes are enclosed 2 or 3 together within the branching sheaths. Bushlike tufts are produced by their habit of growth and these sometimes attain macroscopic proportions. The species are differentiated by size, by sheath (often lamellate) characteristics and type of arrangement of the false branches. They are customarily found intermingled with

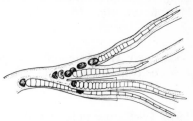

Fig. 430.   *Dichothrix gypsophila* (Kuetz.) Born. et Flah.

miscellaneous algae in the typchoplankton; are sometimes attached and form tufted mats over submersed plant stems. Eleven species have been reported from the United States, most of which are widely distributed.

593b Filaments not freely branched, if branched the branches not lying parallel within the sheath of the main filament............594

594a Branching at regular intervals, solitary or in pairs, the branches tapering, heterocysts mostly terminal, but also intercalary. Fig. 431...*Scytonematopsis*

This is the only member of the Rivulariaceae in which the tapering false branches arise at regular intervals (Some species of *Rivularia* are a possible exception.) Heterocysts are both basal and intercalary, and usually branches, solitary or in pairs, arise just below them. Plants are very similar to *Tolypothrix* (Fig. 446) or *Scytonema* (Fig. 445) except for the decided tapering of the trichomes. The only species reported from the United States has been found in the hot springs of Yellowstone National Park.

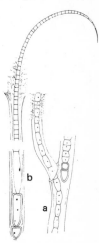

Fig. 431. *Scytone-matopsis* h y d noides Copeland. (a) habit of branching; (b) heterocyst and tapering filament. (Redrawn from Copeland).

594b Branching absent or scarce and irregular, the heterocysts basal. Fig. 410...*Calothrix*

595a (588) Trichome branches formed by the lateral division of cells in the main axis (true branching)...................................596

595b Trichomes unbranched or with false branches (sections of trichomes developing a series of cells to one side of a break in the main axial row of cells)...600

596a Individual trichome sheath not apparent; colony of trichomes invested by a mucilage; heterocysts usually on the ends of short branches. Fig. 432...*Nostochopsis*

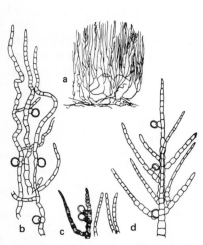

The branched trichomes in this genus are enclosed in a rather firm mucilage which gives an erect strandlike or tubelike form to the thallus. The trichomes are composed of *Anabaena*like cells and bear true branches. The heterocysts are borne laterally along the trichome or on the ends of short branches (rarely intercalary also). The trichomes are more or less parallel and erect in the gelatinous matrix. In flowing water the thalli may lie prostrate; whereas in quiet water the thalli may stand erect, reach the surface and then flatten out. Apparently only 1 species has been reported from the United States; is widely distributed.

Fig. 432. *Nostochopsis lobatus* Wood. (a) diagram of filament arrangement in colony; (b)-(d) filaments and lateral heterocysts.

596b Individual trichome sheath evident; heterocysts in the same series with the main axis, or cut off laterally from them but not on the ends of branches...597

597a Filaments closely aggregated, forming an attached, gelatinous thallus, 1-2 mm. in diameter. Fig. 433...........................Capsosira

In this genus there are small, bulbous, mucilaginous colonies attached to submersed substrates. The individual trichomes which bear true branches are surrounded by individual sheaths that are yellowish. Heterocysts are usually lateral, but may be intercalary in the trichomes which do not taper toward the apices. There is but 1 species reported from the United States, and from only 1 station, in Connecticut.

Fig. 433. *Capsosira Brebissonii* Kuetz. (a) habit of attached colony; (b) portion of filament showing lateral heterocysts. The sheath is thin and soft, without a definite limiting membrane.

597b Filaments not forming a definitely shaped, gelatinous thallus, but spreading irregularly...598

598a Filaments with more than 1 series of cells within a wide, gelatinous sheath; heterocysts small, cut off laterally from the vegetative cells and scarce. (Branches often have cells in 1 series.) Fig. 434..Stigonema

Although there are several species reported from the United States, *Stigonema turfaceum* (Berk.) Cook and *S. ocellatum* (Dillw.) Thur. are by far the most common. The latter is one which frequently does not show the multiseriate arrangement of cells. The sheath is wide and distinctly lamellate, the cells showing individual sheaths. The heterocysts typically are cut off laterally from vegetative cells; often are scarce and difficult of discernment. Usually they are olive-brown. The cells in some species are connected by narrow strands (similar to many of the genera in the Rhodophyta). *Stigonema* forms brownish, olive-green or blue-green growths on

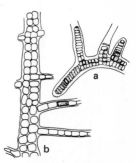

Fig. 434. (a) *Stigonema muscicola* Borzi (*Fischerella muscicola* (Thur.) Gom.; (b) *S. turfaceum* (Berk.) Cook.

submersed reed stems, on exposed roots and other aquatic vegetation. On moist soil or wet rocks and cement some species form velvety expanses. *Stigonema ocellatum* invariably is found in acid water and desmid habitats.

598b Filaments with 1 series of cells; heterocysts within the series of vegetative cells (intercalary), not lateral.............599

599a Branches extending parallel with the main axial trichome. Fig. 435...*Thalpophila*

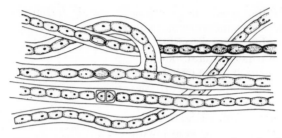

Fig. 435. *Thalpophila imperialis* Copeland. (Redrawn from Copeland.)

As shown in the illustration, *Thalpophila* trichomes have true branching as in *Hapalosiphon* (Fig. 436), but the branches are predominantly unilateral and lie parallel with the main axis. The branching habit produces a cordlike thallus with each trichome within its own sheath. *Thalpophila* has been found only in the geyser waters of Yellowstone National Park.

599b Branches arising and extending at right angles to the main filament. Fig. 436..*Hapalosiphon*

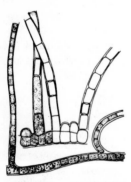

Fig. 436. *Hapalosiphon hibernicus* W. et W.

This genus is differentiated readily from *Stigonema* (Fig. 434) by the cells being arranged in a single series, by the intercalary heterocysts, and by the close, relatively firm and sometimes lamellate sheath. The habit of branching separates it from *Thalpophila* (Fig. 435). Whereas *Stigonema* cells are round or oval and often interconnected, *Hapalosiphon* cells are mostly rectangular, barrel-shaped or short-cylindric. The trichomes often have constrictions at the cross walls. The plants mostly sprawl over a substrate, branching and rebranching. The younger branches, especially when growth is vigorous, possess cell characteristics different from those of the main axis and hence in some instances students have been led to identify the outer portions of the thallus as different species. *Hapalosiphon* occurs more frequently in acid (soft) water than in hard; at least 1 common species is terrestrial. Twenty species have been reported from the United States, some of which are widely distributed; others decidedly localized.

601a Individual trichome sheath firm and definite, heterocysts basal (rarely intercalary also). Fig. 437.................*Microchaete*

Plants of this genus are mostly epiphytic (or loosely adjoined to filamentous algae), with part of the filament lying parallel with the substrate, then curving away. The trichomes do not taper (or scarcely so) and although there may be intercalary heterocysts they usually are basal, 1 to 3 in a series. Nine species are reported from the United States, differentiated on size and habit of growth.

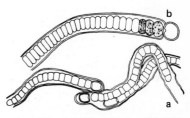

Fig. 437. (a) *Microchaete diplosiphon* Gom.; (b) *M. robusta* Setch. et Gard.

601b Individual sheath soft, often indistinct and confluent with colonial mucilage; heterocysts either all terminal or all intercalary..**602**

603a Spores adjacent to the heterocysts which are at one end of the trichome (rarely at both ends). Fig. 438......*Cylindrospermum*

The chief characteristic of this genus is the location of the heterocysts and akinetes — always terminal and usually only 1 at the end of the trichome which does not taper. Occasionally a heterocyst may occur at both ends of a trichome. The trichomes lie in somewhat parallel fashion within a soft mucilage, forming patches or films over submersed

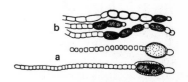

Fig. 438. (a) *Cylindrospermum majus* Kuetz.; (b) *C. marchicum* Lemm.

vegetation; usually are bright blue-green. The akinetes occur singly or in a series of 3 immediately behind the terminal heterocyst. Frequently a dense 'nest' of spores will be found where there has been a colony of *Cylindrospermum*. Of the 21 species reported from the United States a few are terrestrial.

603b Spores not adjacent to the heterocysts; heterocysts regularly at both ends of the trichome. Fig. 439................*Anabaenopsis*

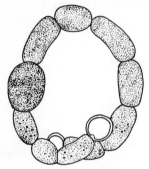

The trichomes of this genus are usually relatively short (8 to 20 cells), and usually coiled. Heterocysts are terminal and the akinetes are formed remote from them. Five species have been reported from the plankton in the United States.

Fig. 439. *Anabaenopsis Elenkinii* Miller. (Redrawn from G. M. Smith.)

604a(602) Thallus composed of many trichomes, usually parallel within the colonial mucilage....................................605

604b Plant a solitary trichome, or if aggregated, not parallel but entangled within the colonial mucilage..............................607

605a Trichomes enclosed in abundant mucilage, arranged to form a hollow, attached, tubular thallus. Fig. 440....................*Wollea*

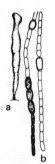

The trichomes of this species lie more or less parallel in long, gelatinous, tubelike strands which grow vertically from the bottom of standing water. The cells are barrel-shaped or *Anabaena*like, and the intercalary heterocysts are oval or cylindrical or nearly so. The species illustrated is the only one known.

Fig. 440. *Wollea saccata* (Wolle) Born. et Flah. (a) habit of colony; (b) trichomes in detail showing heterocysts and akinetes in a series.

605b Thallus not a gelatinous, saclike tube....................................606

606a Trichomes parallel, forming a free-floating flakelike bundle, each trichome containing near the middle a single heterocyst and an akinete (not adjacent), the akinete appearing at maturity; trichome sometimes tapering slightly at the extremeties. Fig. 441.. .....*Aphanizomenon*

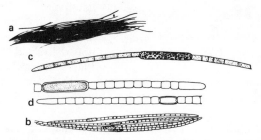

Fig. 441. *Aphanizomenon flos-aquae* (L.) Ralfs. (a) diagram of colony; (b) a few trichomes from the colony; (c), (d) trichomes in detail showing medial akinete.

Species of this genus lie parallel in bundles of macroscopic proportions and usually occur so profusely that the water seems to be filled with bits of chopped grass. The cells are short cylindric or barrel-shaped and are the same diameter throughout except that there may be a slight tapering at the apices of the trichome. Each trichome contains 1 heterocyst and 1 akinete produced near the midregion of the filament but not adjoined. The cells contain pseudovacuoles which give the plants great buoyancy and this accounts for the fact that profuse growths become concentrated at the surface where floating scums result. This leads to deterioration of the plants and a release of pigments (and possibly endotoxins). This condition leads to increased bacterial action and either directly or indirectly *Aphanizomenon* becomes a spoiler of water for both domestic and recreational purposes. Three species have been reported from the United States. The one illustrated is the most common but is known to occur in a number of 'strains' as evidenced by laboratory culture.

606b Trichomes not parallel, or if so, forming indefinitely shaped flakes or clumps; mostly not macroscopic. Fig. 404...............
....*Anabaena*

607a (604) Trichomes planktonic, solitary.....................................608

607b Trichomes colonial, in a gelatinous mass.............................609

608a Vegetative cells and heterocysts compressed, wider than long; disc-shaped. Fig. 442..*Nodularia*

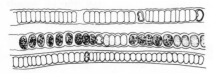

Fig. 442.   *Nodularia spumigena* Mert.

Filaments of this species are at once recognizable by the very short, compressed (almost disclike) cells and heterocysts. The sheath is rather thin and close; is mucilaginous and sometimes not discerned immediately. Plants are either eu- or tychoplanktonic. The species illustrated is the most common of 6 that have been reported from the United States.

608b Cells globose to cylindric or barrel-shaped, not compressed as above. Fig. 405..*Anabaena*

609a (607) Plant mass definite in shape, usually globular, bounded by a firm, gelatinous tegument (sometimes forming an expanded, gelatinous or rubbery sheet); colonies microscopic or macroscopic. Fig. 443..*Nostoc*

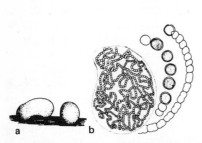

Fig. 443. (a) *Nostoc pruniforme* Ag., showing habit of colonies; (b) *N. linckia* (Roth) Born. et Flah., with 2 trichomes in detail showing heterocysts and akinetes.

This genus is characterized by the firm outer tegument of the mucilage which encloses numerous coiled threads of beadlike cells. The colonies retain a definite shape, mostly globular although a few species form rubbery or leathery expansions, especially *Nostoc commune* Vauch. which is widely distributed but is especially abundant in alpine meadows and on the tundra of the Arctic. The colonies vary in size from microscopic to thalli 10 cm. in diameter, (*N. amplissimum* Gard.) known as Mare's Eggs. *N. caeruleum* Lyngb. is planktonic; occurs as minute blue balls sometimes very abundant especially in soft-water lakes. *N. parmeloides* Kuetz. forms small, olive-green, shelving thalli on the down stream side of rocks, especially in mountain brooks. The thalli, up to 1.5 cm. across, invariably contain the egg or larva of a midge fly.

609b Plant mass not definite in shape; mucilage soft, not bounded by a firm tegument..**610**

610a Trichomes forming small bundles (often occurring solitary), within a gelatinous sheath, either entangled or parallel. Fig. 444...*Aulosira*

This genus is much like *Microchaete* (Fig. 437) and is sometimes classified with it. Some authorities differentiate it on the basis of the soft sheath, the intercalary heterocysts and the akinetes which also are intercalary and about the same diam-

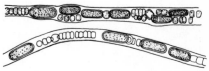

Fig. 444. *Aulosira laxa* Kirch.

eter as the heterocysts. Two species have been reported from the United States.

610b Trichomes not forming bundles. Fig. 405....................*Anabaena*

611a (600) Branches arising in pairs about miday betweeen 2 heterocysts (branching also rarely solitary). Fig. 445.......*Scytonema*

This genus exhibits false branching, the branches arising either singly or in pairs where there has been a break in the trichome of the main axis. Sheaths are either close and thin, or wide and lamellate; often are yellow or brown. Heterocysts are intercalary. Plants occur intermingled with other algae in the tychoplankton, or form clots attached to the stems of aquatic plants. Some species are terrestrial. *Scytonema* should be compared with *Tolypothrix* (Fig. 446) in which branches arise

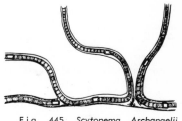

Fig. 445. *Scytonema Archangelii* Born. et Flah.

only at a heterocyst or near a series of them. Twenty-five or more species have been reported from the United States, most of them widely distributed.

611b Branches arising singly just below a heterocyst or a series of them. (branching sometimes rare and not regular, requiring a search through a number of plants to determine this character)..**612**

612a Sheath close and firm; 1 trichome in a sheath....................**613**

612b Sheath usually wide and soft; at least more than 1 trichome within a sheath..**614**

613a Branches frequent, arising just below the heterocyst which is always intercalary. Fig. 446..................................*Tolypothrix*

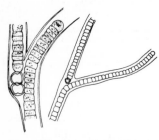

Fig. 446. *Tolypothrix distorta* Kuetz.

This genus is differentiated from *Scytonema* (Fig. 445) principally by the fact that the false branch always arises below a heterocyst. The plants form tangled, brownish clumps, either adherent to stems of aquatic plants, or sometimes forming brown, cottony tufts planktonic and very abundant in hard-water lakes. At least 20 species have been reported from the United States.

613b Branches rare; heterocysts terminal (rarely intercalary also). Fig. 431..*Microchaete*

614a (612) Trichomes parallel within a fairly wide sheath; plant mass developing bushy tufts; heterocysts basal in the trichome. Fig. 447..*Desmonema*

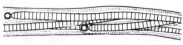

Fig. 447. *Desmonema Wrangelii* (Ag.) Born. et Flah.

The falsely branched filaments of this genus differ from others in the Scytonemataceae by having several trichomes within a single sheath. The filaments are gregarious and form masses of macroscopic size on moist subaerial substrates. They usually show erect tufts. The species illustrated is the only one reported from the United States.

614b Trichomes twisted and entangled in a wide sheath; heterocysts intercalary. Fig. 448..*Diplocolon*

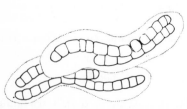

Fig. 448. *Diplocolon Heppii* Naeg. (Redrawn from G. M. Smith.)

This plant forms an expanse on moist subaerial substrates such as dripping rocks and banks. The trichomes are falsely branched, have intercalary heterocysts and are enclosed several together in a wide, gelatinous sheath; often form rather short hormogonia. Only 1 species is known for the United States.

615a (560) Plants attached; cells club-shaped or grobular-angular mostly isodiametric); gregarious, forming cushionlike masses or horizontal expanses, or solitary (especially when cylindric and club-shaped); epiphytic or growing on shells; cells usually showing endospores (segments of the protoplast rounded up and forming reproductive bodies which are sporelike)......
....616

615b Plant not attached (or only incidentally adherent); cells mostly spherical, hemispherical or rod-shaped, not forming cushionlike masses or horizontal expanses; cells often incidentally attached to plants or to substrates; endospores lacking..........
....625

616a Cells erect, club-shaped or subcylindric, straight or slightly curved...617

616b Cells some other shape; gregarious, forming horizontal expanses which may show a slight tendency to elongate in branches, or as cushions..618

617a Protoplast dividing by cleavage planes in the apex to form endospores which are cut off successively. Fig. 449...............
....*Chamaesiphon*

These club-shaped or cylindrical plants grow as epiphytes on filamentous algae and whereas they may be solitary they usually occur in gregarious patches. When mature the ends of the protoplasts become cut off, the segments forming endospores which drift away as regenerative elements. A patch of the plants will show many different stages of development from these spores.

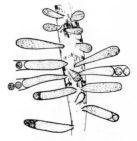

Fig. 449. *Chamaesiphon incrustans* Grun.

617b Protoplast divided throughout its length to form endospores simultaneously. Fig. 450...*Stichosiphon*

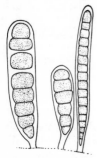

Plants in this genus are similar to those of *Chamaesiphon* (Fig. 449) but differs in that the entire protoplast becomes segmented by simultaneous cleavage to form endospores. The club-shaped plants are epiphytic on filamentous algae, especially members of the Cladophoraceae.

Fig. 450. *Stichosiphon regularis* Geitler, showing simultaneous cleavage of entire protoplast to form endospores.

618a (616) Plant mass composed of cells in 1 layer. (See *Chlorogloea*, Fig. 454, however)...**619**

618b Plant mass in the form of a cushion with the cells arranged in vertical rows or as false filaments.......................................**622**

619a Colony not attached; cells closely arranged in packets. Fig. 451...*Myxosarcina*

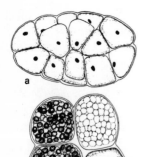

In this genus the plants are essentially unicellular but, by cell division, packets of angular cells are formed which are enclosed in a common mucilage. Some of the cells are usually seen filled with endospores. The plants are free-floating. The only species reported from the United States occurs in the hot springs of Yellowstone National Park.

Fig. 451. *Myxosarcina amethystina* Copeland. (a) colony; (b) cells with endospores. (Redrawn from Copeland.)

619b Cells not arranged as above; colony sessile......................**620**

620a Plant mass composed of a few closely arranged, pyriform cells; endospores formed by a cleavage in 3 planes. Fig. 452 ....*Dermocarpa*

Dermocarpa occurs as a solitary cell but often individuals are closely aggregated, forming compact clumps on aquatic plants or other submersed substrates. The cell frequently shows the contents divided into numerous spherical endospores. The plants are epiphytic on filamentous algae. Several species are reported from the United States, differentiated by cell size and shape.

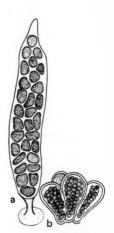

Fig. 452. (a) *Dermocarpa rostrata* Copeland. (Redrawn from Copeland); (b) *D. prasina* (Reinsch) Born. et Thur. (Redrawn from Reinsch.)

620b Plant mass a definite colony of many cells......................**621**

621a Cells globular or slightly angular from mutual compression, forming prostrate, pseudofilamentous growths on substrates. Fig. 453..*Xenococcus*

This genus is largely marine but there are at least 4 fresh-water species in the United States. The plants occur as patches of blue-green cells, compactly arranged as epiphytes on filamentous algae. Cells form endospores although they may multiply rapidly by fission.

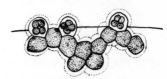

Fig. 453. *Xenococcus Schousbei* Thur.

621b Cells compactly arranged in globular masses forming tubercular growths epiphytic or endophytic, enclosed in a common sheath and involving a large number of small round or oval cells. Fig. 454...*Chlorogloea*

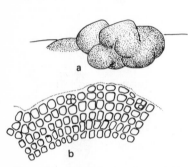

Fig. 454. *Chlorogloea microcystoides* Geitler. (a) colony; (b) optical section to show cell arrangement.

Like *Xenococcus* (Fig. 453) this genus is both marine and fresh-water. The cells are globular or oval and are loosely arranged within a wide, gelatinous sheath. The thallus may have short upright extensions in some species. The plant appears much like an attached colony of *Chroococcus* (Fig. 464) but the cells produce endospores in reproduction. Only 1 species has been reported from the United States and seems to be very rare.

622a (618) Cells surrounded by a sheath; plant mass thick, cartilaginous, usually macroscopic. Fig. 455...............*Chondrocystis*

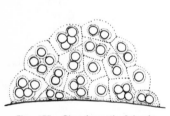

Fig. 455. *Chondrocystis Schauinslandii* Lemm.

The species illustrated here forms extensive, cushionlike masses on exposed subaerial surfaces and often are heavily encrusted with lime. The colonial mass is enclosed by a tough mucilage in which families of cells are surrounded by individual sheaths. This is the only species of the genus reported from the United States, occurring in the western section.

622b Cells not enclosed by a thick sheath; plant mass usually macroscopic (in well-developed thalli)...................................623

623a Plant mass forming a flat layer or cushion...........................624

623b Plant mass cushionlike; cells forming erect series which are similar to branched filaments. Fig. 456.......................................
....*Entophysalis (Oncobyrsa)*

The species illustrated is the most common in the genus. It has compactly arranged series of cells in which the filamentous plan can be determined more certainly than in *Pleurocapsa* (Fig. 458). The thallus is a mound of cells, encased in a tough mucilage on filamentous algae. Although the general habit is is that of members of the Chamaesiphonaceae, there have no endospores observed. The name is synonymous with *Oncobyrsa*. Two species are reported from the United States.

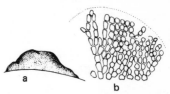

Fig. 456. *Entophysalis* (Oncobyrsa) sp. (a) habit of colony; (b) diagram of cell arrangement.

624a Thallus a pseudofilamentous growth in the shells of mollusca. Fig. 457..*Hyella*

This plant presents itself as a prostrate cushion of indefinite and entangled short filaments, growing within the shells of molluscs. There are both relatively long, horizontally growing filaments and short, upright ones. Almost any cell in the thallus may develop endospores. About half of the known species are marine but 2 freshwater forms have been reported from the United States.

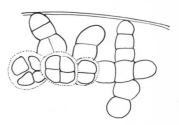

Fig. 457. *Hyella fontana* Huber et Jadin, some cells with endospores.

624b Thallus an encrusting growth with rhizoidal extensions on the ventral side, the upper or outer portion consisting of uniseriate or multiseriate branches, all very compact with sheaths fused together. Fig. 458.............................*Pleurocapsa*

In this genus the attached plant mass is essentially filamentous but the cells are so closely appressed that the filamentous, branching habit cannot be determined readily without dissecting the colony. Encrusting thalli often show some differentiation between the lower or inner cells and those near the surface which produce the endospores. Nine species have been reported from the United States.

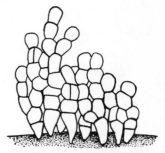

Fig. 458. *Pleurocapsa minor* Hansg.

This is a rather simple although plant which probably is of more common occurrence than is evidenced by records of it from the United States. The cells are globular or oval, solitary or in pairs, without a mucilaginous sheath being apparent. The densely granular central body of the cells seems to be more complex than for other genera of the Chroococcaceae. *Synechocystis* is found in the tychoplankton. Five species are reported from the United States, 1 reported from hot springs.

Fig. 459. *Synechocystis aquatilis* Sauv.

631a Cells arranged to form a flat plate; cell division in 2 directions in 1 plane. Fig. 460...*Merismopedia*

This genus is readily distinguished by the definite, rectilinear arrangement of spherical
or oval cells in rectangular plates.
Colonies increase in size by fission of cells in 2 directions. *Meris-*
mopedia convoluta Bréb. is an uncommon species in which the
colonies become very large (visible to the unaided eye) sheets
with enrolled margins. There are
several species in the United
States, differentiated by cell size,
presence or absence of pseudovacuoles, and by size of the
colony.

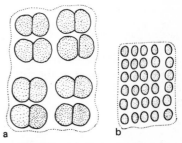

Fig. 460. (a) *Merismopedia elegans*
var. *major* G. M. Smith; (b) *M. glauca*
(Ehr.) Naeg.

631b Cells arranged to form cubical colonies of many individuals;
   cell division in 2 planes; cubes of cells enclosed by sheaths.
   Fig. 461...*Eucapsis*

This colonial blue-green alga is
regarded by some as being a *Chro-*
ococcus. But the cubical, sarcinalike arrangement of the cells with
separate sheaths around groups of
8 or 16 cells distinguishes *Eucapsis*.
Cell division occurs regularly in 3
planes. Only 1 species and its varieties is known for the United States
although 2 or 3 are reported from
Europe.

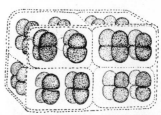

Fig. 461. *Eucapsis alpina* Clem-
ents et Shantz.

632a (630) **Cells heart-shaped or round, occurring at the ends of short, radiating, gelatinous strands of mucilage (focus down into the colony and reduce illumination to detect presence of radiating strands). Fig. 462.......***Gomphosphaeria*

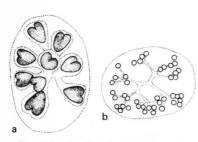

These plants are characterized by having cells in globular or oval colonies (that are free-floating), closely or distantly arranged at the ends of mucilaginous strands that radiate from the center of the thallus. *Gomphosphaeria lacustris* Chod. is frequently found in the euplankton, whereas *G. aponina* Kuetz. occurs mostly in the tychoplankton. In the latter species the cells often appear heart-shaped because fission is initiated at the outer wall and the cells are lobed at the apex.

Fig. 462. (a) *Gomphosphaeria aponina* Kuetz.; (b) *G. lacustris* Chod.

632b **Cells not at the ends of radiating strands**............................633

633a **Groups of many cells enclosed in concentric layers of mucilage; colonial investment intermingling (confluent) with the sheaths of other groups and so forming gelatinous masses, mostly on moist, subaerial substrates; sheaths showing definite, concentric rings, often colored brown or red. Fig. 463..............**
....*Gloeocapsa*

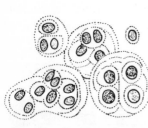

This is a genus in which globular cells are enclosed, many 'families' together, within gelatinous masses of considerable size. Cells, pairs of cells, or clusters are surrounded by lamellate sheaths. Many species, especially when few cells are involved, can scarcely be differentiated from *Chroococcus* (Fig. 464) and there is a disposition among some specialists to place the 2 genera together. Plants are either aquatic, or more commonly on moist subaerial substrates. Some species have highly pigmented sheaths and appear as red or orange-colored masses on damp soil and rocks. Forty-four species are indefinitely reported from the United States.

Fig. 463. *Gloeocapsa punctata* Naeg.

633b Colonial mucilage not intermingling with that of other colonies; families of few (2 to 8) cells separated from one another,
usually free-floating but commonly inhabiting soil and moist
substrates of all kinds; sometimes adherent to aquatic plants;
colonial sheath usually not showing concentric layers. Fig. 464
....*Chroococcus*

There are numerous species
in the genus, many of them
inadequately described and differentiated. The genus is
separated from *Gloeocapsa*
(Fig. 463) mostly on the basis
of the fewness of cells in a
colony and by the fact that
'families' of cells are not enclosed in a much lamellated
sheath. The colonies are composed of 2, 4 or 8 cells. A few
species are adherent (or apparently epiphytic) but most are
either eu- or tychoplanktonic.
Some are commonly found on
moist subaerial substrates. *C.*

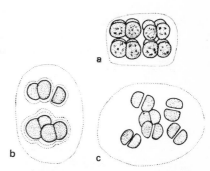

Fig. 464. (a) *Chroococcus Prescottii*
Drouet et Daily; (b) *C. limneticus* var.
distans G. M. Smith; (c) *C. limneticus*
Lemm.

turgidus (Kuetz.) Naeg. is a large species in which cells occur in
2's and 4's within a stratified sheath and one that is invariably
found in desmid habitats where the water is acid.

634a (628) Cells arranged to form a flat plate..............................635

634b Cells forming irregularly globular or oval colonies, some-
times clathrate...636

635a Cells arranged in rectilinear series. Fig. 460.....*Merismopedia*

635b Cells irregularly arranged. Fig. 465....................*Holopedium*

This genus differs from *Merismope-
dium* (Fig. 460) by having cells irregularly arranged in a flat or curled
plate. Five species have been reported
from the United States, differentiated
by cell size and nature of the colonial
mucilage.

Fig. 465. *Holopedium irregulare* Lag.

636a (634) Colony globular, rather definite in shape......................637

636b Colony irregular in outline..639

637a Cells very numerous and crowded within the colonial mucilage (in some species showing false vacuoles which refract
the light so that the cells appear brownish, black or purplish).
Fig. 466...*Microcystis*

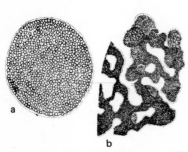

Fig. 466. *Microcystis flos-aquae* (Wittr.) Kirch.; (b) *M. aeruginosa* Kuetz.
emend. Elenkin.

The marblelike cells of this
genus are closely compacted
and irregularly arranged in definitely shaped but mostly irregular colonies, enclosed in
mucilage. *Microcystis flos-
aquae* (Wittr.), Kuetz. however, occurs in nearly globular
colonies, whereas in *M. aeruginosa* Kuetz. the colonies are
highly irregular and clathrate
when mature. Some species
contain pseudovacuoles (gas
pockets) and float high in the
water. Hence they produce surface scums and like *Aphanizomenon* (Fig. 441) cause a great deal of disturbance in lakes and
reservoirs. Dense growths may lead directly or indirectly to
the death of fish through suffocation or by poisoning, and the toxin
produced by some species causes the death of cattle and birds.
It is interesting that where some species occur (*M. aeruginosa*,
e.g.) the habitat is completely dominated by the plant to the ex-
clusion of almost all other forms of Cyanophyta. It has been
noted often that a lake may be densely overgrown with either
Microcystis or with *Alphanizomenon*, but usually not the two together. There are several species reported from the United States,
differentiated by cell size, presence or absence of pseudovacuoles,
and by nature of the sheath, colony, shape, *etc.*

637b Cells densely crowded but evenly spaced or regularly ar-
ranged..638

638a Cells in 1 layer at the periphery of the mucilage. Fig. 467
....*Coelosphaerium*

In this genus the cells are arranged (as the name suggests) in a hollow colony, the cells forming a peripheral layer immediately within the colonial sheath. Cells are either round, or oval and somewhat radiately arranged. Two species are commonly found in the euplankton of hard-water lakes. *Coelosphaerium Naegelianum* Unger is readily identified by the presence of pseudovacuoles which cause the colony to appear dark brown or purplish, or even blackish.

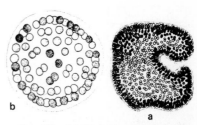

Fig. 467. (a) *Coelosphaerium Naegelianum* Unger; (b) *C. Kuetzingianum* Naeg.

638b Cells distributed throughout the colonial mucilage; cells evenly spaced, often in pairs. Fig. 468... ....*Aphanocapsa*

Whereas *Microcystis* (Fig. 466) has cells compactly arranged or crowded within a gelatinous sheath, in this genus the cells are evenly and rather regularly spaced, often occurring in pairs. The cells are spherical; do not have pseudovacuoles. Some are minute and intergrade with bacteria; are sometimes mistaken for them. *Aphanocapsa* is mostly euplanktonic, several species being reported from the United States. The genus is included under *Anacystis* by some authors.

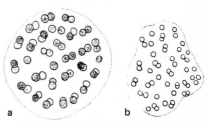

Fig. 468. (a) *Aphanocapsa Grevillei* (Hass.) Rab.; (b) *A. elachista* W. et W.

639a (636) Cells crowded, usually with refractive pseudovacuoles. Fig. 466..*Microcystis*

639b Cells evenly spaced within the mucilage; false vacuoles lacking. Fig. 468..*Aphanocapsa*

640a (625) Cells quadrangular, arranged in flat plates. Fig. 469 ....*Tetrapedia*

Fig. 469. Tetrapedia Reinschiana Archer, diagram showing arrangement of rectangular cells.

Tetrapedia Reinschiana Arch. is a rare and dubious plant that has quadrangular cells arranged in multiples of 4 to form a flat, rectangular plate. Other species may be solitary and either 3- or 4-angled, some with minute spines. Five of the 11 known species occur in the United States.

640b Cells some other shape..**641**

641a Cells solitary or in colonies of few cells................................**642**

641b Cells numerous within a globular, amorphous, gelatinous matrix..**648**

642a Without a gelatinous sheath. Fig. 470..............*Synechococcus*

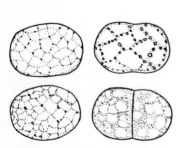

Fig. 470. *Synechococcus aeruginosus* Naeg.

This is a solitary oval unicell which does not possess a gelatinous sheath. Cells may be in pairs as a result of recent fission. They are relatively large for Cyanophyta of this type (may be up to 35μ in length) and are often conspicuous in the microscope mount because of their bright blue color. Five species and their varieties have been reported from the United States.

642b With a gelatinous sheath (sometimes discerned with difficulty), or enclosed by a gelatinous matrix................................**643**

643a Cells elongate, pointed at the ends; fusiform. Fig. 471..........
....*Dactylococcopsis*

These are fusiform-shaped cells, arranged with their long axes mostly parallel with that of the fusiform colonial sheath. Some species, however, do not exhibit a definite sheath. Mostly colonial, some forms occur as solitary cells, either straight, slightly bowed or spirally twisted. They should be compared with *Ankistrodesmus* (Fig. 122) in which some species have similarly shaped cells. At least 1 species has been described from snow fields; 8 have been reported from the United States.

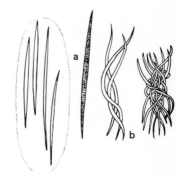

Fig. 471. (a) *Dactylococcopsis acicularis* Lemm.; (b) *D. fascicularis* Lemm.

643b Cells not pointed at the ends..644

644a Cells heart-shaped, (or oval); at the ends of radiating strands of mucilage; colonies globular. Fig. 462.........*Gomphosphaeria*

644b Cells not at the ends of radiating strands...........................645

645a Cells radiately disposed. Fig. 472............................*Marssoniella*

In this genus there are pyriform cells which are more or less definitely arranged in a radiate fashion about a common center, enclosed by mucilage that does not exhibit a definite sheath. The narrow end of the cells is directed outward. The genus is to be expected in the euplankton. Only 1 species is reported from the United States; widely distributed.

Fig. 472. *Marssoniella elegans* Lemm.

645b Cells not radiately disposed...646

646a Individual cell sheath distinct; cells elongate to rod-shaped, many in a common sheath. Fig. 473............................*Gloeothece*

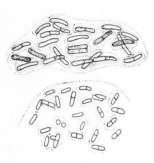

In this genus the cells are elongate cylinders, bacilliform, or may be merely elongate ovals. The cells are enclosed many together within a common mucilaginous sheath and each cell or pair of cells has its individual sheath. The cells are often crowded and irregularly arranged, much like a *Microcystis* with rod-shaped cells. Species should be compared with *Aphanothece* (Fig. 476), a genus with which some authors combine *Gloeothece*.

Fig. 473.   Gloeothece linearis Naeg.

646b Cells bacilliform, in a wide sheath.......................................647

647a Cells elongate-cylindric and curved; few (4 to 10) within a wide gelatinous sheath. Fig. 474........................*Rhabdoderma*

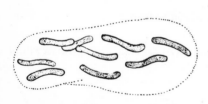

In this genus the cells are elongate and cylindrical, even vermiform and are much like *Gloeothece* (Fig. 473) except that there is no individual cell sheath. The plants occur in small colonies of 4 or 8 to 16 in the plankton of lakes; sometimes are in the tychoplankton and intermingled with miscellaneous algae. About 5 species

Fig. 474.   Rhabdoderma lineare Schm. et Lauterb.

have been reported from the United States, differentiated on size and cell proportions.

647b Cells elongate-cylindric, solitary or a few attached end to end in a wide, gelatinous sheath. Fig. 473..............*Gloeothece*

648a (641) Cells arranged at the periphery of a globular, gelatinous matrix (colony hollow). Fig. 467......................*Coelosphaerium*

648b Colony formed otherwise..649

649a Cells numerous within a tubular sheath which is pointed at the ends. Fig. 475..*Bacillosiphon*

The cells in this genus are elongate, bacilliform (similar to *Aphanothece*, Fig. 476), but arranged with their long axes parallel in gelatinous strands which may be lime-impregnated. The single species has been reported from hot springs in Yellowstone National Park.

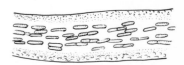

Fig. 475. *Bacillosiphon induratus* Copeland. (Redrawn from Copeland).

649b Colony otherwise...**650**

650a Cells irregularly scattered throughout a shapeless mass (or somewhat globular); colonial mucilage often firm, the colonies retaining their shape when removed from the water; individual cell sheaths lacking. Fig. 476..........................*Aphanothece*

Cells are elongate cylinders, bacilliform or elongate-oval, occurring in colonies which may be either microscopic or macroscopic. Some species form firm, olive-green gelatinous balls remindful of *Nostoc* colonies (Fig. 443) and are sometimes mistaken for them

Fig. 476. *Aphanothece Castagnei* (Bréb.) Rab.

when not examined microscopically. The cells (similar to *Gloeothece*, Fig. 473) do not have individual sheaths; occur in much larger colonies. The colonies often develop on lake bottoms, become loosened and float to the surface and then are washed ashore, sometimes forming a 'soupy' mass. Sixteen species are recognized from the United States but some of the reports are confused with *Gloeothece*.

650b Individual cell sheaths distinct. Fig. 473...................*Gloeothece*

651a (503) Frustule (diatom shell)* elongate, rod-shaped, boat-shaped, rectangular or wedge-shaped, 2 or more times longer than wide...**664**

651b Frustules isodiametric or nearly so; round, triangular, or oval, but less than twice the diameter in length.................**652**

_____

*See note on p. 13 for the preparation of diatom mounts.

652a Frustules rectangular in side (girdle)* view, joined in chains
by interlocking of long, slender, spinelike horns which arise
from the corners of the valves; frustules without a raphe;
horns hollow or solid. Fig. 477...............................*Chaetoceros*

---

*Diatoms exhibit two general expressions of form and according to a standard classification system there are two Orders. One is the elongate, 'cigar'-shaped, 'boat'-shaped or wedge-shaped cell with bilateral symmetry in the arrangement of wall markings, constituting the Pennales. The other includes round, 'pill-box'-shaped, or nearly isodiametric cells with radiate ornamentations, the Centrales.

The wall or shell of the diatom is called a frustule. It is not a plain, simple envelope but is composed of two sections, one slightly larger and overlapping the smaller much as a box lid. The larger or upper section is called the epitheca, the smaller, inner section the hypotheca. The 'lid' and the 'box' are adjoined by overlapping side pieces, the cingula (singular cingulum). The flattened or broad surface is called a valve and has marginal flanges to which the side pieces, the cingula fit. In some genera there may be supplementary or additional connecting bands, called intercalary bands. When the shell is seen from the top or bottom it is said to be in valve view; when seen from the side so that the line shows that is formed by the overlapping of the connecting bands the frustule is said to be in girdle view. The cell may be quite different in appearance in these two views.

The siliceous shells have decorations and markings in an almost endless variety: linear etchings, rows of puncta (dots), costae (ribs), vertical canals (pores). Externally there may be ridges or flanges on the valves; internally, partitions or septations (septa). In certain Pennales genera the valves (or at least one of the two) may contain a longitudinal groove or furrow, the raphe (seen in valve view) as a distinct line, usually straight and in the midregion, but it may be sigmoid or to one side of center. Sometimes the raphe lies within a marginal rib or keel. The raphe is not continuous throughout the full length of the valve but is interrupted at the mid point by an internal swelling on the wall called the central nodule. There may be nodules at either pole of the cell (polar nodules). The central nodule may be large and lobed and referred to as a stauros. A false or pseudoraphe results when the wall decorations form lines (striae) in from the margin but leave an arrow, linear, smooth central region. This 'line' or smooth field may appear on one or both valves. Care and patience must be used in diatom identification to determine the presence or absence of a raphe or pseudoraphe on one or both valves.

The Centrales which are circular in value view do not possess a raphe; may have spines or horns. The radiate markings may be evenly disposed or interrupted by smooth zones, or form patterns according to the size and shape of the smooth and marked areas.

Observations by electronmicroscopists in recent years have disclosed refinements in the decorations and markings of the frustule. Lines under the light microscope actually may be rows of minute puncta, *etc.* These disclosures have necessitated a change in terminology relating to wall markings. The terms employed in the accompanying key are based on observations made by the customarily used light microscope.

This genus is well-named because of the long, hornlike processes, one at either pole of the oval cells as seen in valve* view. In girdle view the cells are quadrate, with a horn at each angle. The horns of adjacent cells interlock so that filaments are formed. Most species are marine but some may occur in brackish water, such as Devils Lake, North Dakota.

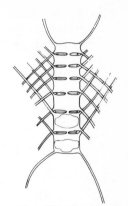

Fig. 477. *Chaetoceros Elmorei* B o y e r, girdle view showing only portions of the very long polar horns. (Redrawn from Boyer).

652b Frustules without spinelike horns..653

653a Frustules triangular in valve view; seldom seen lying in girdle view; raphe and pseudoraphe lacking. Fig. 478......................
....*Hydrosera*

These beautifully ornamented frustules are triangular in valve view, quadrate in girdle view and in cross section are somewhat orbicular. The genus is mostly marine but species may be found in estuaries and in coastal ponds. *Hydrosera* is regarded as synonymous with *Triceratium* by some diatomists.

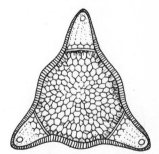

Fig. 478. *Hydrosera triquetra* Wall., valve view.

653b Frustules some other shape...654

654a Frustules circular in valve view..................................655

654b Frustules oval, broadly elliptic, slipper-shaped or rhomboid
....658

*See notes on p. 282.

655a Valve with a single, undecorated, mammillate protrusion or thickening just within the margin; (frustules sometimes broadly elliptic or rhomboid). Fig. 479............................*Actinocyclus*

Fig. 479. *Actinocyclus* sp., valve view showing portion of wall ornamentation.

The pill-box frustule (member of the Centrales) has a large pustulelike swelling just within the margin of the epivalve. The puncta or areolae are radiately arranged as in *Coscinodiscus* (Fig. 481) which are usually larger and more conspicuous in the center of the valve. Some species are broadly elliptic in valve view rather than circular. Most members of the genus are marine, but the one illustrated occurs in Lake Erie and presumably throughout the Great Lakes region.

655b Valve without intramarginal protrusions...............................656

656a Valve with an intramarginal zone of costae encircling the cell; smooth or finely punctate within the marginal circle of costae; (markings in the center of the valve various, but mostly smooth). Fig. 480..*Cyclotella*

Fig. 480. *Cyclotella Meneghiniana* Kuetz., valve view of a species in which the central region is smooth and the marginal zone coarsely punctate.

These circular cells (Centrales) are narrowly rectangular in girdle view and often lie parallel with one another to form chains or short filaments. In valve view there is a zone of radiate costae just within the valve margin and a central, smooth or punctate area. Species are planktonic, often occurring with *Stephanodiscus* (Fig. 482).

656b Valve marked by rows of puncta radiating from a central area to the margin; frustules drum-shaped or rectangular in girdle view...657

657a Valves evenly ornamented by rows of puncta forking as they extend to the margin, from a central region where they are irregularly disposed, with an intramarginal circle of fine teeth; plants euplanktonic, sometimes tychoplanktonic. Fig. 481..*Coscinodiscus*

These are pill-box-shaped frustules, (Centrales), circular in valve view, narrowly rectangular in girdle view. Radiating from the center where there is an area of irregularly arranged puncta are decussating rows of areolae or puncta. Just within the margin in many species is a circle of short, sharp spines. The radiating puncta do not quite converge in the midregion. Compare with *Stephanodiscus,* Fig. 482. There are about 450 species in the plankton of both marine and fresh waters. This genus and *Stephanodiscus* are common within blue-green algal

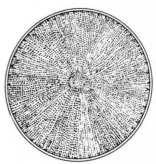

Fig. 481. *Coscinodiscus lacustris* Grun., valve view showing radial striae of coarse puncta and minute marginal spines.

blooms and seem to be more prevalent in hard water lakes than in acid waters.

657b Valves unevenly ornamented with radiating rows of puncta, converging at the center but interrupted by smooth, radiating zones between the rows of puncta; intramarginal circle of coarse spines which extend beyond the edge of the valve. Fig. 482...*Stephanodiscus*

These are relatively large, drum-shaped cells (Centrales), usually showing a circle of prominent spines just within but extending beyond the margin of the valve. In valve view there are radiating rows of puncta (sometimes multiseriate rows) alternating with clear, smooth zones. The central area of irregularly arranged puncta is usually less extensive than in *Coscinodiscus* (Fig. 481) and the rows of puncta nearly converge. The girdle view (rectangular) is smooth and there are no intercalary bands. The species illustrated is common in hard-water

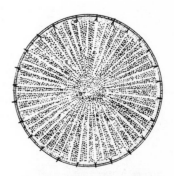

Fig. 482. *Stephanodiscus niagarae* Ehr., valve view; alternating smooth and punctate radial zones; marginal teeth prominent.

or basic lakes; occurs mostly in the euplankton. About 5 species have been reported from the United States; widely distributed.

658a (654) Frustules broadly elliptic or oval in valve view but commonly short-rectangular, the corners protruding and outturned; no raphe or pseudoraphe. Fig. 483...............*Biddulphia*

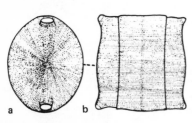

Fig. 483. *Biddulphia laevis* Ehr. (a) valve view; (b) girdle view.

This genus contains variably shaped cells, mostly rectangular in girdle view, broadly oval in valve view. The chief characteristic is a blunt process extending from the ends of the valves. There is a broad intercalary band. The areolae are in radiating linear series in valve view and in parallel series in girdle view. Most species are marine, usually solitary but sometimes adjoined in chains.

658b Frustules with a raphe or a pseudoraphe, oval or rhomboidal in valve view...659

659a Frustules rhomboidal to circular in valve view, arched and saddle-shaped in girdle view; pseudoraphe in 1 valve at right angles to that of the other valve. Fig. 484.........*Campylodiscus*

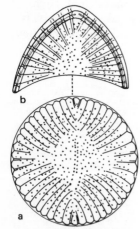

Fig. 484. *Campylodiscus hibernicus* Ehr. (a) valve view; (b) girdle view, showing marginal keel in which the raphe lies. (Redrawn from G. M. Smith).

The clear areas are regarded by some diatomists as not being justifiably called pseudoraphes. When seen vertically these cells are circular in outline but are folded or bent to form a 'saddle' when seen from the side. Costae extend inward from the edge of the valve. In girdle view the cell takes on various shapes according to the angle of observation. The cells occur solitarily; mostly marine but at least 3 species have been reported from fresh water in the United States.

659b Frustules oval or broadly elliptic, not bent nor saddle-shaped
....660

660a Frustules broadly elliptic or slipper-shaped, with prominent marginal costae; raphe lateral in a marginal keel.................661

660b Frustules oval or narrowly elliptic, with a pseudoraphe, or with a raphe not in a marginal keel...662

661a Frustules slipper-shaped, surface of valve transversely undulate, seen when the cell is viewed from the side; transverse striae often faint, occurring in zones or bands across the valve; some species much longer than wide. Fig. 485......
....*Cymatopleura*

Although sometimes linear, most species are broadly elliptic or football-shaped in valve view. The cells are rectangular in girdle view but have wavy margins because the valves are transversely undulate. In this view the marginal, often short costae are very prominent. The valve appears zoned or banded when the frustules are seen in valve view. There is a keel along the valve margins in which the raphe lies. A pseudoraphe can be determined in some species. The cells are solitary; are both marine and fresh-water.

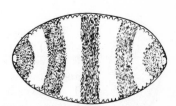

Fig. 485. *Cymatopleura elliptica* (Bréb.) W. Smith, valve view; the surface undulations represented by clear and shaded areas. (Redrawn from G. M Smith).

661b Frustules broadly oval, egg-shaped, or slipper-shaped, the surface of the valve not undulate; costae extending inward from the margin showing prominently; some species twisted in girdle view. Fig. 486..*Surirella*

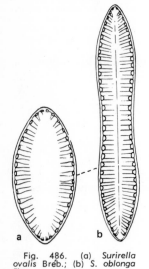

These boat-shaped or oval cells (Pennales) are usually identified readily by the very prominent costae which extend from the margin as seen in valve view, with a clear, linear region along the axis. Some species are spirally twisted. The raphe is marginal in both valves. Cells are solitary in both eu- and tychoplankton; are relatively large diatoms.

Fig. 486. (a) *Surirella ovalis* Bréb.; (b) *S. oblonga* Ehr.

662a (660) Raphe in hypovalve; pseudoraphe in epivalve; with central and polar nodules in the hypovalve; cells epiphytic. Fig. 487..*Cocconeis*

Fig. 487. *Cocconeis pediculus* Ehr., valve view showing enlarged clear area in the midregion of the hypovalve.

The frustules are broadly ovoid-elliptic in valve view. The epivalve shows an axial pseudoraphe and is convex whereas the hypovalve is concave, or flat and shows a raphe; with a central and polar nodules. The valves have prominent transverse striae but the pattern differs on the 2 valves. In many there is a clear marginal band formed by an interruption of the striae on the valve which has the raphe. The frustules are epiphytic on filamentous algae or on aquatic plants, sometimes occurring so abundantly as to form a coating over the host substrate.

662b Raphe in both epi- and hypovalve; frustules oval or variously
    shaped..663

663a Frustules with transverse septa which show as bands across
    the cell in valve view; raphe in a canal, the canal with pores.
    Fig. 488..*Denticula*

These cells are subrectangular in girdle
view but the margins are slightly convex.
The girdle is smooth and there are intercalary bands. The transverse septa are
seen extending from the margin to the
junction of the valves and the girdle.
These show as costae or ribs. In valve
view the frustules are narrowly elliptic or
lanceolate with a keel next to one margin.
There are transverse septa, and the wall
has fine, transverse striae. The cells may
be solitary or in short ribbons.

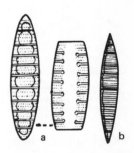

Fig. 488. (a) *Denticula
elegans* Kuetz.; (b) *D. ten-
uis* Kuetz.

663b Frustules without transverse septa; raphe in a central axis
    of the valve; a prominent central nodule which extends both
    directions on either side of the raphe; the valve with costae
    which may be marked by longitudinal ribs. Fig. 489................
    ....*Diploneis*

The frustules in this genus are broadly elliptic in valve view; rectangular in girdle view.
In some the cells are elongate in valve view
and with a median constriction. There are no
septa. The central nodule where the valve wall
is distinctly thickened is quadrangular and has
elongated projections which extend as ribs on
either side of the raphe, a feature not clearly
evident in fresh-water species. The axial field
is enlarged in the midregion. Across the valve
are somewhat converging costae between which
are prominent pores so arranged as to form
longitudinal lines. Free-floating or sedentary
species occur; about 12 being reported from
the United States.

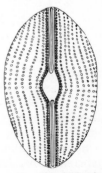

Fig. 489. *Diploneis
elliptica* (Kuetz.) Cl.,
valve view.

664a (651) Frustules bilaterally undulate in valve view; the poles capitate; some species in girdle view somewhat triangular, the septa showing as inward projecting processes extending to the intercalary bands. Fig. 490............................*Terpsinoe*

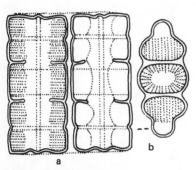

The frustules, although quadrangular in girdle view are conspicuously undulate-elliptic or even triangular in valve view. The septa are evident in valve view where they show as perpendicular extensions from the wall. The cells may be solitary or in chains. Apparently only 1 species has been reported from the United States.

Fig. 490. *Terpsinoe americana* (Bailey) Ralfs. (a) girdle view; (b) valve view. (Redrawn from Schmidle).

664b Frustules shaped otherwise, without septa, or if present, not so arranged..**665**

665a Frustules capsule-shaped, cylindrical or quadrangular in girdle view, often with 1 or 2 spinelike extensions at the poles; often filamentous..**666**

665b Frustules without spines at the poles..............................**668**

666a Frustules with intercalary bands; cells solitary.................**667**

666b Frustules without intercalary bands; cells arranged in filaments of cylindrical cells; the walls often coarsely punctate and in some species the poles with spines or teeth. Fig. 491
....*Melosira*

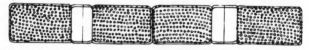

Fig. 491. *Melosira granulata* (Ehr.) Ralfs.

These are capsulelike cells, (Centrales), cylindrical as they lie end to end in relatively long filaments (in girdle view). The valves are either flat or convex in which instance there are teeth at the poles which aid in adjoining the cells. In some there is a sulcus or ringlike incision around the midregion, the girdle being smooth. The wall is punctate, coarsely or faintly so. The species illustrated shows rows of very prominent puncta, whereas others seem to be smooth until examined with oil immersion. The girdle is also ornamented when there is no sulcus. The genus frequently occurs in abundance in the euplankton.

667a Frustules rectangular in girdle view showing many inter-
    calary bands forming curved imbricated lines; with 2 spines
    at each pole. Fig. 492...*Attheya*

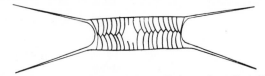

Fig. 492.   *Attheya Zachariasi* Brun. (Redrawn from Hustedt).

This curiously shaped frustule is remindful of a miniature squid
egg-case. The numerous intercalary plates separate the valves to
the extent that a rectangular shape is produced in girdle view—
with the 4 corners extended into long, diverging spines. The 2 valves
are at either end of the rectangle. In some species there is a horn
borne midway between the other two on the valve poles. Compare
with *Rhizosolenia* (Fig. 493).

667b Frustules extended at the poles to form a single spine; inter-
    calary bands forming straight imbricated lines; wall markings
    usually lacking. Fig. 493......................................*Rhizosolenia*

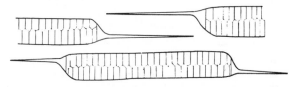

Fig. 493.   *Rhizosolenia eriensis* H. L. Smith. (Redrawn from G. M. Smith).

In this genus the cylindrical cells lie in girdle view with the
2 valves widely separated by intercalary bands. These may be
faint and difficult of discernment. The valves are mostly caplike
in this view and terminate in a long, slender spine. The walls are
not decorated but the imbricate intercalary bands form a pattern.
The walls are delicate and do not withstand the usual (especially
acid) cleaning treatment by which diatom frustules are clarified.

668a (665) Frustules cylindrical in girdle view (quinine capsule-
    shaped), attached end to end in filaments; polar margins often
    with denticulations. Fig. 491...*Melosira*

668b Frustules not cylindrical, not attached in filaments............669

669a Frustules triangularly divided (3-parted) with a pseudoraphe in each valve; frustules non-septate. (Questionably a diatom.) Fig. 494..*Centronella*

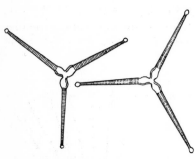

These uniquely shaped cells have tri-radiate, branched valves. The apices of the valve lobes are slightly capitate. The midregion is smooth but on either side of the pseudoraphe are fine, transverse striae. The frustules are non-septate. Apparently this little-understood 'diatom' has been reported only from Europe.

Fig. 494. Centronella Reichelti voigt., valve view. (Redrawn from Schoenfelt).

669b Frustules not triangularly divided...670

670a Frustules without a raphe; pseudoraphe showing in both valves...671

670b Frustules with a raphe in at least 1 valve.............................680

671a Frustules in girdle view elongate-rectangular, forming a circular colony in which the cells radiate from a common center like spokes of a wheel, the frustules slightly enlarged at the poles. Fig. 495..*Asterionella*

Species of this genus are planktonic, often very abundant, and are readily identified by the spokelike arrangement of the rectangular frustules about a common center. The poles are enlarged, more so at the adjoined than at the free (outer) ends. The pseudoraphe is narrow and often discerned with difficulty. Septa are lacking. Some species may form a bloom in favorable habitats and often are involved in water spoilage. The common species are usually found in hard-water lakes.

Fig. 495. Asterionella formosa Hass., colonial arrangement of cells in girdle view.

672a Frustules wedge-shaped in girdle view, adjoined side by side to form flat, circular or semicircular, or fan-shaped colonies (sometimes forming spiral bands). Fig. 496..................*Meridion*

The wedge-shaped cells in this genus have 1 or 2 intercalary bands between the girdles. The frustules lie in girdle view, side by side in a complete or incomplete, circular plate. In valve view they are cuneate and show (usually) transverse coastae interspersed by striae. The species illustrated is common in waters which support a luxuriant blue-green algal flora, but is found also in temporary pools, sometimes coating the bottom of ditches and trickles of water with a brown scum.

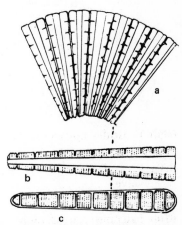

Fig. 496. *Meridion circulare* (Grev.) Ag. (a) part of colony; (b) girdle view; (c) valve view.

674a Central smooth area present, extending to ventral margin in the midregion where there is a slight swelling on the concave margin. Fig. 497..*Ceratoneis*

The cells are arched or somewhat boomerang-shaped, with attenuated or slightly capitate poles in valve view. In the midregion there is an enlargement on the ventral or concave margin, and a conspicuous clear area in the midregion. There is a conspicuous pseudoraphe. In girdle view the frustules are narrowly rectangular with truncate ends. Transverse striae on the valves are prominent. Most records are from cold, mountain streams.

F i g. 497.
*Ceratoneis ar-
cus* (E h r.)
Kuetz.

674b Central smooth area lacking; pseudoraphe narrow throughout the length of the valve; margins showing pointed undulations in valve view. Fig. 498............................*Amphicampa*

Frustules in this genus are mostly slightly arched or bowed and have both margins (as seen in valve view) undulate, or with toothlike projections. In girdle view cells are elongate-rectangular. The valves are marked by transverse striae. The pseudoraphe lies near the inner or concave margin. Apparently only 1 species is known from the United States.

F i g. 498.
*A m phicampa
e r u c a* Ehr.,
v a l v e view.
(R e d r a w n
f r o m Ehren-
berg).

675a (673) Frustules attached in zig-zag chains (sometimes semi-stellate, rotate or radiate colonies); longitudinal septa present, *straight;* rows of transverse puncta visible in valve view; frustules not showing transverse costae. Fig. 499....*Tabellaria*

Frustules in this genus are short or elongate rectangles as seen in girdle view. They are attached at the corners to one another, forming zig-zag chains or filamentous arrangements. There are narrowly elongate, septa which show in girdle view. In valve view the cells, showing longitudinal septa, are narrowly elongate, subcylindrical with capitate poles and a median swelling. There is a pseudoraphe border-

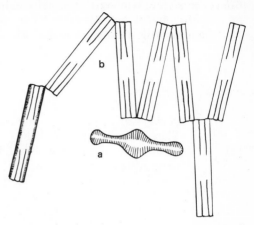

Fig. 499. (a) *Tabellaria* sp., valve view; (b) *T. fenestrata* (Lyngb.) Kuetz., girdle view in zig-zag chains.

ed by transverse striae. Species are common in both eu- and tycho-plankton.

675b Frustules not arranged in zig-zag chains, or if so, with *curved* septa..**676**

676a Frustules with curved septa; costae present, appearing as septa; frustules arranged in bands (sometimes in zig-zag chains). Fig. 500.......................................*Tetracyclus*

The cells in this genus are rectangular in girdle view, with truncate poles that have rounded corners. The 2 valves are widely separated by intercalary bands, and appear as caps at the ends of the cells. In valve view the cells are oval, elliptic or cruciform and show transverse false septa. The wall is not ornamented. Three species are reported from the United States, occurring in the tycho-plankton, or benthic, forming part of the film on submersed substrates.

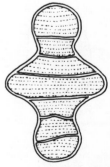

Fig. 500. *Tetracyclus lacustris* Ralfs, v a l v e view.

676b Frustules without septa...**677**

677a Frustules with prominent costae in the valve.......................**678**

677b Frustules without prominent costae...................................**679**

678a Valve view symmetrical, usually elliptic or subcylindric, often with subcapitate poles; in valve view with a faint pseudoraphe; girdle view rectangular. Fig. 501......................*Diatoma*

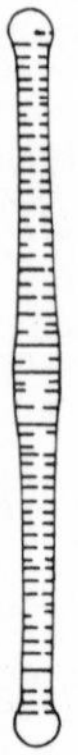

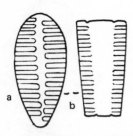

Species in this genus are variously shaped in valve view; oval or elongate, but rectangular in girdle view. There usually are intercalary bands. There are costae across the valves interspersed by striae. The valve and the girdles are finely punctate. In the valves is a narrow pseudoraphe where the wall is not punctate. Frustules usually form zig-zag chains; adjoined by pads at the corners of the cells. Compare with *Tabellaria* (Fig. 499).

Fig. 501. *Diatoma vulgare* Bory var., valve view.

678b Valve view symmetrical, egg-shaped; asymmetrical and wedge-shaped in girdle view; transverse costae conspicuous. Fig. 502...*Opephora*

These elliptic or egg-shaped cells in valve view are cuneate and asymmetrical wedge-shaped in girdle view. There are prominent striae on the valves but no costae. Elsewhere the wall is smooth. In valve view the pseudoraphe shows. Three species have been reported from the United States.

Fig. 502. *Opephora Martyi* Herib. (a) valve view; (b) girdle view.

679a (677) Frustules quardate or rectangular in girdle view, attached side by side to form ribbons (rarely in chains); valve view fusiform, the poles narrowed from enlarged central region. Fig. 503...*Fragilaria*

The frustules are narrowly elongate, fusiform in valve view (sometimes cross-shaped or triangular); rectangular in girdle view and usually show intercalary bands. The pseudoraphe is broad and distinct (usually) and occurs in both valves. The prominent striae actually are composed of rows of puncta. The most common species form ribbons with the valves attached side by side (rarely in zig-zag chains). A dozen or more species occur in both eu- and tycho-plankton.

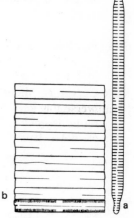

Fig. 503. (a) *Fragilaria* sp., valve view; (b) *F. capucina* Desm., diagram to show ribbonlike arrangement in girdle view.

679b Frustules elongate and straight (rarely slightly curved), needle-shaped in both views, or with slightly capitate poles; pseudoraphe between transverse striae; frustules solitary or in radiating colonies, attached to substrate, single or in clumps, at one end by short, gelatinous stalks. Fig. 504................*Synedra*

These mostly needlelike cells are commonly solitary but often form erect, radiating clusters when attached, or free-floating. Some are fusiform in valve view or are bilaterally undulate. In valve view is a pseudoraphe, narrow or wide, bordered by transverse striae. These are absent in the midregion of the cell in some species. *Synedra* is common in the plankton and in scums on substrates. They often occur in clusters with one pole attached to filamentous algae, forming radiate tufts. There are about 25 species in the United States.

Fig. 504. *Synedra* sp., valve view showing absence of striae in midregion.

680a (670) Frustules lunate or slightly curved in valve view; rect-angular or boat-shaped in girdle view..................................681

680b Frustules some other shape in valve view............................684

681a Curvature slight (frustules often nearly straight); frustules bearing a keel near the margin of the valve in which the raphe is enclosed, the location of the keel marked by a row of dots; frustule quadrangular in cross section. Fig. 505 ....*Hantzschia*

Like *Nitzschia* (Fig. 519) frustules of *Hantzschia* are beanpod-shaped in valve view. In this view the girdle shows a broad, clear area; rectangular in girdle view. There are fine, transverse striae across the valve. There is a keel along one margin of each valve. Unlike *Nitzschia* the keeled margin of one valve lies opposite that of the other valve. The raphe lies within the keel and from the fissure a row of pores open into the cell cavity, forming "carinal dots." The frustules are rectangular in optical section. There are only 2 or 3 species reported from fresh water of the United States.

F i g. 505.
H a n tzschia
a m p h ioxys
Grun.

681b Curvature decidedly evident; frustules not bearing a keel on the valve; asymmetrical in longitudinal axis; the raphe usually lying much closer to the ventral (concave) margin................682

682a Arcuate valve view showing prominent transverse lines of the septa of the frustule (appearing as costae); raphe along the ventral margin and in the midregion bent inwardly to form a 'V' as seen in valve view; frustules epiphytic on filamentous algae and aquatic plants. Fig. 506............................*Epithemia*

The frustules are slightly bowed with the dorsal (convex) side more strongly curved as seen in valve view. The axial field lies along the concave margin but forms a V-shaped bending in the mid-region. The raphe lies within a canal in the axial field. The girdle view of the frustule is rectangular and shows broad, clear (undecorated) smooth girdles. In the valve view there are prominent transverse septa (which appear as costae), and rows of puncta. There may be a longitudinal septum also. The frustules are commonly found as epiphytes on filamentous algae with the concave side down.

Fig. 506. *Epithemia* sp., valve view showing v-shaped pattern formed by inbending of smooth axial field.

682b Frustules without transverse septa (costae) showing in the valve view..683

683a Axial view expanded in the midregion, forming a clear area in the valve ornamentation which extends to the ventral margin of the curved frustule; cells usually with concave margin against a substrate. Fig. 507...*Amphora*

Frustules in this genus are crescent-shaped in valve view but broadly elliptic with truncate poles in girdle view. The raphe presents two curved lines near the ventral margin of the valve, the two curves meeting over the central nodule which lies next to the ventral margin of the cell. The cells usually are found lying with the concave surface of the hypovalve uppermost when viewed under the microscope, but in nature occurs with the concave face against the substrate (often filamentous algae).

Fig. 507. *Ampora* sp., valve view showing eccentric raphe.

683b Axial field central and small, not expanded as above; frustules forming linear colonies in gelatinous tubes, or attached singly at the ends of gelatinous stalks (often found floating free); lunate, with a slight swelling in the midregion of the ventral margin. Fig. 508..*Cymbella*

Fig. 508. Cym-bella cistula (Hempr.) Kirch. (?), valve view, showing eccentric raphe, bent in-ward at the poles toward the con-cave margin.

These are mostly gracefully curved, crescent-shaped cells which are slightly tumid along the concave margin in the midregion as seen in valve view. The axial field in which the raphe lies is eccentric and enlarged in the midregion. In valve view rows of prominent puncta extend from the margin in a converging pattern. Although usually free-floating, the frustules are often found at the ends of branching, gelatinous strands; sometimes are enclosed densely within long, gelatious tubes.

684a (680) Frustules S-shaped or sigmoid; wall ornamented with transverse and logitudinal striae which make a pattern of intersections. Fig. 509..*Gyrosigma*

The frustules of *Gyrosigma* are sigmoid in valve view, as is the narrow axial field which is en-larged in the midregion. The valve is marked by intersecting longitudinal and transverse striae. In girdle view the frustules are lanceolate. The ends of the raphe at the central area bend or are hooked in opposite directions. The cells occur singly. *Gyrosigma* is a relatively common genus; has about 20 species reported from the United States.

Fig. 509. Gyro-sigma acumina-tum (Kuetz.) Cleve. valve view.

684b Frustules not sigmoid..685

685a Frustules broadly elliptic, slipper-shaped or boat-shaped in valve view, the margins showing prominent, often short costae; surface of valve undulate; in girdle view elongate but with the sides undulate; pseudoraphe often indistinct. Fig. 485 ....*Cymatopleura*

685b Frustules without such costae; not undulate, not showing marginal undulations in girdle view.....................................686

686a Raphe along both margins of the valve; located within a keel 687

686b Raphe not marginal; keel present or absent.......................688

687a Valve sharply bent to form a saddle; pseudoraphe in each valve but at right angles to one another; raphe in a marginal keel. Fig. 484...*Campylodiscus*

687b Valve usually twisted, sometimes flat; prominent costae extending from the valve margin toward the smooth pseudoraphe area. Fig. 486...*Surirella*

688a (686) Frustule in valve view curved and 'bone'-shaped, 1 pole distinctly larger than the other; transverse rows of puncta in valve viw. Fig. 510...*Actinella*

Species are either solitary or colonial, forming stellate clusters. Cells in this genus are all elongate and subcylindric, but the poles are enlarged and unsymmetrically so. In valve view there are numerous transverse rows of puncta. In some species there are fine, intramarginal spines. The raphe lies along the concave margin of the valve, extending only part way diagonally from the polar nodules. The species illustrated is the only one reported from the United States and is rare.

F i g. 510. A c t i nella punctata Lewis, valve view.

688b Frustules some other shape...689

689a Valve with 'wings,' furnished with a sigmoid keel vertical to the face of the valve; boat-shaped in valve view; 8-shaped or hourglass-shaped in girdle view. Fig. 511.........*Amphiprora*

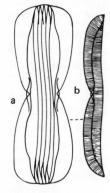

The frustules are elongate boat-shaped in valve view but 8-shaped or hourglass-shaped in girdle view. The valve has a curious vertical flange or keel which extends in a sigmoid fashion. The raphe lies in the outer margin of the keel. The wall is decorated with longitudinal rows of puncta which form parallel striae. Species may be free-floating or adherent in mucilage on moist substrates. Most species are marine.

Fig. 511. *Amphiprora paludosa* W. Smith. (a) girdle view; (b) valve view.

689b Valves without a sigmoid keel, some other shape than above in girdle view..690

690a Pseudoraphe in 1 valve; true raphe in the other.................691

690b Raphe in both valves..693

691a Girdle view bent, wedge-shaped with poles usually truncate, attached by stalks or mucilage plugs to substrates; valve view cuneate. Fig. 512..*Rhoicosphenia*

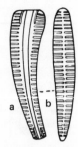

In valve view these cells are elongate-oblanceolate, narrower at one end than the other and somewhat wedge-shaped in both views. The hypovalve shows a raphe and there is a pseudoraphe in the convex epivalve. In girdle view the cells are curved cuneate. The intercalary bands are not decorated. Coarse transverse striae (rows of puncta) show in both views. There are 2 longitudinal septa which are parallel to the face of the valve. The species illustrated is the only one reported from the United States; occurs attached by a gelatinous stalk to algae or aquatic plants.

Fig. 512. *Rhoicosphenia curvata* (Kuetz.) Grun. (a) girdle view; (b) valve view. (Redrawn from G. M. Smith).

These frustules are symmetrical in valve view but not when seen from the side. They are, in general, elliptic or fusiform in valve view, undulate-rectangular and bent in girdle view. The epivalve shows a pseudoraphe, the hypovalve a raphe. There may be a distinctive lateral horseshoe-shaped clear area in the midregion of the valve which has the pseudoraphe. The cells may be free, or more commonly attached by a gelatinous stalk to various substrates, sometimes forming packets or filaments. There are over 30 species which have been reported from the United States.

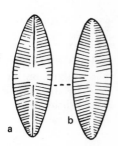

Fig. 513. *Achnanthes lanceolata* (Bréb.) Grun. (a) hypovalve view showing raphe; (b) epivalve view showing pseudoraphe. *A. coarctata* (Bréb.) Grun is a common species which is on stalks, epiphytizing filamentous algae.

694a Frustules straight and relatively narrow, sometimes slightly capitate at one pole; margin of frustule smooth in valve view; costae on both lateral margins; raphe extending only 2/3 the distance from the polar nodules. Fig. 514......................*Peronia*

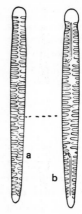

These cells are elongate or cigar-shaped with rounded poles. One pole is often larger than the other as seen in valve view. The raphe in one valve extends from the poles only about 2/3 of the distance to the midregion and is slightly curved near the inner end. The other valve has a short pseudoraphe and a short raphe. The valves have prominent marginal coastae. Cells are free-floating or benthic; only 2 or 3 species have been reported from the United States.

Fig. 514. *Peronia erinacea* Bréb. et Arn., valve views; (a) valve without raphe; (b) valve with short raphe near poles.

694b Frustules bent or curved in the apical regions; wavy or undulate on one margin as seen in valve view; transversely striate; raphe not extending the full length of the valve. Fig. 515..*Eunotia*

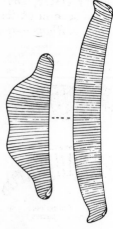

Species of this genus are solitary, or in filaments. The frustules are slightly bowed and are undulate on one or both margins as seen in valve view. In some species the raphe shows only near the polar nodules, and in some a pseudoraphe lies near the ventral margin. The face of the valves is transversely striate. The polar nodules are conspicuous and from them to the ventral (concave) margin a short raphe extends. There are many species common in especially soft-water or desmid habitats. This is a large genus with over 45 species reported from the United States.

Fig. 515. *Eunotia* spp., 2 cell shapes in valve view.

The keel is central but the valves and the raphe are twisted. This genus has elongate fusiform cells with 3 spiral lines The lines are marked with numerous dots. This unique diatom appears not to have been reported from the United States.

Fig. 516. *Cylindrotheca* sp., valve view.

In this genus the cells are much different in shape as seen in girdle and in valve views. In valve view the frustule is narrow with the poles bowed, giving the appearance of a 'half-cell' with an enlargement on the midregion on the convex margin. The girdle view is much wider than the valve view. The ventral margin is almost straight, except for the narrow, curved polar region. The valve bears a keel to one side and in this lies the raphe. The valves are coarsely costate, the costae alternating with the striae. In girdle view the cells are

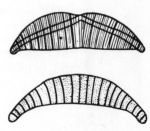

Fig. 517. *Rhopalodia* sp., valve view of 2 species.

elongate, somewhat quadrate in general outline but with a swelling on each side in the midregion. The girdle is smooth, but extending in from the margin are coarse costae which, in the polar regions, converge toward the center of the cell. The genus is entirely freshwater in distribution, but apparently only 2 species have been found in the United States.

698b Raphe in a canal with pores; lanceolate or elliptic in valve view. Fig. 488...*Denticula*

699a (697) Keels on margins of valve opposite one another; quadrangular in cross section. Fig. 505............................*Hantzschia*

699b Keels on alternate margins of the valve...............................**700**

700a Frustules occurring in colonies; keel central. Fig. 518..............
....*Bacillaria*

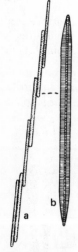

The species illustrated is placed by some diatomists in the genus *Nitzschia* (Fig. 519). The narrowly elongate cells, with produced apices are united side by side to form ribbons. The cells slide back and forth along the sides of the frustules and draw the ribbon out into an extended, pseudofilament arrangement—then slide back and extend in the opposite direction; hence the name "carpenter's rule" diatom. The keel is central or nearly so and is conspicuously punctate. The raphe is in the keel and is diagonally opposite the raphe in the other valve. Species are both marine and brackish.

Fig. 518. *Bacillaria paradoxa* Gmel. (a) diagram of cells sliding out to form elongate, pseudofilamentous colony; (b) single cell, valve view.

700b Frustules solitary; keel eccentric, diagonally opposite one another; rhomboid in cross section. Fig. 519...............*Nitzschia*

The frustules of this genus are narrowly linear and tapered at the poles in both valve and girdle views. The cells may be straight or slightly sigmoid. Along one margin of a valve is a keel which is opposite the unkeeled margin of the other valve (one raphe diagonally opposite the other). The raphe lies within the keel. The fissure of the raphe has a row of pores that open into the cell cavity. These are called carinal dots. There are prominent transverse rows of puncta on the valve faces. Although commonly solitary, *Nitzschia* often occurs in gelatinous, tubelike strands.

Fig. 519. *Nitzchia* sp., valve view showing location of marginal keel.

701a (695) Frustules asymmetrical in either the transverse or the longitudinal axis; key- or wedge-shaped in valve view, slightly larger at one end than the other.......................................**702**

701b Frustules symmetrical in both axes.......................................**703**

702a Striae composed of puncta in a double series, interrupted near the margin of the valve so that a longitudinal line is formed; attached. Fig. 520.......................................*Gomphoneis*

These cells are wedge-shaped or cuneate, unsymmetrical in both girdle and valve views (transversely). There is an elongate, axial field which is enlarged in the midregion. The frustules are very similar to *Gomphonema* (Fig. 521) but there is a fine but definite line running parallel with the margin of the valve. The striae are composed of a double row of puncta. Frustules are attached or free-floating.

Fig. 520. *Gomphoneis herculeana* (Ehr.) Cleve, valve view showing raphe with curvature in the midregion.

702b Striae composed of puncta in a single series; attached on branched stalks. Fig. 521..*Gomphonema*

Species in this genus have frustules that are wedge-shaped or clavate, larger at one end than the other. In both girdle and valve view the frustules are transversely unsymmetrical. The elongate axial field is enlarged in the midregion where there is often an eccentric, coarse punctum. There are coarse striae extending inward from the valve margins. The puncta form a single row. The cells are usually found attached on branched, gelatinous stalks at their narrow end. Compare with *Gomphoneis* (Fig. 520).

Fig. 521. *Gomphonema lanceolatum* var. *insignis* (Greg.) Cl., valve view showing eccentric punctum.

703a (701) Frustules with septa..**704**

703b Frustules without septa..**705**

704a Frustules quadrangular in girdle view; usually in zig-zag chains; longitudinally septate, the septa with openings in the center and at the poles. Fig. 522................................*Diatomella*

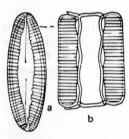

In valve view frustules are narrowly elongate, broadly rounded at the poles and enlarged in the midregion. In girdle view the cells are rectangular. There are 2 intercalary bands and 2 longitudinal septa in which there are 3 holes, one at each pole and one at the midregion. The valves have marginal transverse rows of striae leaving a wide central clear longitudinal field. The septa show in both valves. Frustules may be solitary, filamentous, or in zig-zag chains.

Fig. 522. *Diatomella* sp. (a) valve view; (b) girdle view showing intercalary bands.

704b Frustules narrowly rectangular in girdle view; naviculoid in valve view; septa with large central opening and parallel linear openings which form 2 lateral series of minute, transverse canals. Fig. 523...*Mastogloia*

Frustules in this genus are symmetrical in both longitudinal and transverse axes. They are elongate-elliptic in valve view (sometimes capitate); rectangular in girdle view. The girdle is smooth but the intercalary bands have areolae. There is a raphe in a straight, clear axial field which is conspicuously enlarged in the midregion. There are 2 longitudinal septa. In valve view there are transverse striae on either side of the axial field. Cells are solitary and mostly marine; 4 or 5 species are reported from the United States.

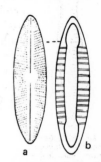

Fig. 523. *Mastogloia Danseii* Thw. (a) valve view; (b) diagram showing internal septa. (Redrawn from G. M. Smith.)

705a (703) Raphe extending within a siliceous, riblike thickening **706**

705b Raphe not bordered by siliceous ribs...................................**708**

706a Valve with an enlarged, undecorated central area in the region of the central nodule; especially evident in large species; frustule broadly elliptic; valve costate. Fig. 489......... ....*Diploneis*

706b Valve without an enlarged clear area in the central region; valve not costate; frustule linear-lanceolate..........................**707**

707a Central nodule greatly elongated, the raphe appearing in 2 relatively short sections in the apical region. Fig. 524............
....*Amphipleura*

These are elongate and narrow, boat-shaped cells in valve view. The conspicuous differentiating character is the greatly enlarged central nodule that extends 2/3 of the length of the valve and is divided to form 2 parallel extensions toward the poles. The raphe lies between the divisions of the siliceous ribs. The valve has minute transverse striae of punctations which sometimes can be seen only under special optical conditions, hence it appears smooth under ordinary magnification. The puncta may show also forming longitudinal lines. Frustules are solitary and usually benthic in calcareous waters especially.

Fig. 524. *Amphipleura pellucida* Kuetz., valve view showing greatly elongated central nodule. (Redrawn from Boyer).

707b Central nodule shorter, with 2 siliceous ribs extending toward the apices; raphe lying within the ribs. Fig. 525.....................
....*Frustulia*

Like *Amphipleura* (Fig. 524) *Frustulia* has an elongate central nodule but it is relatively shorter (less than 1/2 the length of the cell). The cells are boat-shaped in valve-view; rectangular in girdle view and without intercalary bands and septa. Two ribs from the central nodule run parallel to the raphe and unite with the polar nodules. There are both transverse and longitudinal striae leaving a small, clear central area. Frustules are either solitary or lie side by side in a gelatinous, tubular colony. At least 5 species are reported from the United States.

Fig. 525. *Frustulia rhomboides* (Ehr.) De Toni, valve view showing raphe between 2 ribs. (Redrawn from Smith).

708a (705) Valves with 'wings' bearing a sigmoid keel, 8-shaped in girdle view. Fig. 511...*Amphiprora*

708b Valves without a keel...**709**

709a Transverse valve markings interrupted, thus the frustule shows longitudinal lines paralleling the margins of the valve **710**

709b Transverse markings not so interrupted.................................**712**

710a Interruption of transverse lines forming a zig-zag pattern or line. Fig. 526..*Anomoeoneis*

The frustules are elongate boat-shaped in valve view with narrowly rounded (sometimes capite) apices, whereas they are rectangular in girdle view. In the valve view a narrow axial field (clear of wall markings) is enlarged in the midregion. The raphe is narrow and either straight or hooked in the same direction in the central region. Lateral to the central field are fine, transverse striae which are interrupted by clear spaces in such a way that a zig-zag pattern is formed over the face of the valve. This is a fresh-water genus; benthic or in the tychoplankton; 8 species reported from the United States.

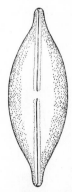

Fig. 526. Anomoeo-
neis sphaerophora var.
sculpta O. F. Muell. (Re-
drawn from Reimer).

710b Interruptions not forming zig-zag pattern...............................**711**

711a Transverse markings formed of puncta. Fig. 527........*Neidium*

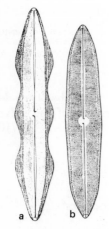

Fig. 527. (a) *Neidium magellanicum* Cl., valve view showing curvature of raphe in midregion. (Redrawn from Frenguelli); (b) *N. iridis* var. *subundulata* (A. C.-Eul.) Reimer. (Redrawn from Reimer).

These boat-shaped cells in valve view show prominent, but discontinuous transverse and punctate striae. Although mostly with convex lateral margins, some are straight or even concave. The striae are conspicuously interrupted by blank places in two lateral lines just within the margins of the valves. There is a clear axial field which is enlarged in the midregion and takes on various shapes. There are not septa. At the central nodule the raphe forms 2 hooks which usually turn in opposite directions. At the poles the raphe may be divided. The frustules are rectangular in girdle view. Compare with *Caloneis* (Fig. 528), another strictly fresh-water genus. There are over 20 species reported from the United States.

711b Transverse markings of continuous lines. Fig. 528......*Caloneis*

Fig. 528. *Caloneis bacillum* (Grun.) C l e v e, valve view showing clear area in midregion and curvature of raphe. (Redrawn from Foged).

Cells are elongate cigar-shaped, but slightly widened in the midregion where the axial field is also enlarged. There are both central and polar nodules. There are parallel transverse striae extending from the lateral margins of the valve. There are no septa nor intercalary bands. The frustules are rectangular in girdle view. Just within the margins of the valve is a parallel line which crosses the transverse striae which often appear as coastae. These parallel lines are caused by pores in the striae which open into the cell cavity. There are many species in both fresh and salt water habitats.

712a (709) Clear area in longitudinal axis sigmoid. Fig. 529.........
....*Scoliopleura*

Frustules are elongate-oval to naviculoid or fusiform in valve view; lanceolate in girdle view. The outstanding characteristic of this genus is the sigmoid axial field. Within this lies a sigmoid raphe. There may be a line on either side of the axial field bordering the transverse striae (rows of puncta). There are 4 longitudinal chloroplasts in each cell. Species are both marine and fresh-water.

Fig. 529. *Scoliopleura* sp., valve view with sigmoid raphe.

712b Clear area of axial field not sigmoid.....................................713

713a Valves with costae forming the transverse markings; costae punctate. Fig. 530...*Brebissonia*

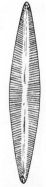

These cells are attached by branched, gelatinous strands to a substrate, sometimes aquatic plants. The cells are lanceolate-boat-shaped in valve view; quadrangular in girdle view. The girdles are distinctly ornamented between which are several smooth intercalary bands. The 2 sections of the raphe lie in a clear, longitudinal axial field and between 2 parallel ridges (which are inconspicuous). There are 2 or several intercalary bands between the girdles. Very prominent striae extend from the margins of the valve toward the axial field. The genus is mostly marine but at least 2 species have been reported from fresh water in the United States.

Fig. 530. *Brebissonia Boeckii* (Ehr.) G r u n., valve view s h o w i n g raphe between parallel ridges. (Redrawn from Boyer).

713b Valves with ornamentation formed by puncta, or without evident markings...714

714a Lateral valve markings strongly oblique, interrupted in the midregion by an undecorated area over the central nodule which extends to the margins of the valve (forming a stauros). Fig. 531...*Stauroneis*

These are mostly naviculoid cells (in valve view), with either capitate or acutely rounded poles. The conspicuous feature (the stauros) is a broad, central nodule which extends to both lateral margins of the valve. In this region alone there are no transverse striae which throughout the remainder of the valve are prominent and which converge from the lateral margins to the axial field. There is a straight raphe lying in this field. Septa are lacking. The genus is common and there are many (depending on interpretations of diatomists) widely distributed species in the United States. There are also many marine species.

Fig. 531. *Stauroneis parvula* var. *prominula* Grun., valve view showing transverse stauros. (Redrawn from Foged).

714b Central undecorated clear area not extending to the margins of the valve...**715**

715a Transverse ornamentations composed of costae, the axial field usually broad. Fig. 532...*Pinnularia*

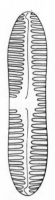

These mostly solitary and free-floating frustules vary considerably in shape but mostly they are naviculoid with broadly rounded poles in valve view. Some species are enlarged in the midregion. The conspicuous feature is the prominent transverse coastae or costaelike striae on either side of a relatively wide, straight axial field. The striae open into the cavity of the cell. The raphe in this field is sigmoid. There are no septa. In girdle view the frustules are rectangular with truncate poles. Some species have cells which are perhaps the largest among fresh-water diatoms. A few species, especially *Pinnularia viridis* (Nitzsch) Ehr. have the characteristic habit of lying side by side (in valve view) in groups of 4. There are many marine species.

Fig. 532. *Pinnularia borealis* Ehr., valve view showing c o s t a e. (Redrawn from Foged).

715b Transverse ornamentations composed of puncta, the axial field narrow and linear, the raphe straight. Fig. 533................
....*Navicula*

This is a large genus with very many species in both fresh and salt water; benthic or in the plankton. The cells vary considerably in shape, especially in valve view but in the main they are naviculoid or cigar-shaped, with narrowly rounded or capitate poles; sometimes distinctly rostrate at the apices. There is a raphe in both valves. There may be internal plates but not complete septa. Striae are composed of puncta, sometimes very coarse and form what appear to be costae. The frustules are eu- or tychoplanktonic or may occur in films on submersed substrates. Compare with *Pinnularia* (Fig. 532). The striae or rows of puncta are convergent toward the central, clear area of the axial field which is distinctly en-

Fig. 533. (a) *Navicula Petersenii* Hustedt; (b) *N. digitoradiata* fa. *minor* F o g e d. (Redrawn from Foged).

larged in the midregion. The field in general is straight and narrow and the raphe within it is straight. In girdle view the cells are rectangular.

APPENDIX

A Brief Synopsis of Unicellular Green Algae not Included in the Pictured Key to Genera Because Differentiating Characters must be Determined by Culturing and by Observations of Reproductive Details, Both Vegetative and Asexual. (Genera mostly isolated from soil.)

I. Tetrasporales: Cells often with pseudocilia, containing contractile vacuoles; solitary or colonial in copious mucilage; vegetative reproduction by ordinary cell division. See Figs. 78, 79, 85.

A. Hypnomonadaceae
Spherical unicells with contractile vacuoles.

1. *Actinochloris* Korschikoff.
Cells globular, up to 150 μ in diameter; chloroplast stellate, with the arms flattened against the wall; pyrenoid central; contractile vacuoles several, occurring between lobes of the chloroplast; cells becoming multinucleate in age.

II. Chlorococcales (Including Chlorosphaerales):* solitary, colonial or forming coenobia; reproducing largely by autospores, commonly also by zoospores; contractile vacuoles lacking, although zoospores may show the tetrasporine-volvocine type of contractile vacuole and red eye-spot; sexual reproduction iso-aniso- or oogamous.

A. Pyrenoid Present.

1. Chloroplast axial.

a. *Axilosphaera* Cox et Deason
Cells spherical, up to 18 μ in diameter; chloroplast axial, lobed with an eccentric pyrenoid; surface view of cell showing ends of lobes, giving the appearance of several parietal plates. From soil.

b. *Borodinella* Miller
Cells spherical, solitary or grouped after cell division, floating at the surface of the water, forming some-

---

*The order Chlorosphaerales has been suggested by Dr. Walter Herndon for all non-motile, unicellular and colonial forms which carry on vegetative cell division (cell bipartition); reproducing by motile and non-motile spores but which do not produce sarcinalike packets; without contractile vacuoles; includes Chlorosphaeraceae and Coccomyxaceae.

what tetrahedral colonies after cell division; chloroplast stellate with a central pyrenoid; reproduction by biflagellate zoospores containing contractile vacuoles.

c. *Borodinellopsis* Dykstra
Spherical cells up to 30 μ in diameter; chloroplast stellate, with a pyrenoid, the arms flattened against the cell wall; cell division internal, forming tetrahedrally arranged, non-motile daughter cells; asexual reproduction by biflagellate zoospores which retain an ovoid shape for some time (unlike *Borodinella*) after becoming stationary. Plants from soil.

2. Chloroplast parietal (continuous or perforate)
a. *Chlorosphaeropsis* (Vischer) Herndon
Cells spherical, about 17 μ in diameter, solitary at first, becoming clumped; the chloroplast at first a parietal plate but soon becoming reticulate and covering the wall; pyrenoid median in the chloroplast; reproduction by elongate-ellipsoid, biflagellate zoospores. From soil.

b. *Fasciculochloris* McLean et Trainor
Cells at first oblong-ovoid, becoming spherical, up to 14 μ in diameter; chloroplast a parietal cup with 1 or more pyrenoids; cells dividing to form quartets of daughter cells; asexual reproduction by biflagellate, walled zoospores that have an eye-spot.

c. *Heterotetracystis* Cox et Deason (Chlorosarcinaceae?)
Cells spherical, up to 18 μ in diameter, solitary or in 2's and 4's; chloroplast parietal but massive, with a pyrenoid, the chloroplast becoming netlike or reticulate; asexual reproduction by oval-elliptic zoospores which retain their shape for a time after becoming sedentary; in culture often forming orange-colored cysts. Soil organism.

d. *Neochloris* Starr
Cells spherical, up to 65 μ in diameter, with a wall which may be thin or laminate; chloroplast cup-shaped (somewhat similar to *Gloeocystis*, Fig. 85), with 1 to several pyrenoids; asexual reproduction by biflagellate, ovoid zoospores. Plants from soil.

e. *Spongiochloris* Starr
Cells spherical (or subspherical), up to 100 μ in diameter; chloroplast a parietal reticulum with inward projecting (spongy) portions; pyrenoids 1 to several; asexual reproduction by equally-flagellated,

naked zoospores which become spherical upon attachment. Plants from soil.

f. *Spongiococcum* Deacon
Cells spherical, about 20 μ in diameter; chloroplast a fine reticulum, both parietal and spongy (as in *Spongiochloris*, with at least 1 eccentric pyrenoid; reproduction by oval or elongate, walled, *Chlamydomonas*-like zoospores; vegetative cell division by internal cleavage to form several (16 ?) individuals. Plants from soil.

g. *Tetracystis* Brown et Bold
Cells spherical or subspherical, solitary or aggregated, up to 20 μ in diameter; chloroplast a parietal but massive body which may be perforate; vegetative cell division forming tetrads of daughter cells; asexual reproduction by biflagellate zoospores which become spherical upon attachment. Plants from soil.

B. Pyrenoid Absent.
  1. Chloroplasts many, irregular platelets, parietal.
    a. *Dictyochloropsis* Geitler
    Cells spherical, subaerial, up to 75 μ in diameter; chloroplasts numerous, irregular, lobed platelets and vermiform bodies; pyrenoids lacking; reproduction by 16-64 autospores.
  2. Chloroplast a bilobed, dumbell-shaped body.
    a. *Pulchrasphaera* Deason
    Cells spherical, up to 25 μ in diameter; chloroplast parietal and lobed or dumb-bell-shaped, the lobes often perforate, without pyrenoids; cells gregarious but not forming packets following cell division; reproduction by oval, biflagellated zoospores which become spherical immediately upon attaching; eye-spot present in zoospore. Plants from sand.
  3. Chloroplast parietal plates, or reticulate, the fenestrations varying in size.
    a. *Dictyochloris* Vischer
    Cells spherical, up to 75 μ in diameter; chloroplast reticulate and covering most of the wall, without a pyrenoid; reproduction by naked, somewhat unequally flagellated zoospores; cells becoming coenocytic in age. Plants from soil.
    b. *Dictyococcus* Gerneck
    Cells spherical, up to 60 μ in diameter; chloroplasts

numerous angular, parietal plates as seen in surface view, with inward projecting lobes; pyrenoid lacking; cells becoming coenocytic in age; reproduction by biflagellate zoospores. Genus similar to *Bracteacoccus*, Fig. 199.

c. *Friedmannia* Chantanchat et Bold
Cells spherical with a parietal, irregularly lobed or segmented chloroplast; pyrenoid lacking; cells dividing to form tetrahedral clumps; asexual reproduction by biflagellate, naked oval zoospores with an eye-spot. (Originally placed in the Chlorosarcinaceae).

A Check List of the More Common Genera of Fresh-water Algae According to Families, Orders and Phyla[1]

(See Index for references to page numbers to locate genera.)

I. PHYLUM (DIVISION) CHLOROPHYTA[2]

A. SUB-PHYLUM
   CHLOROPHYCEAE

1. Order Volvocales

   Family Pyramimonaceae
   Pyramimonas
   p. 54 fig. 56

   Family Tetraselmiaceae
   Tetraselmis (Platymonas)
   p. 51 fig. 48

   Family Polyblepharidaceae
   Dunaliella
   p. 52 fig. 52
   *Hyaliella** (colorless)
   Mesostigma
   p. 53 fig. 54
   Polyblepharides
   p. 53 fig. 55
   *Polytomella** (colorless)
   Quadrichloris (Tetrachloris)
   p. 55 fig. 58
   Raciborskiella
   p. 56 fig. 61
   Spermatozoopsis
   p. 54 fig. 57
   Stephanoptera
   p. 52 fig. 51

   Family Chlamydomonadaceae
   Brachiomonas
   p. 48 fig. 42
   Carteria
   p. 51 fig. 49
   Chlamydomonas
   p. 35 fig. 17
   Chlorogonium
   p. 47 fig. 41
   *Diplostauron**
   *Furcilia**
   *Gloeomonas**
   Haematococcus
   p. 33 fig. 14
   Lobomonas
   p. 49 fig. 43
   *Platychloris**

Polytoma
p. 43 fig. 32
Scherffelia
p. 50 fig. 47
Smithsonimonas
p. 49 fig. 45
Sphaerellopsis
p. 49 fig. 44
*Tetrablepharis**
p. 51

Family Phacotaceae
Cephalomonas
p. 45 fig. 35
Coccomonas
p. 47 fig. 40
Dysmorphococcus
p. 45 fig. 34
Granulochloris
p. 47 fig. 39
Pedinopera
p. 50 fig. 46
Phacotus
p. 46 fig. 38
Pteromonas
p. 44 fig. 33
Thoracomonas
p. 46 fig. 37
Wislouchiella
p. 46 fig. 36

Family Volvocaceae
Astrephomene
p. 62 fig. 72
Eudorina
p. 61 fig. 70
Gonium
p. 56 fig. 60
Pandorina
p. 59 fig. 66
Platydorina
p. 55 fig. 59
Pleodorina
p. 61 fig. 71
Stephanoon
p. 60 fig. 69
Stephanosphaera
p. 60 fig. 68

---

1. Genera indicated (*) are not treated in this key.
2. For the most part the arrangement follows a plan used by Bourrelly (1966).

**See footnote, p. 316.

II. PHYLUM (DIVISION) EUGLENOPHYTA

1. Order Euglenales
   Family Euglenaceae
   Ascoglena
      p. 37 fig. 21
   *Cryptoglena**
   Euglena
      p. 33 fig. 13
   Euglenomorpha
      p. 41 fig. 28
   Eutreptia
      p. 42 fig. 30
   Lepocinclis
      p. 43 fig. 31
   Phacus
      p. 42 fig. 29
   *Strombomonas**
   Trachelomonas
      p. 41 fig. 27
   Family Astasiaceae (Colorless)
   *Astasia**
   *Distigma**

*Menoidium**
*Rhabdomonas**

Family Peranemaceae
(Colorless)
   *Anisonema**
   *Dinema**
   *Entosiphon**
   *Euglenopsis**
   *Heteronema**
   *Jenningsia**
   *Notosolenus**
   *Peranema**
   *Petalomonas**
   *Sphenomonas**
   *Tropidoscyphus**
   *Urceolus**

2. Order Colaciales
   Family Colaciaceae
   Colacium
      p. 85 fig. 118

III. PHYLUM (DIVISION) PYRRHOPHYTA

A. CLASS DESMOKONTAE
   1. Order Desmomonadales
      Family Prorocentraceae
      Exuviella
         p. 230 fig. 381

B. CLASS DINOPHYCEAE
   1. Order Dinokontae
      Family Gymnodiniaceae
      Amphidinium
         p. 234 fig. 386
      Gymnodinium
         p. 233 fig. 384
      Gyrodinium
         p. 232 fig. 383
      Massartia
         p. 233 fig. 385
      Family Gonyaulacaceae
      Gonyaulax
         p. 235 fig. 388
      Family Glenodiniaceae
      Glenodinium
         p. 236 fig. 390
      Hemidinium
         p. 235 fig. 389
      Family Peridiniaceae
      Peridinium
         p. 234 fig. 387

Family Ceratiaceae
Ceratium
   p. 231 fig. 382

2. Order Dinocapsales
   Family Gloeodiniaceae
   Gloeodinium
      p. 227 fig. 376
   Urococcus
      p. 35 fig. 18

3. Order Dinococcales
   Family Dinococcaceae
   Cystodinium
      p. 226 fig. 374
   Hypnodinium
      p. 227 fig. 375
   Raciborskia
      p. 224 fig. 369
   Stylodinium
      p. 224 fig. 370
   Tetradinium
      p. 223 fig. 367
   Family Blastodiniaceae
   Oodinium
      p. 224 fig. 368

VII. PHYLUM (DIVISION) PHAEOPHYTA

VIII. PHYLUM (DIVISION) RHODOPHYTA

IX. PHYLUM (DIVISION) CYANOPHYTA

INDEX AND PICTURED GLOSSARY

Figures in italic face refer to pages where the genus name appears in the key. Numbers 321 to 333 refer to pages where the names appear in the checklist of genera, families, orders and phyla.

A

Acanthochloris, *211*, 328
Acanthosphaera, *126*, 323
  Zachariasii, 126
Achnanthaceae, 331
Achnanthes, *303*, 331
  coarctata, 303
  lanceolata, 303
ACICULAR: needlelike in shape. Fig. 534

Fig. 534

ACID BOG: having soft water, low or lacking in dissolved minerals; pH below neutral (7.0)
Acrochaetium, *192*, 332
Actidesmium, *96*, 324
  Hookeri, 96
Actinastrum, *94*, 324
  gracillimum, 94
  Hantzschii, 94
Actinella, *301*, 331
  punctata, 301
Actinochloris, *316*, 322
Actinocyclus, *284*, 330
Actinotaenium, 67, 68, 115, 122, 326
Aegagropila, *183*, 325
  profunda, 183
AERIAL: Subaerial: algal habitat on moist soil, rocks, trees, *etc.*; involving a thin film of water.
Akaryonta, 19
AKINETE: a type of spore formed by the transformation of a vegetative cell into a thick-walled resting cell, containing a concentration of food material.
Albrightia, 248, 249, *333*
  tortuosa, 249
Alcohol
  food reserve, 18
  preservative, 12
ALKALINE WATER: containing a predominating amount of hydroxyl-ions as compared with hydrogen-ions; abundant in electrolytes; hard water lakes ordinarily are alkaline.
Alligator, 8
Allorgeia, *121*, 326
  Valiae, 121

ALPINE: altitudes above tree line; SUB-ALPINE: upper limits of forest zone.
ALVEOLAE: small cavities; minute chambers.
Ambrosia, 107
AMOEBOID: like an amoeba; creeping by extensions of highly plastis protoplasm (pseudopodia).
AMORPHOUS: without definite shape; without regular form.
Amphicampa, *294*, 330
  eruca, 294
Amphichrysis, 329
Amphidinium, *234*, 327
  Klebsii, 234
Amphipleura, *310*, 331
  pellucida, 310
Amphiprora, *302*, *311*, 331
  paludosa, 302
Amphithrix, 246, *247*, 333
  janthina, 246
Amphora, *299*, 331
Amscottia, *121*, 326
  mira, 121
Anabaena, 15, 110, *244*, 263, 264, 265, 333
  spiroides var. *crassa*, 244
  subcylindrica, 244
Anabaenopsis, *262*, 333
  Elenkinii, 262
Anacystis (Aphanocapsa), 332
  p. 277 fig. 468
ANASTOMOSE: to separate and come together again at another point or level; a meshwork. Fig. 535

Fig. 535

Ancylonema, 28, *142*, 326
  Nordenskioldii, 142
Angiosperms
ANISOGAMETE: a sex cell which shows only slight differentiation in respect to maleness or femaleness, 15, 18
Anisonema, 327
Ankistrodesmus, 9, *88*, *95*, *100*, *102*, 103, *104*, *111*, 279, 323
  Braunii, 88
  convolutus, 88
  falcatus, 88
  fractus, 88
  spiralis, 88

Ankyra, 103, *104*, 111, 322
  Judayi, 103, 104
Anomoeoneis, *311*, 331
  sphaerophora var. *sculpta*, 311
ANTAPICAL: the posterior or rear pole or region of an organism, or of a colony of cells.
ANTERIOR: the forward end; toward the top.
ANTHERIDIUM: a single cell or a series of cells in which male gametes are produced; sometimes applied to the multicellular *spherule* in the Characeae which is a specialized, complex branch in which antheridial cells are produced. (See Figs. 1, 2, 3)
ANTHEROZOID: male sex cell; sperm.
Apatococcus, 62, *86*, 87, 324
  lobatus, 87
APEX: the summit, the terminus; end of a projection; inner part of an incision; the upper end of a filament of cells.
Aphanizomenon, 263, 276, 333
  flos-aquae, 263
Aphanocapsa, *277*, 332
  elachista, 277
  Grevillei, 277
Aphanochaetaceae, 325
Aphanochaete, 157, *171*, 325
  polychaete, 157
  repens, 157
Aphanothece, *281*, 332
  Castagnei, 281
APICAL: See apex
Apiocystis, *66*, 322
  Brauniana, 66
APLANOSPORE: non-motile thick-walled spore formed many within an unspecialized vegetative cell; a small resting spore.
Apodochloris, 322
Araceae, 107
Arachnochloris, *211*, 328
  minor, 211
ARBUSCULAR: branched or growing like a tree or bush.
ARCUATE: curved, sharply bow-shaped. Fig. 536

Fig. 536

Arisaema, 8, 187
ARMORED: See thecate.
Arthrodesmus, 123, *124*, 326
  Fuellebornei, 123
  octocornis, 123

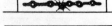

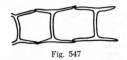

Fig. 547

I

Fig. 548

J

K

L

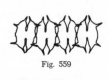

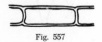

Fig. 561

Fig. 562

Fig. 563

Fig. 564

Fig. 565

Fig. 566

Fig. 567

Fig. 568

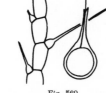

Fig. 569

Fig. 570

Fig. 571

Fig. 572

Fig. 573

Fig. 574

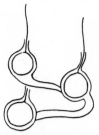

Fig. 575

Fig. 576

Fig. 577